Atlas of Polymer and Plastics Analysis

HUMMEL/SCHOLL

Atlas of Polymer and Plastics Analysis

Second, completely revised edition

Vol. 1 Polymers: Structures and Spectra

By Prof. Dr. Dieter O. Hummel, Cologne

Vol. 2 Plastics, Fibres, Rubbers, Resins; Starting and Auxiliary Materials, Degradation Products

By Prof. Dr. Dieter O. Hummel, Cologne

Vol. 3 Additives and Processing Aids

Spectra and Methods of Identification

By Dr. Friedrich Scholl, Stuttgart

Carl Hanser Verlag
Munich · Vienna

VCH Verlagsgesellschaft
Weinheim · Basel · Cambridge · New York

VCH Publishers
New York · Weinheim · Basel · Cambridge

HUMMEL/SCHOLL

Atlas of Polymer and Plastics Analysis

Second, completely revised edition

Vol. 2
Plastics, Fibres, Rubbers, Resins;
Starting and Auxiliary Materials, Degradation Products

Part b/II
Bibliography and Index

By Prof. Dr. Dieter O. Hummel, Cologne

in Collaboration with Dr. Agnes Solti, Budapest/Cologne

Carl Hanser Verlag
Munich · Vienna

VCH Verlagsgesellschaft
Weinheim · Basel · Cambridge · New York

VCH Publishers
New York · Weinheim · Basel · Cambridge

Prof. Dr. Dieter O. Hummel
Institut für Physikalische Chemie der Universität Köln
Luxemburger Straße 116
D-5000 Köln 41
Federal Republic of Germany

Published jointly by
Carl Hanser Verlag, Munich (Federal Republic of Germany)
VCH Verlagsgesellschaft, Weinheim (Federal Republic of Germany)
VCH Publishers, New York, NY (USA)

Editorial Director: Dr. Hans F. Ebel
Production Director: Dipl.-Ing. (FH) Hans Jörg Maier
Composition, Printing and Bookbinding: Wiesbadener Graphische Betriebe GmbH, D-6200 Wiesbaden 1

Library of Congress Card No. 85-154032

A CIP catalogue record for this book is available from the British Library.

Deutsche Bibliothek Cataloguing in Publication Data

Atlas of polymer and plastics analysis / Hummel ; Scholl. – Munich ;
Vienna : Hanser ; Weinheim ; New York ; Cambridge ; Basel : VCH-
Verl.-Ges. ; New York ; Weinheim ; Basel ; Cambridge : VCH Publ.
    Dt. Ausg. u.d.T.: Atlas der Polymer- und Kunststoffanalyse. – Teilw. nur in
    d. Verl. Hanser, München, Wien, u. VCH-Verl.-Ges., Weinheim, Deerfield
    Beach, Fl.
    ISBN 3-446-12589-2 (Hanser)
    ISBN 3-527-25800-0 (VCH, Weinheim ...)
    ISBN 0-89573-012-X (VCH, New York ...)
NE: Hummel, Dieter O. [Mitverf.]; Scholl, Friedrich [Mitverf.]

Vol. 2. Plastics, fibres, rubbers, resins, starting and auxiliary materials,
    degradation products : [spectra and methods of identification].
    Pt. b.
    2. Bibliography and text / by Dieter O. Hummel. With co-operation
    by Agnes Solti. – 2., completely rev. ed. – 1988
    ISBN 3-446-13835-8 (Hanser) Kunststoff
    ISBN 3-527-26091-9 (VCH, Weinheim ...) Kunststoff
    ISBN 0-89573-074-X (VCH, New York ...) Kunststoff

© Carl Hanser Verlag, D-8000 Munich, and VCH Verlagsgesellschaft mbH, D-6940 Weinheim
Federal Republic of Germany, 1988

Printed in the Federal Republic of Germany

Notes on the use of the bibliography

This bibliography primarily contains more recent literature from ca. 1977 to 1987. The most important older publications are also included. The excellent work by DECHANT (1972)*, which unfortunately only appeared in one edition, contains a practically complete collection of references to 1971 (if that is at all possible).

Later literature on the subject is to be found in the work by SIESLER and HOLLAND-MORITZ**.

The decimal classification of this bibliography does not correspond to the classification of the text volume. The references in each section corresponding to a particular decimal number are arranged alphabetically according to the initial letters of the name of the first author. Particularly important monographs are included not only under class 1 "Books, reviews" but also under each pertinent specialist topic. The topics which do not form part of the major thrust of this work (*UV* spectroscopy, *ESR* spectroscopy and thermal analysis to name just these) are only represented by a few important publications.

* J. DECHANT in collaboration with R. DANZ, W. KIMMER, R. SCHMOLKE, *Ultrarotspektroskopische Untersuchungen an Polymeren*, Akademie-Verlag, Berlin 1972.
** H.W. SIESLER, K. HOLLAND-MORTIZ, *Infrared and Raman Spectroscopy of Polymers*, Marcel Dekker, New York, 1980.

Contents

Contents

Contents

Bibliography

1 Books, reviews

1.1 Descriptions of materials

1.1.1 Polymers general; fibers, elastomers, liquid crystals; polymer mixtures

H. Batzer (ed.), *Polymere Werkstoffe*, Bd. I *Chemie und Physik*; Georg Thieme, Stuttgart etc. 1985

A. Blumstein (ed.), *Polymeric Liquid Crystals*; Plenum Publ. Corp., New York 1984

L. L. Chapoy (ed.), *Recent Advances in Liquid-Crystalline Polymers*; Elsevier, New York 1985

F. Ciardelli, C. Carlini, Optically active polyolefins; in R. B. Seymour, T. Cheng (eds.), *History of Polyolefins*; Reidel, Dordrecht 1986

A. Ciferri, W. R. Krigbaum, R. B. Meyer (eds.), *Polymer Liquid Crystals*; Academic Press, New York 1982

J. Economy (ed.), *New and Specialty Fibers, Appl. Polym. Symp. 29*; Interscience/Wiley, New York etc. 1976

B. v. Falkai (ed.), *Synthesefasern*; Verlag Chemie, Weinheim 1981

F. Fourne, *Synthetische Fasern — Herstellung, Verarbeitung und Verwendung*; Wissenschaftl. Verlagsanstalt, Stuttgart 1964

I. H. Hall (ed.), *Structure of Crystalline Polymers*; Elsevier Applied Science, New York etc. 1984

C. D. Han (ed.), *Polymer Blends and Composites in Multiphase Systems*; *Adv. Chem. Ser. 206*; ACS, Washington, DC 1984

F. Happey, *Applied Fibre Science* (3 vols.); Academic Press, New York 1978...80

Z. Jedliński (ed.), *Advances in the Chemistry of Thermally Stable Polymers*; Polish Scientific Publishers, Warszawa 1977

H. Kelker, R. Hatz, *Handbook of Liquid Crystals*; Verlag Chemie, Weinheim 1980

D. Klempner, K. C. Frisch (eds.), *Polymer Alloys: Blends, Blocks, Grafts, and Interpenetrating Networks*; Plenum Publ. Corp., New York 1977...83

V. V. Korshak, V. A. Samyatina, N. I. Bekassova, *Boroorganic Polymers* (Russ.), Isdatel'stvo „Nauka", Moskau 1975

M. Kryszewski, E. Martuscelli, A. Galeski (eds.), *Polymer Blends: Processing, Morphology, Properties*, Vol. II; Plenum Press, New York etc. 1984

M. Lewin (ed.), *Fiber Science, J. Appl. Polym. Sci., Appl. Polym. Symp. 31*; Interscience/Wiley, New York 1977

H. F. Mark, N. M. Bikales, C. G. Overberger, G. Menges (eds.), *Encyclopedia of Polymer Science and Engineering*, 1st ed. 1964...71, 2nd ed. 1986...90; Wiley Interscience, New York etc.

J. E. Mark, A. Eisenberg, W. W. Graessley, L. Mandelkern, J. L. Koenig, *Physical Properties of Polymers*; American Chemical Society, Washington, DC 1984

E. Martuscelli, R. Rosario, M. Kryszewski (eds.), *Polymer Blends*; Plenum Press, New York etc. 1979

E. Martuscelli, R. Palumbo, M. Kryszewski (eds.), *Polymer Blends: Processing, Morphology, Properties*, Vol. I; Plenum Press, New York etc. 1980

E. Martuscelli (ed.), *New Polymeric Materials*; V. + New Science Press, Utrecht 1987

C. A. May (ed.), *Epoxy Resins*, 2nd ed.; Marcel Dekker, New York 1988

K. L. Mittal (ed.), *Polyimides: Synthesis, Characterization, and Applications* (2 vols.); Plenum Publ. Corp., New York etc. 1984

G. Oertel (ed.), *Polyurethane Handbook*; Hanser/Wiley, Munich/Chichester 1985

D. R. Paul, S. Newman (eds.), *Polymer Blends* (2 vols.); Academic Press, New York 1978

N. A. J. Platzer, *Copolymers, Polyblends, and Composites*; *Adv. Chem. Ser. 142*; ACS, Washington, DC 1975

Hj. Saechtling, *Kunststoff-Taschenbuch*, 23rd ed.; Carl Hanser, Munich 1986

H. Saechtling, *International Plastics Handbook* (2nd ed.); Hanser/Wiley, Munich/Chichester 1987 (translation of *Kunststoff-Taschenbuch*, 23rd ed.)

R. B. Seymour, H. F. Mark (eds.), *Applications of Polymers*; Plenum, New York 1988

H. Ulrich, *Introduction to Industrial Polymers*; Hanser/Wiley, Munich/Chichester 1982

R. Vieweg, K. Krekeler (eds.), *Kunststoff-Handbuch*;

I	D. Braun: Grundlagen	
II	G. Wick: Polyvinylchlorid	
III	E. Becker: Abgewandelte Naturstoffe	
IV	A. Schley, A. Schwarz: Polyolefine	
V	G. Daumiller: Polystyrol	
VI	A. Müller: Polyamide	
VII	A. Höchtlen: Polyurethane	
VIII	L. Goerden: Polyester	
IX	F. Esser: Polymethacrylate	
X	E. Becker: Duroplaste	

XI   M. Reiher, H. Scheurlen: Epoxidharze, fluorhaltige Polymerisate, Silicone; Carl Hanser, Munich etc. 1975ff.

D. J. Walsh, J. S. Higgins, A. Maconnachie (eds.), *Polymer Blends and Mixtures*; Kluwer Acad. Publ., Dordrecht etc. 1985

I. M. Ward, *Developments in Oriented Polymers, 1*; Applied Science Publ., Essex 1982

G. Woods, *The ICI Polyurethanes Book*; Wiley, Chichester etc. 1987

B. Wunderlich, *Macromolecular Physics*;
Vol. 1: *Crystal Structure, Morphology, Defects*; Academic Press, New York etc. 1973
Vol. 2: *Crystal Nucleation, Growth, Annealing*; ibid. 1976
Vol. 3: *Crystal Melting*; ibid. 1980

1.1.2 Resins, paints, coatings

U. Biethan et al., *Lacke und Lösemittel*; Verlag Chemie, Weinheim 1979

M. Fischer, F. Lohse, R. Schmid, *Makromol. Chem. 181* (1980) 1251...87; Struktureller Aufbau und physikalisches Verhalten vernetzter Epoxidharze

E. W. Flick, *Industrial Synthetic Resins Handbook*; Noyes Publ., Park Ridge, NJ 1985

H. Kittel (ed.), *Lehrbuch der Lacke und Beschichtungen*;
I/1 P. Baur, F. M. Depke, H. Kittel: Grundlagen, Bindemittel; 1971
I/2 I. Bauer et al.: Grundlagen, Bindemittel; 1973
I/3 H. Disselhoff et al.: Grundlagen, Bindemittel; 1974
II E. A. Becker et al.: Pigmente, Füllstoffe, Farbstoffe; 1974
III M. Giesen et al.: Lösemittel, Weichmacher, Additive, Zwischenprodukte; 1976

IV F. M. Depke et al.: Lack- und Beschichtungssysteme, Formulierung; 1976, Verlag W. A. Colomb/H. Heenemann GmbH, Berlin etc.

A. Knop, W. Scheib, *Chemistry and Application of Phenolic Resins*; Springer, Berlin 1979

A. Knop, L. A. Pilato, *Phenolic Resins*; Springer, Berlin etc. 1985

R. Lambourne (ed.), *Paint and Surface Coatings*; Ellis Horwood/John Wiley, Chichester etc. 1987

R. R. Myers, J. S. Long (eds.), *Treatise on Coatings*;
1/I Film-Forming Compositions; 1967
1/II Film-Forming Compositions; 1968
1/III Film-Forming Compositions; 1972
2/I Characterization of Coatings: Physical Techniques; 1969
2/II Characterization of Coatings: Physical Techniques; 1976
3 Pigments; Marcel Dekker, New York

A. M. Paquin, *Epoxydverbindungen und Epoxydharze*; Springer, Berlin etc. 1958

G. D. Parfitt, A. V. Patsis (eds.), *Organic Coatings, Science and Technology*, Vol. 8; Marcel Dekker, New York 1986

1.1.3 Additives

R. Büll, G. v. Rosenberg, H. Götte, W. Brotz, J. Lange, O. Malitschek, J. Kaupp, W. Strassenberger, *Vom Wachs*, Hoechster Beiträge zur Kenntnis der Wachse; 2 Vols., 23 Beiträge, Hoechst AG, Frankfurt/M.-Höchst 1960…5

G. V. Chilingarian, T. F. Yen (eds.), *Bitumens, Asphalts and Tar Sands*; Elsevier, Amsterdam etc. 1978

R. Gächter, H. Müller (eds.), *Taschenbuch der Kunststoff-Additive*; Carl Hanser, Munich 1983

R. Gächter, H. Müller (eds.), *Plastics Additives Handbook*; Carl Hanser, Munich etc. 1984

H. Gnamm, O. Fuchs, *Lösungsmittel und Weichmachungsmittel*, 8th ed.;
Vol. I: Physikalische Grundlagen und Eigenschaften der Lösungen von nieder- und hochmolekularen Verbindungen;
Vol. II: Löslichkeitstabellen von Makromolekülen;
Vol. III: Eigenschaften der Lösungsmittel und Weichmachungsmittel; Wissenschaftliche Verlagsgesellschaft, Stuttgart 1980

E. Gulinsky, *Pflanzliche und tierische Fette und Öle*; Curt R. Vincentz Verlag, Hanover 1963

W. Hofmann, *Vulkanisation und Vulkanisationshilfsmittel*; Bayer AG, Leverkusen 1965

J. E. Kresta (ed.), *Polymer Additives*; Plenum Press, New York 1984

L. Michaels, S. S. Chissick, *Asbestos*, Vol. 1: *Properties, Applications, and Hazards*; John Wiley, New York 1979

J. Stepek, H. Daoust, *Additives for Plastics*, Vol. 5 of *Polymer Properties and Applications*; Springer, Berlin 1983

1.2. Identification, analysis, testing (non-spectroscopic)

L. S. Bark, N. S. Allen, *Analysis of Polymer Systems*; Applied Science Publ., Essex 1982

F. A. Bovey, F. H. Winslow, *Macromolecules — An Introduction to Polymer Science*; Academic Press, New York 1979

D. Braun, *Erkennen von Kunststoffen. Qualitative Kunststoffanalyse mit einfachen Mitteln*; Hanser, Munich etc. 1986 (2nd ed.)

D. Braun, *Simple Methods for Identification of Plastics*; Hanser Publishers/Macmillan, New York 1982

T. R. Crompton, *Chemical Analysis of Additives in Plastics*, 2nd ed.; Pergamon Press, Oxford etc. 1977

T. R. Crompton, *The Analysis of Plastics*; Pergamon Press, Oxford etc. 1984

K.-F. Elgert, *Kunststoffe. Analyse*; Ullmanns Encyklopädie, 4th ed. Vol. 15, 371…96; Verlag Chemie, Weinheim 1978

W. Fresenius, H. Günzler et al., *Analytiker-Taschenbuch* (7 Bände bis 1987); Springer, Berlin etc.

J. Haslam, H. A. Willis, D. C. M. Squirrel, *Identification and Analysis of Plastics*, 2nd ed.; Iliffe, London 1972

M. Hoffmann, H. Krömer, R. Kuhn, *Polymeranalytik (2 Bände) Makromolekulare Strukturen, physikalische Methoden, Anwendungskriterien*; Georg Thieme, Stuttgart 1977

D. O. Hummel, *Kunststoff-, Lack- und Gummi-Analyse*; Carl Hanser, Munich 1958

G. Kämpf, *Charakterisierung von Kunststoffen mit physikalischen Methoden, Verfahren und praktische Anwendung*; Carl Hanser, Munich etc. 1982

C. P. A. Kappelmeier (ed.), *Chemical Analysis of Resin-Based Coating Materials*; Interscience, New York etc. 1959

H. P. Kaufmann, *Analyse der Fette und Fettprodukte*; Springer, Berlin 1958

G. M. Kline (ed.), *Analytical Chemistry of Polymers*; Interscience Publ., New York etc. 1962

J. L. Koenig, *Chemical Microstructure of Polymer Chains*; John Wiley, New York 1980

A. Krause, A. Lange, *Kunststoff-Bestimmungsmöglichkeiten*; Carl Hanser, Munich 1979

A. Krause, A. Lange, M. Ezrin, *Plastic Analysis Guide. Chemical and Instrumental Methods*; Hanser, Munich etc. 1983

L.-H. Lee, *Characterization of Metal and Polymer Surfaces*;
Part I: Electron Spectroscopy for Chemical Analysis
Part II: Infrared and Laser Raman Spectroscopy
Part III: Microscopy for Polymers
Part IV: Surface-Chemical and Radiation Analyses; Academic Press, New York etc. 1977

J. Mitchell (ed.), *Applied Polymer Analysis and Characterization*; Hanser Publishers, Munich etc. 1987

H. Ostromow, *Analyse von Kautschuken und Elastomeren*; Springer, Berlin etc. 1981

K. Schmidtke, Methoden zum chemischen Charakterisieren von EP-Harzen und Prepregs für die Wareneingangskontrolle, in VDI-Kunststofftechnik: *Verarbeiten und Anwenden von kohlenstofffaserverstärkten Kunststoffen*; VDI-Verlag, Düsseldorf 1981

J. V. Schmitz (ed.), *Testing of Polymers* (2 vols.); Wiley-Interscience, New York etc. 1965 and 1966

E. Schröder, G. Müller, K.-F. Arndt, *Leitfaden der Polymercharakterisierung*; Akademie-Verlag, Berlin 1982

E. Schröder, J. Franz, E. Magen (ed.), *Ausgewählte Methoden der Plastanalytik*; Akademie-Verlag, Berlin 1976

M. Stratmann, *Erkennen und Identifizieren der Faserstoffe*; Spohr, Stuttgart 1973

M. Stratmann, Identification of textile fibers; in J. Mitchell (ed.), *Applied Polymer Analysis and Characterization*; Carl Hanser, Munich etc. 1987

1.3 *IR* Spectroscopy

1.3.1 Fundamentals

A. J. Barnes, W. J. Orville-Thomas, *Vibrational Spectroscopy — Modern Trends*; Elsevier, Amsterdam etc. 1977

L. J. Bellamy, *Advances in Infrared Group Frequencies*; Methuen, London 1968

L. J. Bellamy, *Advances in Infrared Group Frequencies, Vol. 2: The Infrared Spectra of Complex Molecules*, 2nd ed.; Chapman and Hall, London 1980

E. G. Brame, J. G. Grasselli (eds.), *Infrared and Raman Spectroscopy*; Marcel Dekker, New York etc. 1976

W. Brügel, *Einführung in die Ultrarotspektroskopie*, 4th ed.; Steinkopff, Darmstadt 1969

R. J. H. Clark, R. E. Hester (eds.), *Advances in Infrared and Raman Spectroscopy* (ca. 10 vols.); John Wiley, Chichester etc.

J. T. Clerc, E. Pretsch, J. Seibl, *Structural Analysis of Organic Compounds by Combined Application of Spectroscopic Methods*; Akadémiai Kiadó, Budapest 1981

N. B. Colthup, L. H. Daly, S. E. Wiberley, *Introduction to Infrared and Raman Spectroscopy*, 2nd ed.; Academic Press, New York 1975

J. W. Cooper, *Spectroscopic Techniques for Organic Chemists*; John Wiley & Sons, New York 1980

J. R. Durig (ed.), *Analytical Applications of FT-IR to Molecular and Biological Systems*. NATO Advanced Study Institute Series, C, Vol. 57; Reidel Publishing Co., Dordrecht 1980

J. R. Durig (ed.), *Chemical, Biological and Industrial Applications of Infrared Spectroscopy*; John Wiley, Chichester etc. 1985

A. Fadini, F.-M. Schnepel, *Schwingungsspektroskopie: Methoden, Anwendungen*; G. Thieme, Stuttgart etc. 1985

J. R. Ferraro, L. J. Basile (eds.), *Fourier Transform Infrared Spectroscopy. Applications to Chemical Systems*, Vol. 1; Academic Press, New York 1978

J. R. Ferraro, *Vibrational Spectroscopy at High External Pressures*; Academic Press, Orlando etc. 1984

S. K. Freeman (ed.), *Interpretive Spectroscopy*; Reinhold Publ. Corp., New York 1965

R. W. Frei, J. D. MacNeil, *Diffuse Reflectance Spectroscopy in Environmental Problem-Solving*; CRC Press, Cleveland 1973

J. G. Grasselli, D. G. Cameron (eds.), *Fourier and Computerized Infrared Spectroscopy*, SPIE vol 53; Washington, DC 1985

P. R. Griffiths, *Chemical Infrared Fourier Transform Spectroscopy*; Wiley-Interscience, New York 1975

P. R. Griffiths, Developments in Fourier-Transform Infrared Spectrometry, in R. J. H. Clark, R. E. Hester (eds.), *Advances in Infrared and Raman Spectroscopy*, Vol. 10; John Wiley, Chichester etc. 1983

P. R. Griffiths, J. A. de Haseth, *Fourier Transform Infrared Spectroscopy*; John Wiley, Chichester etc. 1986

H. Günzler, H. Böck, *IR-Spektroskopie*, 2nd ed.; Verlag Chemie, Weinheim 1983

H. J. Hediger, *Infrarotspektroskopie: Grundlagen, Anwendungen, Interpretation*; Akad. Verlagsges. Frankfurt/M. 1971

H. J. Hediger, *Quantitative Spektroskopie*; Hüthig, Heidelberg 1985

W. Herres, *HRGC-FTIR: Capillary Gas Chromatography — Fourier Transform Infrared Spectroscopy Theory and Applications*; Hüthig, Heidelberg 1987

M. Hesse, H. Meier, B. Zeeh, *Spektroskopische Methoden in der organischen Chemie*; Georg Thieme, Stuttgart 1979

T. Hirschfeld, E. W. Stark, Near-infrared reflectance analysis of foodstuff; in G. Charamboulos (ed.), *Analysis of Food and Beverages*; Academic Press, New York 1984

W. Kemp, *Organic Spectroscopy*; Macmillan, London 1975

J. L. Koenig, *FTIR of interfaces*, in D. Leyden (ed.), *Silanes, Surfaces and Interfaces*; Gordon and Treach, New York 1986

I. N. Levine, *Molecular Spectroscopy*; John Wiley & Sons, New York 1975

J. E. Mark, A. Eisenberg, W. W. Graessley, L. Mandelkern, J. L. Koenig, Molecular spectroscopy, in *Physical Properties of Polymers*; ACS Symp. Ser., Washington, DC 1984

A. E. Martin, *Infrared Interferometric Spectrometers*; Elsevier, Amsterdam 1980

R. G. J. Miller, B. C. Stace, *Laboratory Methods in Infrared Spectroscopy*, 2nd ed.; Heyden + Son Ltd., London 1972

K. D. Möller, W. G. Rothschild, *Far Infrared Spectroscopy*; Wiley Interscience, New York 1971

E. Pretsch, T. Clerc, J. Seibl, W. Simon, *Strukturaufklärung organischer Verbindungen*, 2nd ed.; Springer, Berlin etc. 1981

A. Rosencwaig, *Photoacoustic and Photoacoustic Spectroscopy*; John Wiley, New York 1980

F. Scheinmann, *An Introduction to Spectroscopic Methods for the Identification of Organic Compounds*, Volume 1 + 2; Pergamon Press, Oxford 1970, 1974

B. Schrader, *Infrarot- und Ramanspektrometrie*, Ullmanns Encyklopädie der technischen Chemie, 4th ed. Vol. 5; Verlag Chemie, Weinheim 1980

R. M. Silverstein, G. C. Bassler, T. C. Morrill, *Spectrometric Identification of Organic Compounds*; John Wiley, New York 1981

A. L. Smith, *Treatise Anal. Chem. 1* (1981) 249...476; Infrared spectroscopy

G. Socrates, *Infrared Characteristic Group Frequencies*; John Wiley, New York 1980

E. Steger et al., K. Doerffel et al., *Strukturaufklärung — Spektroskopie und Röntgenbeugung*, 2 Vols.; Verlag Chemie, Weinheim 1973; VEB Deutscher Verlag für Grundstoffindustrie, Leipzig 1973

T. Theophanides (ed.), *Fourier Transform Infrared Spectroscopy — Industrial, Chemical and Biochemical Applications*; Kluwer Acad. Publ., Dordrecht etc. 1984

L. C. Thomas, *Interpretation of the Infrared Spectra of Organophosphorus Compounds*; Heyden, London etc. 1974

G. Varsányi, *Assignments for Vibrational Spectra of 700 Benzene Derivatives*; Akadémiai Kiadó, Budapest 1973

H. Volkmann, *Handbuch der Infrarot-Spektroskopie*; Verlag Chemie, Weinheim 1972

H. Weitkamp, R. Barth, *Einführung in die quantitative Infrarot-Spektrophotometrie*; G. Thieme, Stuttgart 1976

W. W. Wendlandt, H. G. Hecht, *Reflectance Spectroscopy*, Wiley-Interscience, New York 1966

H. A. Willis, *Adv. Infrared Raman Spectrosc. 2* (1976) 81...139; Industrial plant applications of infrared and Raman spectroscopy

1.3.2 Macromolecular systems

D. R. Anderson, *Chem. Anal. (N.Y.) 41* (1974) 247...86; Infrared, Raman and ultraviolet spectroscopy (of organosilicon compounds)

F. J. Boerio, J. L. Koenig, *J. Macromol. Sci., Rev. Macromol. Chem. C7* (2) (1972) 209...49; Vibrational spectroscopy of polymers

E. G. Brame, J. G. Grasselli (eds.), *Infrared and Raman Spectroscopy*, Pt. C (Biological Science, Polymers, Surfaces); Marcel Dekker, New York etc. 1977

E. G. Brame (ed.), *Applications of Polymer Spectroscopy*; Academic Press, New York 1978

S. C. Brown, A. B. Harvey, *Pract. Spectrosc. 1* (1977) 873...932; Infrared and Raman spectroscopy of polymers

M. M. Coleman, P. C. Painter, *J. Macromol. Sci., Rev. Macromol. Chem. C16* (2) (1977...8) 197...313; Fourier transform infrared studies of polymeric materials

M. M. Coleman, D. F. Varnell, J. P. Runt, A critical assessment of the application of *FT-IR* spectroscopy to the study of crystalline/compatible polymer blends, in D. Klempner, K. C. Frisch (eds.), *Polymer Alloys* III; Plenum Publ. Corp., New York etc. 1983

J. Dechant, with R. Danz, W. Kimmer, R. Schmolke, *Ultrarotspektroskopische Untersuchungen an Polymeren*; Akademie-Verlag, Berlin 1972

L. D'Esposito, J. L. Koenig, Applications of Fourier transform infrared to synthetic polymers and biological macromolecules, in J. R. Ferraro, L. J. Basile (eds.), *Fourier Transform Infrared Spectroscopy, Applications to Chemical Systems*, Vol. 1; Academic Press, New York 1978

N. J. Harrick, Reflection spectroscopy, nature of the spectra, in L. H. Lee, *Characterization of Metal and Polymer Surfaces*, Vol. 2, *Polymer Surfaces*; Academic Press, New York etc. 1977

J. Haslam, H. A. Willis, D. C. M. Squirrel, *Identification and Analysis of Plastics*; Iliffe Books, London 1965; Heyden, London 1972

J. C. Henniker, *Infrared Spectrometry of Industrial Polymers*; Academic Press, London New York 1967

K. Holland-Moritz, K. W. Siesler, *Appl. Spectrosc. Rev. 11* (1976) 1...55; Infrared spectroscopy of polymers

D. O. Hummel, *Pure Appl. Chem. 11* (1965) 497...533; Fortschritte bei der infrarotspektroskopischen Analyse makromolekularer Systeme

D. O. Hummel, *Infrared Spectra of Polymers in the Medium and Long Wavelength Regions*; Interscience Publ., New York etc. 1966

D. O. Hummel, F. Scholl, *Atlas der Kunststoff-Analyse*,
Vol. 1: Polymere und Harze
Vol. 2: Hilfsmittel; Carl Hanser/Verlag Chemie, Munich/Weinheim 1968 and 1973

D. O. Hummel (ed.), *Polymer Spectroscopy*; Verlag Chemie, Weinheim 1974

D. O. Hummel, F. Scholl, *Atlas der Polymer- und Kunststoffanalyse*, 3 Vols.; Carl Hanser/Verlag Chemie, Munich/Weinheim 1978...84

D. O. Hummel (ed.), *Proceedings of the 5th European Symposium on Polymer Spectroscopy*; Verlag Chemie, Weinheim 1979

D. O. Hummel, *IR-Spektrometrie von Polymeren*, in Fresenius et al. (eds.), *Analytiker-Taschenbuch*, Vol. 6; Springer, Berlin 1986

H. Ishida (ed.), *Fourier-Transform Infrared Characterization of Polymers*; Plenum, New York 1987

K. J. Ivin (ed.), *Structural Studies of Macromolecules by Spectroscopic Methods*; John Wiley, London 1976

R. J. Jakobsen, Application of *FT-IR* to surface studies, in J. R. Ferraro, L. J. Basile (eds.), *Fourier Transform Infrared Spectroscopy, Applications to Chemical Systems*, Vol. 1; Academic Press, New York 1978

W. Klöpffer, *Introduction to Polymer Spectroscopy*; Springer, Berlin 1984

J. L. Koenig, *Adv. Polym. Sci. 54* (1984) 89...147; Fourier transform infrared spectroscopy of polymers

J. L. Koenig, *FTIR* studies of polymer films, surfaces and interfaces, in M. Mathlouthi (ed.), *Food Packaging and Preservation*; Elsevier, New York 1986

M. Kraft, *Struktur und Absorptionsspektroskopie der Kunststoffe*; Verlag Chemie, Weinheim 1973

G. Melber, H. Szymanski, Pyrolysis in Infrared Spectroscopy, in H. Szymanski, *Progress in Infrared Spectroscopy*, Vol. 3; Plenum Press, New York 1967

G. Natta, G. Zerbi (eds.), *J. Polym. Sci. C 7* (1964); Vibrational spectra of high polymers

P. C. Painter, M. M. Coleman, J. L. Koenig, *The Theory of Vibrational Spectroscopy and Its Application to Polymeric Materials*; John Wiley, New York etc. 1982

H. W. Siesler, K. Holland-Moritz, *Infrared and Raman Spectroscopy of Polymers*; Marcel Dekker, New York etc. 1980

R. G. Snyder, *Methods Exp. Phys. 16* (A) (1980) 73...148; Infrared and Raman spectra of polymers

W. E. Steger (ed.), *Progress in Polymer Spectroscopy*; Teubner, Leipzig 1986

H. Tadokoro, *Structure of Crystalline Polymers*; John Wiley, New York 1979

H. A. Willis, Combination of spectroscopic methods in polymer structure analysis, in D. O. Hummel (ed.), *Proceedings of the 5th European Symposium on Polymer Spectroscopy*; Verlag Chemie, Weinheim 1979

G. Zerbi, *Makromol. Chem. Suppl. 5* (1981) 253...95; Modern techniques of vibrational spectroscopy in macromolecular science

R. G. Zhbankov, B. I. Stepanov (eds.), *Infrared Spectra of Cellulose and Its Derivatives*; John Wiley, New York 1966

G. Zundel, *Hydration and Intermolecular Interaction — Infrared Investigations with Polyelectrolyte Membranes*; Academic Press, New York 1969

1.3.3 Additives

J. P. Coates, L. C. Setti, *Oils, Lubricants and Petroleum Products: Characterization by Infrared Spectra*; Marcel Dekker, New York 1985

C. D. Craver (ed.), *Infrared Spectra of Plasticizers and Other Additives*, 2nd ed.; The Coblentz Society, Kirkwood, MO 1981

Y. Sekikawa, S. Yoshiaki, M. Shimasa, *Kanzei Chuo Bunsekishoho 16* (1976) 97...133; Infrared spectra of inorganic compounds

M. Wandel, H. Tengler, H. Ostromov, *Die Analyse von Weichmachern*; Springer, Berlin 1967

G. Zundel, U. Böhner, J, Fritsch, H. Merz, B. Vogt, *Infrared spectrophotometry in food technology*, in D. W. Gruenwedel, J. R. Whitaker (eds.), *Food Analysis*, Vol. 2, *Physicochemical Techniques*; Marcel Dekker, New York etc. 1984

1.3.4 Compilations of data

British Pharmacopoeia, *Infrared Reference Spectra and Supplements*; British Pharmacopoeia Commission, London

Coblentz Standard Spectra; Coblentz Society, Norwalk, CT/Heyden + Son, London/Rheine

C. D. Craver (ed.), *The Coblentz Society Desk Book of Infrared Spectra*; The Coblentz Society, Kirkwood, MO

C. D. Craver (ed.), *Plasticizers and Other Additives, A Special Collection of IR-Spectra*; The Coblentz Society, Kirkwook, MO

P. C. Gillette, J. B. Lando, J. L. Koenig, A survey of infrared spectral data processing techniques, in J. R. Ferraro, L. J. Basile (eds.), *Fourier Transform Infrared Spectroscopy*; Academic Press, New York etc. 1985

J. Grasselli, W. Ritchey, *Atlas of Spectral Data for Organic Compounds*; Chemical Rubber Co., Cleveland, OH 1975

H. J. Hediger, *Kommentare zu Infrarot-Banden, KIRBA-Kartei*; H. J. Hediger, Eigenacker, CH Eglisau

IRDC Standard Spectra; The Infrared Data Committee of Japan, Nankodo Co., Tokyo

V. A. Koptyug (ed.), *Atlas of Spectra of Aromatic and Heterocyclic Compounds* (ca. 15 vols.); Novosibirsk Institute of Organic Chemistry

L. Láng (ed.), *Absorption Spectra in the Infrared Region* (5 vols.); Akadémiai Kiadó, Budapest

A. J. Luff, *DMS-Arbeitsatlas der Infrarotspektroskopie*; Verlag Chemie/Butterworth, Weinheim/London 1972

R. Mecke, F. Langenbucher, *Infrared Spectra of Selected Chemical Compounds*; Heyden + Son, London 1970

R. G. J. Miller, H. A. Willis (ed.), H. J. Hediger, *IRSCOT-Infrared Structural Correlation Tables*; Heyden + Son, London 1964/1965

M. Passlack, W. Bremser, M. Beckmann, H. Wagner, *Infrared Spectral Data*; VCH Verl. Ges., Weinheim etc. 1986

C. J. Pouchert, *The Aldrich Library of Infrared Spectra*; Aldrich Chem. Comp./EGA-Chemie, Steinheim/Albuch, 1975

J. W. Robinson (ed.), *Handbook of Spectroscopy*; CRC Press, Boca Raton 1974

Sadtler Standard Spectra; Sadtler Research Labs., Philadelphia, PA/Heyden + Son, London/Rheine

Sadtler/Heyden, *The Infrared Spectra Atlas of Monomers and Polymers*; Sadtler Res. Labs., Philadelphia, PA/Heyden + Son, London 1980

B. Schrader, W. Meier, *Raman/IR-Atlas organischer Verbindungen*; Verlag Chemie, Weinheim 1974/1975

J. T. Vandeberg, D. G. Anderson et al. (eds.), *An Infrared Spectroscopy Atlas for the Coatings Industry*; Federation of Societies for Coatings Technology, Philadelphia, PA 1980

1.3.5 Computers

J. Bargon (ed.), *Computational Methods in Chemistry*; Plenum Publ. Corp., New York 1980

P. G. Barker, *Computers in Analytical Chemistry*; Pergamon Press, Oxford etc. 1984

R. Norman Jones, *Comp. Chem. Instrum. 7* (1977) 1...69; Modular computer programs for infrared spectrophotometry

D. J. Malcome-Lawes, *Microcomputers and Laboratory Instrumentation*; Plenum, New York 1985

J. Mattson, H. B. Mark, H. C. MacDonald (eds.), Infrared, correlation, and Fourier transform spectroscopy, in *Computers in Chemistry and Instrumentation*, Vol. 7; Marcel Dekker, New York 1977

J. S. Mattson, C. A. Smith, *Comput. Chem. Instrum. 7* (1977) 71...118; An on-line minicomputer system for infrared spectrophotometry

H. L. C. Meuzelaar, T. L. Isenhour (eds.), *Computer-Enhanced Analytical Spectroscopy*; Plenum, New York 1987

H. A. Willis (ed.: R. A. G. Carrington), *Computers for Spectroscopists*; Adam Hilger, London 1974

D. D. Wolff, M. L. Parsons, *Pattern Recognition Approach to Data Interpretation*; Plenum, New York 1983

E. Ziegler (ed.), *Computer in der Chemie, Praxisorientierte Einführung*; Springer, Berlin 1984

J. Zupan (ed.), *Computer Supported Spectroscopic Databases*; Ellis Horwood/John Wiley, Chichester etc. 1986

1.4 Raman spectroscopy

H. Baranska, A. Labudzinska, J. Terpinski, *Laser Raman Spectrometry*; Ellis Horwood, London 1987

B. Bulkin, J. G. Grasselli (eds.), *Chemical Applications of Raman Spectroscopy*; Wiley, New York 1988

A. Harvey (ed.), *Chemical Applications of Nonlinear Raman Spectroscopy*; Academic Press, New York 1981

K. W. F. Kohlrausch, *Ramanspektren*; Heyden + Son, London etc. 1972 (reprint of the original: Akad. Verlagsges., Leipzig 1943)

B. Schrader, *Raman-Spektrometrie*; Analytiker-Taschenbuch (ed.: R. Bock et al.), Vol. 3; Springer, Berlin etc. 1983

B. Schrader, *Fresenius Z. analyt. Chem. 314* (1983) 363...82; Ramanspektrometrie

M. M. Suschtschinskij, *Ramanspektren von Molekülen und Kristallen* (ed.: H. Kriegsmann); Heyden + Son, Rheine 1974

1.5 Nuclear and electron spin resonance spectroscopy

J. Bestgen, Kernparamagnetismus, in D. O. Hummel (ed.), *PC — Aufgaben zur Physikalischen Chemie*; de Gruyter, Berlin 1979

F. A. Bovey, *Polymer Conformation and Configuration*; Academic Press, New York 1969

F. A. Bovey, *High Resolution NMR of Macromolecules*; Academic Press, New York 1972

F. A. Bovey, High resolution carbon-13 studies of polymer structure, in K. J. Ivin (ed.), *Structural Studies of Macromolecules by Spectroscopic Methods*; John Wiley, London etc. 1976

R. F. Boyer, S. E. Keinath (eds.), *Molecular Motion in Polymers by ESR*; Harwood Acad. Press, New York 1978

E. Breitmaier, W. Voelter, ^{13}C-*NMR-Spectroscopy*; Verlag Chemie, Weinheim 1974

E. Breitmaier, G. Haas, W. Voelter, *Atlas of Carbon-13 NMR Data*; Heyden, London 1975

W. Bremser et al., *Carbon-13 NMR Spectral Data*, 4th ed.; VCH Verlagsgesellschaft, Weinheim 1986

W. Brügel, *Kernresonanz-Spektrum und chemische Konstitution*; D. Steinkopff, Darmstadt 1967

Bruker-Physik, *Data Bank ^{13}C*; Karlsruhe 1976

J. T. Clerc, E. Pretsch, S. Sternhell, ^{13}C-*Kernresonanzspektroskopie — Methoden der Analyse in der Chemie*; Akademische Verlagsgesellschaft, Frankfurt/M. 1973

C. Dybowski, R. L. Lichter (eds.), *NMR Spectroscopy Techniques*; Marcel Dekker, New York etc. 1987

H. Fischer, D. O. Hummel, Electron spin resonance, in D. O. Hummel (ed.), *Polymer Spectroscopy*; Verlag Chemie, Weinheim 1974

H. G. Fitzky, Elektronen-Spin-Resonanz — Anwendungen und Verfahrensweisen, in Fresenius et al. (eds.), *Analytiker-Taschenbuch*, Vol. 4; Springer, Berlin etc. 1984

H. Günther, *NMR-Spektroskopie*; Georg Thieme, Stuttgart 1973

H. Günther, *NMR Spectroscopy — An Introduction*; John Wiley, Chichester etc. 1980

U. Haeberlen, High resolution *NMR* spectroscopy in solids, selective averaging, in J. Waugh (ed.), *Advances in Magnetic Resonance*; Academic Press, New York etc. 1976

E. J. Haws, R. R. Hill, D. J. Mowthorpe, *The Interpretation of Proton Magnetic Resonance Spectra — A Programmed Introduction*; John Wiley, Chichester etc. 1973

S. Hvilsted, U. Jørgensen, *Analyse af Multikomponent Acryl Bindemidler*; Appendix C (^{13}C-*NMR*), Appendix H (^{1}H-*NMR*), Appendix *IR*; Scandinavian Paint and Printing Ink Research Institute, Agern Allé, DK Hørsholm 1986

K. J. Ivin, Some recent applications of ^{13}C-*NMR* spectroscopy to the determination of structure in hydrocabon polymers, in D. O. Hummel (ed.), *Proceedings of the 5th European Symposium on Polymer Spectroscopy*; Verlag Chemie, Weinheim 1979

H.-O. Kalinowski, S. Berger, S. Braun, ^{13}C-*NMR-Spektroskopie*; G. Thieme, Stuttgart 1984

E. Klesper, G. Sielaff, High resolution nuclear magnetic resonance spectroscopy, in D. O. Hummel (ed.), *Polymer Spectroscopy*; Verlag Chemie, Weinheim 1974

R. A. Komoroski (ed.), *High Resolution NMR Spectroscopy of Synthetic Polymers*; VCH Verl. Ges., Weinheim etc. 1986

R. N. Majumdar, Determination of polymer chain microstructure by fluorine-19 nuclear magnetic resonance spectroscopy, in J. Mitchell (ed.), *Applied Polymer Analysis and Characterization*; Carl Hanser, Munich etc. 1987

M. Mehring, *Principles of High Resolution NMR in Solids*; Springer, Berlin etc. 1983

W. J. Moore, D. O. Hummel, *Physikalische Chemie*, 4th ed.; Walter de Gruyter, Berlin 1986; 20. Chapter: Magnetismus und magnetische Resonanzspektroskopie

Q.-T. Pham, R. Petiaud, H. Waton, *Proton & Carbon NMR Spectra of Polymers*, Vol. 2; John Wiley, Chichester etc. 1983

Q.-T. Pham, R. Petiaud, M. F. Llauro, H. Waton, *Proton & Carbon NMR Spectra of Polymers*, Vol. 3; John Wiley, Chichester etc. 1984

B. Rånby, J. F. Rabek, *ESR Spectroscopy in Polymer Research*; Springer, Berlin etc. 1977

B. Rånby, Applications of ESR to polymer research, in R. F. Boyer, S. E. Keinath (eds.), *Molecular Motions in Polymers by ESR*; Harwood Acad. Publ., London New York 1980

J. C. Randall, *Polymer Sequence Determination: Carbon-13 NMR Method*; Academic Press, New York 1978

J. C. Randall (ed.), *NMR and Macromolecules — Sequence, Dynamic, and Domain Structure*; ACS Symp. Ser. 247, Washington, DC 1984

H.-K. Roth, F. Keller, H. Schneider, *Hochfrequenzspektroskopie in der Polymerforschung*; Akademie-Verlag, Berlin, DDR 1983

Sadtler Commercial Spectra, Proton NMR — Polymers, 60 MHz (2 vols.), 100 MHz (1 vol.); Sadtler Res. Labs., Philadelphia (in Europe from Heyden + Son, London and Rheine)

Sadtler Carbon-13 NMR of Monomers and Polymers; Sadtler Res. Labs., Philadelphia 1979 (in Europe from Heyden + Son, London and Rheine)

R. Sastre, J. L. Acosta, *Rev. Plast. Mod. 25* (1973) 885...99; Determinación de la composición de un copolímero por metodos espectroscópicos, I. Resonancia magnetica nuclear

D. Shaw (ed.), *Fourier Transform NMR Spectroscopy* (2nd ed.); Elsevier, New York 1984

P. Sohár (ed.), *Nuclear Magnetic Resonance Spectroscopy*, 3 vols.; CRC Press, Boca Raton 1983ff.

H. Strehlow, *Magnetische Kernresonanz und chemische Struktur*; Steinkopff, Darmstadt 1968

Y. Takeuchi, P. Marchand (eds.), *Applications of NMR Spectroscopy to Problems in Stereochemistry and Conformational Analysis*; Verlag Chemie International, Deerfield Beach 1986

J. E. Wertz, J. R. Bolton, *Electron Spin Resonance: Elementary Theory and Practical Applications*; Chapman Hall, New York 1986

A. E. Woodward, F. A. Bovey, *Polymer Characterization by ESR and NMR*; ACS Symp. Ser. 142, Washington, DC 1980

1.6 *UV/VIS* spectroscopy

J. L. Acosta, R. Sastre, *Rev. Plast. Mod. 25* (1973) 67...73; Determinación de la composición de copolímeros, II. Espectroscopia ultravioleta

N. S. Allen, J. F. Rabek (eds.), *New Trends in the Photochemistry of Polymers*; Elsevier, London/New York 1986

E. V. Anufrieva, Y. Ya. Gotlib, *Adv. Polym. Sci. 40* (1981) 1...68; Investigations of polymers in solution by polarized luminescence

F. Ciardelli, P. Salvadori (eds.), *Fundamental Aspects and Recent Developments in Optical Rotatory Dispersion and Circular Dichroism*; Heyden, London etc. 1973

L. H. Garcia-Rubio, A. E. Hamielec, J. F. MacGregor, UV-spectrophotometers as detectors for size exclusion chromatography of styrene-acrylonitrile (SAN) copolymers, in T. Provder (ed.), *Computer Applications in Applied Polymer Science*; ACS Symp. Ser. 197, Washington, DC 1982

M. Hesse, H. Meier, B. Zeeh, *Spektroskopische Methoden in der organischen Chemie*, 2nd ed.; Georg Thieme, Stuttgart 1979

W. Klöpffer, *Introduction to Polymer Spectroscopy*; Springer, Berlin 1984

A. Knowles, C. Burgess, *Techniques in Visible and Ultraviolet Spectrometry*, Vol. 3: *Practical Absorption Spectrometry*; Chapman and Hall, London/New York 1984

J. Michl, E. W. Thulstrup, *Spectroscopy with Polarized Light*; VCH Publishers, New York 1986

H. Morawetz, I. Z. Steinberg, *Acad. Sci. USA 366* (1981); Luminescence from biological and synthetic macromolecules

J. Mort, G. Pfister (ed.), *Electronic Properties of Polymers*; John Wiley, New York 1982

H.-H. Perkampus, *UV-VIS-Spektroskopie und ihre Anwendungen*; VCH Verlagsges., Weinheim 1987

1.7 Mass spectrometry

H. Budzikiewicz, *Massenspektrometrie — Eine Einführung*; Verlag Chemie, Weinheim 1972

H. Budzikiewicz, Massenspektroskopie organischer Verbindungen — Ionisierungsverfahren, in R. Bock et al. (eds.), *Analytiker-Taschenbuch*, Vol. 3; Springer, Berlin 1983

H. Budzikiewicz, Massenspektroskopische Analyse ungesättigter Fettsäuren, in R. Bock et al. (eds.), *Analytiker-Taschenbuch*, Vol. 3; Springer, Berlin 1983

J. R. Chapman, *Practical Organic Mass Spectrometry*; John Wiley, Chichester 1985

H. E. Duckworth, R. C. Barber, V. S. Venkatasubramanian, *Mass Spectroscopy*, 2nd ed.; Cambridge Univ. Press, Cambridge etc. 1986

S. Foti, G. Montaudo, Analysis of polymers by mass spectrometry, in L. S. Bark, N. S. Allen (eds.), *Analytical Pyrolysis*; Applied Science Publishers, London 1982

M. L. Gross (ed.), *High-Performance MS, Chemical Applications*; ACS Symp. Ser. 70, Washington, DC 1978

B. J. Gudzinowicz, M. J. Gudzinowicz, H. F. Martin, *Fundamentals of Integrated GC-MS*; Marcel Dekker, New York 1977

D. O. Hummel, H.-D. Schüddemage, K. Rübenacker, Mass spectrometry, in D. O. Hummel (ed.), *Polymer Spectroscopy*; Verlag Chemie, Weinheim 1974

D. O. Hummel, H.-J. Düssel, P. Manshausen, Pyrolysis mass spectrometry of multicomponent polymeric systems, in E. Steger (ed.), *Proceedings of the 7th European Symposium on Polymer Spectroscopy*; Teubner, Leipzig 1986

K. Levsen, On-line Kopplung Hochleistungsflüssigchromatographie-Massenspektrometrie, in W. Fresenius et al.

(eds.), *Analytiker-Taschenbuch*, Vol. 6; Springer, Berlin 1986

P. A. Lyon (ed.), *Desorption Mass Spectrometry*; *ACS Symp. Ser. 291, ACS*, Washington, DC 1985

G. M. Message, *Practical Aspects of Gas Chromatography/ Mass Spectrometry*; Wiley-Interscience, New York 1984

H. L. C. Meuzelaar, J. Haverkamp, F. D. Hileman, *Curie-Point Pyrolysis Mass Spectrometry of Recent and Fossil Biomaterials, Compendium and Atlas*; Elsevier, Amsterdam 1982

H.-R. Schulten, R. P. Lattimer, *Mass Spectrom. Rev. 3* (1984) 231...315; Applications of mass spectrometry to polymers

S. R. Shrader, *Introductory Mass Spectrometry*; Allyn and Bacon, Boston 1974

M. Spiteller, G. Spiteller, *Massenspektrensammlung von Lösungsmitteln, Verunreinigungen, Säulenbelegmaterialien und einfachen aliphatischen Verbindungen*; Springer, Vienna 1973

1.8 Non-destructive chromatographic methods

B. G. Belenkii, L. Z. Vilenchik, *Modern Liquid Chromatography of Macromolecules*; Elsevier, Amsterdam 1983

L. H. Garcia-Rubio, J. F. MacGregor, A. E. Hamielec, Size exclusion chromatography of copolymers, in C. D. Craver (ed.), *Polymer Characterization: Spectroscopic, Chromatographic, and Physical Instrumental Methods*; *Adv. Chem. Ser. 203, ACS*, Washington, DC 1983

G. Glöckner, *Polymercharakterisierung durch Flüssigkeits-Chromatographie*; Hüthig, Heidelberg 1982

P. R. Griffiths, Gas chromatography and Fourier transform infrared, in J. R. Ferraro, L. J. Basile (eds.), *Fourier Transform Infrared Spectroscopy, Applications to Chemical Systems*, Vol. 1; Academic Press, New York etc. 1978

K. Grob, *Making and Manipulating Capillary Columns for Gas Chromatography*; Hüthig, Heidelberg etc. 1986

W. Günther, F. Schlegelmilch, *Gaschromatographie mit Kapillar-Trennsäulen, Grundlagen, Praktikum*; Vogel-Buchverlag, Würzburg 1984/85

J. K. Haken, Gas chromatography, in R. R. Myers, J. S. Long (eds.), *Treatise on Coatings*, Vol. 2: *Characterization of Coatings: Physical Techniques*, Pt. 1; Marcel Dekker, New York 1969

J. G. Kirchner, *Thin-Layer Chromatography*; Interscience Publ., New York 1967

W. McFadden, *Techniques of Combined Gas Chromatography/Mass Spectrometry*; John Wiley, New York etc. 1973

G. Message, *Practical Aspects of Gas Chromatography/Mass Spectrometry*; John Wiley, New York 1984

J. G. Nikelly, *Advances in Capillary Chromatography*; Hüthig, Heidelberg etc. 1986

J. B. Pattison, *A Programmed Introduction to Gas-Liquid Chromatography*; Heyden + Son Ltd./Sadtler Res. Labs., London 1969

K. Randerath, *Dünnschicht-Chromatographie*; Verlag Chemie, Weinheim 1965

P. Sandra (ed.), *Sample Introduction in Capillary Gas Chromatography*, Vol. 1; Hüthig, Heidelberg etc. 1985

G. Schomburg, *Gaschromatographie*; Verlag Chemie, Weinheim 1977

E. Schulte, *Praxis der Kapillar-Gas-Chromatographie*; Springer, Berlin etc. 1983

C. G. Smith, N. E. Skelly, R. A. Solomon, C. D. Chow (eds.), *CRC Handbook of Chromatography: Polymers*; CRC Press, Boca Raton, FL 1982

E. Stahl (ed.), *Dünnschicht-Chromatographie*; Springer, Berlin etc. 1966

I. Tomka, G. Vancso, Determination of molecular mass distribution of polymers by a combination of dynamic light scattering, gel permeation chromatography and other methods, in J. Mitchell (ed.), *Applied Polymer Analysis and Characterization*; Carl Hanser, Munich etc. 1987

D. W. Vidrine, Liquid chromatography detection using *FT-IR*, in J. R. Ferraro, L. J. Basile (eds.), *Fourier Transform Infrared Spectroscopy, Applications to Chemical Systems*, Vol. 1; Academic Press, New York 1978

1.9 Thermal analysis, analytical pyrolysis, polymer degradation and stabilization; other analytical methods

1.9 Thermal analysis, analytical pyrolysis, polymer degradation and stabilization; other analytical methods

B. B. Baker, Infrared spectral examination of volatile effluents from the thermal treatment of polymers, in J. Mitchell (ed.), *Applied Polymer Analysis and Characterization*; Carl Hanser, Munich etc. 1987

V. G. Berezkin, V. R. Alishoyev, I. B. Nemirovskaya, *Gas Chromatography of Polymers*; Elsevier, Amsterdam 1977

V. Brüderle, *Thermofraktographie zur Schnellanalyse von Epoxidharzen und PVC-Weichmachern*; Thesis, Math. Nat. Sci. Faculty, Saarbrücken 1979

J. Chiu, Thermogravimetry for chemical analysis of polymers, in J. Mitchell (ed.), *Applied Polymer Analysis and Characterization*; Carl Hanser, Munich etc. 1987

D. C. De Jongh, Pyrolytic reaction mechanisms, in C. E. Roland Jones, C. A. Cramers (eds.), *Analytical Pyrolysis*; Elsevier, Amsterdam 1977

G. Geuskens (ed.), *Degradation and Stabilization of Polymers*; Appl. Science Publ., London 1975

N. Grassie (ed.), *Developments in Polymer Degradation*, Vol. 7; Appl. Sci. Publ., London 1988

J. K. Haken, *Gas Chromatography of Coating Materials*; Marcel Dekker, New York 1974

W. L. Hawkins (ed.), *Polymer Stabilization*; John Wiley, New York 1972

W. J. Irwin, *Analytical Pyrolysis: A Comprehensive Guide*; Marcel Dekker, New York etc. 1982

H. H. G. Jellinek (ed.), *Degradation and Stabilization of Polymers*, Vol. 1; Elsevier, Amsterdam 1983

C. E. Roland Jones, C. A. Cramers (ed.), *Analytical Pyrolysis*; Elsevier, Amsterdam 1977

H. H. Kausch, H. G. Zachmann, *Characterization of Polymers in the Solid State*; Springer, Berlin etc. 1985

R. L. Levy, *Chromatogr. Rev. 8* (1966) 49...89; Pyrolysis gas chromatography. A review of the technique

S. A. Liebman, E. J. Levy (eds.), *Pyrolysis and GC in Polymer Analysis*; Marcel Dekker, New York 1985

S. L. Madorsky, *Thermal Degradation of Organic Polymers*; Interscience Publ., New York 1964

R. W. May, E. F. Pearson, D. Schothern, *Pyrolysis Gas Chromatography*; Anal. Sci. Monograph No. 3, Chem. Soc., London 1977

H. Ohtani, S. Tsuge, Polymer characterization by high-resolution pyrolysis-gas chromatography, in J. Mitchell (ed.), *Applied Polymer Analysis and Characterization*; Carl Hanser, Munich etc. 1987

B. Rånby, J. F. Rabek, *Photodegradation, Photooxidation and Photostabilization of Polymers*; John Wiley, London 1975

E. Stahl, V. Brüderle, *Adv. Polym. Sci. 30* (1979) 3...88; Polymer analysis by thermofractography

M. P. Stevens, *Characterization and Analysis of Polymers by Gas Chromatography*; Marcel Dekker, New York 1969

E. Turi (ed.), *Thermal Characterization of Polymeric Materials*; Academic Press, Orlando etc. 1981

N. E. Vanderborgh, Laser induced pyrolysis techniques, in C. E. Roland Jones, C. A. Cramers (eds.), *Analytical Pyrolysis*; Elsevier, Amsterdam 1977

B. B. Wheals, Forensic applications of analytical pyrolysis techniques, in C. E. Roland Jones, C. A. Cramers (eds.), *Analytical Pyrolysis*; Elsevier, Amsterdam 1977

2 Methodology of vibration spectroscopy

2.1 Calibration, standards, nomenclature

A. R. H. Cole, *Spectrochim. Acta 41A* (1985) 9...23; Water vapour spectra for the calibration of infrared spectrometers

J. Denaxas, D. O. Hummel, *Makromol. Chem. 126* (1969) 269; Über Taktizität und Taxis

L. May, *Appl. Spectrosc. 27* (1973) 419...20; Spectroscopic nomenclature

K. D. Mielenz, *Anal. Chem. 48* (1976) 1093...4; Comments on spectrometry nomenclature

K. N. Rao, W. W. Brim, V. I. Sinnett, R. H. Wilson, *J. Opt. Soc. Am. 52* (1962) 862...5; Wavelength calibrations in the (far) infrared. IV. Use of a 1000-lines-per-inch Bausch and Lomb plane replica grating

K. N. Rao, C. J. Humphreys, D. H. Rank, *Wavelength Standards in the Infrared*; Academic Press, New York etc. 1966

2.2 Instrumentation, preparation techniques

2.2.1 Preparation techniques for transmission spectroscopy

B. Bak, D. Christensen, *Acta chem. scand. 10* (1956) 692...4; Difficulties at the infrared-spectrophotometric identification and estimation of pure compounds and mixtures by use of potassium bromide disk technique

K. B. Bradley, W. J. Potts, *Appl. Spectrosc. 12* (1958) 77...80; The internally standardized nujol mull as a method of quantitative infrared spectroscopy

G. C. N. Cheesman, L. J. Gaskin, *Anal. Chem. 57* (1985) 1167f.; Preparation of uniform films from latex for infrared analysis

J. P. Coates, *Europ. Spectrosc. News 16* (1978) 25...33; The analysis of aqueous solutions by infrared spectroscopy

G. Duyckaerts, *Spectrochim. Acta 7* (1955) 25...31; Beitrag zur quantitativen Analyse von Pulvern durch ihre *IR*-Absorptionsspektren. I. Theoretische Untersuchung

V. C. Farmer, *Spectrochim. Acta 8* (1957) 374...89; Effects of grinding during the preparation of alkali-halide disks on the infrared spectra of hydroxylic compounds

J. R. Ferraro, L. J. Basile, *Am. Lab. 11/3* (1979) 31 f., 34, 36, 38, 40 f.; The diamond anvil cell as a sampling device in *IR*

W. R. Harp, H. Stone, J. W. Otvos, *Spectrochim. Acta 9* (1957) 148...56; Quantitative infrared absorption spectrometry with the KBr technique

J. H. van der Maas, A. Tolks, *Spectrochim. Acta 18* (1962) 235; The influence of moisture on potassium bromide disks used in infrared spectrometry

P. MacCarthy, S. J. Bowman, *Anal. Chem. 53* (1981) 1151...2; Mulls of deuterated solid samples for infrared spectrometry

L. May, K. J. Schwing, *Appl. Spectrosc. 17* (1963) 166; The use of polyethylene disks in the far infrared spectroscopy of solids

J. W. Otvos, H. Stone, W. R. Harp, *Spectrochim. Acta 2* (1957) 148...56; Theory of radiant energy absorption by randomly dispersed, discrete particles

L. R. Pearson, *ACS Div. Org. Coat. Plast. Chem. Pap. 30* (1970) 91 f.; Infrared analysis of polymer surfaces and strata by potassium bromide abrasion techniques

H. Röpke, W. Neudert, *Z. analyt. Chem. 170* (1959) 78...95; Über die Vorzüge und Grenzen der KBr-Präpariermethode in der *IR*-Spektrographie

H. Rosenkrantz, P. Potvin, P. Skogstrom, *Anal. Chem. 30* (1958) 975...7; Quantitative application of sample dispersion in potassium bromide for infrared analysis of steroids

U. Schiedt, H. Reinwein, *Z. Naturforsch. 7b* (1952) 270; Zur Infrarotspektroskopie von Aminosäuren: Eine neue Präparationstechnik zur Infrarotspektroskopie von Aminosäuren und anderen polaren Verbindungen

B. Smethurst, D. Steele, *Spectrochim. Acta 20* (1964) 242...4; The use of pressed polythene disks in infra-red spectroscopy

M. M. Stimson, M. J. O'Donnell, *J. Am. Chem. Soc. 74* (1952) 1805; The infrared and ultraviolet absorption spectra of cytosine and isocytosine in the solid state

2.2.2 Measurement at high and low temperatures

J. E. Bertie, E. Whalley, *Spectrochim. Acta 20* (1964) 1349...56; Infrared spectra by mulling techniques at liquid-nitrogen temperatures

J. W. Brasch, R. J. Jakobsen, *Spectrochim. Acta 20* (1964) 1644...6; The use of a polyethylene matrix for studying dilution and low-temperature effects in the far infrared

K. Holland-Moritz, I. Modrič, *Progr. Colloid Polym. Sci. 57* (1975) 212...5; Zwei neu entwickelte Zellen für Raman- und infrarotspektroskopische Untersuchungen zwischen 80 K und 650 K

G. Zundel, *Chemie-Ingenieur-Technik 35* (1963) 306...9; Infrarot-Tieftemperatur-Küvette

2.2.3 Micromethods, miscellaneous experimental techniques

C. J. Curry, M. J. Whitehouse, J. M. Chalmers, *Appl. Spectrosc. 39* (1985) 174...80; Ultramicrosampling in infrared spectroscopy using small apertures

M. P. Fuller, P. R. Griffiths, *Appl. Spectrosc. 34* (1980) 533...9; Infrared microsampling by diffuse reflectance Fourier transform spectrometry

M. A. Harthcock, L. A. Lentz, B. L. Davis, K. Krishnan, *Appl. Spectrosc. 40* (1986) 210...14; Applications of transmittance and reflectance micro/*FT-IR* to polymeric materials

R. E. Kagarise, K. B. Whetsel, *Spectrochim. Acta 17* (1961) 869...79; The determination of frequency shifts by differential spectroscopy

K. Krishnan, *ACS Polym. Prepr. 25/2* (1984) 182...4; Application of *FTIR* microsampling techniques to some polymer systems

P. L. Lang, J. E. Katon, D. W. Schiering, J. F. O'Keefe, *Polym. Mat. Sci. Eng. 54* (1986) 381...5; Application of infrared and Raman microspectroscopy to polymer characterization

F. Luigart, *Kunststoffe 70* (1980) 66...7; Pyrolyse-*IR*-Spektroskopie von Polymeren — Analyse im Mikromaßstab

E. Lünebach, D. O. Hummel, *Kunststoffe 54* (1964) 210...2; Vermeiden von Interferenzen in *IR*-Spektren von Kunststoff-Folien

Ch. Lutinski, *Anal. Chem. 30* (1958) 2071; Method for elimination of interference fringes in spectra of thin films

G. W. Peitscher, *Macromol. Chem. Macromol. Symp. 5* (1986) 75...85; Infrarot-Mikrospektroskopie an Polymeren

J. C. Phillips, A. Peterlin, P. F. Waters, *J. Polym. Sci. Polym. Phys. Ed. 19* (1981) 789...802; Apparatus for infrared measurement of sorption/desorption in strained polymeric films

B. F. Plummer, *J. Chem. Educ. 61* (1984) 439; Measuring polymer film thickness by interference patterns

H. Rebhan, F. Luigart, *Farbe Lack 89* (1983) 425f.; Identifizierung des Lackbindemittels von ausgehärteten, silikat- und carbonhaltigen Lacksystemen

A. N. Sabadas, T. B. Razmachnina, M. S. Akutin, *Dokl. Akad. Nauk. SSSR 260* (1981) 390...3 (Russ.); Spectroscopic investigation of submicro defects in polymers

Th. A. Veerkamp, J. R. de Kock, A. Veermans, M. H. Lardinoye, *Anal. Chem. 36* (1964) 2277; Thickness measurement of polymer films for infrared spectrometry by β-ray absorption analysis of ethene-propene copolymers

H. Wagner, J. Bohm, *Spectrochim. Acta 21* (1965) 427...32; Die Verwendung von Siliciumscheiben als Fenstermaterial für *IR*-Untersuchungen an stark korrodierenden Substanzen

2.2.4 Measurement of *IR* dichroism (polarization spectrometry)

B. Amram, L. Bokobza, J. P. Queslel, L. Monnerie, *Polymer 17* (1986) 877...82; Fourier-transform infra-red dichroism study of molecular orientation in synthetic high *cis*-1,4-polyisoprene and in natural rubber

G. Bauer, H. Mikosch, *Monatsh. Chem. 110* (1979) 1441...7; Bestimmung der Richtung des Übergangsmomentes in gestreckten Molekeln durch Messung der *IR*-Dichroismus. 7. Kritische Untersuchungen des Orientierungsgrades der Molekeln in gereckten Polymeren

L. L. Chapoy, R. K. Sethi, P. Ravn Sorensen, K. H. Rasmussen, *Polym. Photochem. 1* (1981) 131...7; Spatial disposition of probe molecules in uniaxially oriented poly(N-vinylcarbazole): a dichroic absorption study

A. Cunningham, G. R. Davies, I. M. Ward, *Polymer 15* (1974) 743...8; Determination of molecular orientation by polarized infra-red radiation in an oriented polymer of high polarizability

J. Dechant, C. Ruscher, *Faserforsch. Textiltechn. 16* (1965) 180...5; Über die Feinstruktur der Polyamide. V. Dichroismus und Zuordnung des Ultrarotspektrums von Polycaprolactam

G. M. Estes, R. W. Seymour, S. L. Cooper, *Macromolecules 4* (1971) 452...7; Infrared studies of segmented polyurethane elastomers. II. Infrared dichroism

L. J. Fina, J. L. Koenig, A method to explore three-dimensional absorption in polymers, in J.G. Grasselli, D. G. Cameron (eds.), *SPIE Symp. Proc.* 553; Washington, DC 1985

L. J. Fina, J. L. Koenig, *J. Polym. Sci. Polym. Phys. Ed. 24* (1986) 2509; Analysis of trichroic infrared absorption in solids. I. Description of the method; *ibid.* 2525. II. One-way drawn polyethylene terephthalate

L. J. Fina, J. L. Koenig, W. L. Gordon, *J. Polym. Sci. Polym. Phys. Ed. 24* (1986) 2541...51; Analysis of trichroic infrared absorption in solids. III. Phase *I* poly(vinylidene fluoride)

M. L. Fridman, S. P. Morozova, L. G. Rajz, *Plast. Massy 1979* (4) 34f. (Russ.); Determination of the degree of orientation in thermoplastic films

W. Glenz, A. Peterlin, *J. Macromol. Sci. Phys. B4* (1970) 473...90; IR-studies of drawn polyethylene. I. Changes in orientation and conformation of highly drawn linear polyethylene

W. Glenz, A. Peterlin, *Kolloid-Z. Z. Polymere 247* (1971) 786...94; Infrarot-Untersuchungen an verstrecktem Polyäthylen

W. Glenz, A. Peterlin, *J. Polym. Sci. A-2 9* (1971) 1191...1217; IR-studies of drawn polyethylene. II. Orientation behavior of highly drawn linear and ethyl branched polyethylene

W. Glenz, A. Peterlin, *Makromol. Chem. 150* (1971) 163...77; IR-studies of drawn polyethylene. III. The orientation of vinyl and methyl end-groups

R. Gotoh, T. Takenaka, N. Hayama, *Kolloid-Z. Z. Polymere 205* (1965) 18; Simultaneous measurements of stress and infrared dichroism on polymers. I. Stress relaxation of vulcanized natural rubber

R. T. Graf, J. L. Koenig, H. Ishida, Fourier transform infrared ellipsometry of thin polymer films, in J. G. Grasselli, D. G. Cameron (eds.), *SPIE Symp. Proc.* 553; Washington, DC 1985; *Anal. Chem. 58* (1986) 64...8

R. T. Graf, F. Eng, J. L. Koenig, H. Ishida, *Appl. Spectrosc. 40* (1986) 498; Polarization modulation Fourier transform infrared ellipsometry of thin polymer films

S. Hosoda, M. Furuta, *Makromol. Chem. Rapid Commun. 2* (1981) 577...83; Infrared dichroism of the methyl group for some ethylene/α-olefin copolymers

S. Hosoda, *Makromol. Chem. 185* (1984) 787...95; Investigation of molecular orientation and conformational change upon drawing for various ethylene/1-butene copolymers by *IR* spectroscopy

I. J. Hutchinson et al., *Polymer 21* (1980) 55...65; *IR* measurement of one-dimensionally stretched poly(ethylene terephthalate) films with constant elongation

H. Ishihara, *J. Macromol. Sci. B22* (1983/84) 763...82; Investigations on segmented poly(urethane urea) elastomers: structure and properties of segmented poly(urethane urea)s with binary hard-segment components

V. A. Khranovskii, *Vysokomol. Soedin. A 22* (1980) 1380...7 (Russ.); Inversion of *IR* dichroism in segmented polyurethane elastomers

V. A. Khranovskii, L. P. Guliko, *J. Macromol. Sci. Phys. B22* (1983) 497...508; *IR* dichroism and orientation of segmented polyurethane-urea elastomers

Y. V. Kissin, *J. Polym. Sci. Polym. Phys. Ed. 21* (1983) 2085...96; Orientation of isotactic polypropylene in crystalline and amorphous phases: *IR* methods

A. Kivinen, M. Ovaska, M. Rasanen, *J. Mol. Struct. 95* (1982) 141...50; Polarized infrared spectra. Pt. 1. Stretched polymer method. Fundamental vibrations of some mono- and disubstituted benzenes

E. Küpper, W. Wilke, *Colloid Polym. Sci. 257* (1979) 113...6; Bestimmung von Orientierungszuständen verstreckter Polyäthylenfolien mittels *IR*-Dichroismus und Röntgenweitwinkelstreuung

S. V. Laptij, *Vysokomol. Soedin. B 21* (1979) 791...4 (Russ.); Peculiarities in the orientation behavior of linear polyurethanes based on tritetramethylene glycol and hexamethylene diisocyanate

S. V. Laptij, Ju. S. Lipatov, Ju. Ju. Kerca, L. A. Kosenko, V. N. Batulev, R. L. Gajduk, *Dokl. Akad. Nauk SSSR 261* (1981) 682...5 (Russ.); Investigation of the inversion of infrared dichroism in linear, crystallizable polyurethanes

J. E. Lasch, E. Dobrovolny, S. E. Molis, S. L. Hsu, *ACS Polym. Prepr. 25/2* (1984) 169 f.; Deformation studies of polymers by time resolved and polarization modulation spectroscopy

D. Levebvre et al., *Polymer 25* (1984) 318...22; Orientation and relaxation in uniaxially stretched poly(2,6-dimethyl-1,4-phenylene oxide)/atactic polystyrene blends

D. H. MacKerron, *Polym. Commun. 26* (1985) 130 f.; Infrared evidence of tie molecules in oriented polyamide films

J. R. Nielsen, R. F. Holland, *J. Mol. Spectr. 6* (1961) 394...418; Dichroism and interpretation of the infrared bands of oriented crystalline polyethylene

J. H. Nobbs, D. I. Bower, I. M. Ward, *J. Polym. Sci. Polym. Phys. Ed. 17* (1979) 259...72; Comparison of polarized fluorescence with polarized Raman and infrared dichroism measures of orientation in uniaxially drawn poly(ethylene terephthalate)

I. Noda, A. E. Dowrey, C. Marcott, *J. Polym. Sci. Polym. Lett. Ed. 21* (1983) 99...103; Dynamic infrared linear dichroism of polymer films under oscillatory deformation

I. Noda, C. Marcott, *ACS Polym. Prepr. 25/2* (1984) 167 f.; Characterization of polymers using polarization-modulation infrared techniques

B. E. Read, R. S. Stein, *Macromolecules 1* (1968) 117...126; Polarized infrared studies of amorphous orientation in polyethylene and some copolymers

B. E. Read, D. A. Hughes, D. C. Barnes, F. W. M. Drury, *Polymer 13* (1972) 485...94; Measurement of infrared dichroism, stress, and strain of elongated polymers

B. E. Read, D. A. Hughes, *Polymer 13* (1972) 495...502; Stress-dichroism studies of the 4.92 μm band of amorphous crosslinked polyethylene

F. Rietsch, B. Jasse, *Polym. Bull. 11* (1984) 287...93; Investigation of the molecular orientation of one-dimensionally stretched polyethylene terephthalate films by polarized infrared spectroscopy and polarization microscopy

R. J. Samuels, *Makromol. Chem. Suppl. 4* (1981) 241...70; Infrared dichroisms, molecular structure, and deformation mechanism of isotactic polypropylene

T. Soen, T. Murakami, Y. Nomura, S. Nomura, *J. Rheol. 24* (1980) 344; Apparatus for dynamic infrared dichroism during sinusoidal strain

C. S. Sung, C. B. Hu, *Macromolecules 14* (1981) 212...5; Orientation studies of segmented polyether poly(urethane urea) elastomers by infrared dichroism

J. F. Tassin, L. Monnerie, L. J. Fetters, *Polym. Bull. 15* (1986) 165...71; Infrared dichroism investigation of molecular viscoelasticity using isotopically labelled block copolymers

Y. Uemura, R. S. Stein, *J. Polym. Sci. Polym. Phys. Ed. 10* (1972) 1691...8; Change in infrared dichroism during and following high-speed elongation of polyethylene

V. N. Vatulev, S. V. Laptij, R. L. Gajduk, Ju. Ju. Kerca, *Vysokomol. Soedin. A 23* (1981) 2470...7 (Russ.); Inversion of infrared dichroism in segmented polyurethane elastomers

I. M. Ward, *Adv. Polym. Sci. 66* (1985) 81...115; Determination of molecular orientation by spectroscopic techniques

2.2.5 Measurement of attenuated total reflectance (*ATR* spectroscopy)

J. C. Andries, H. E. Diem, *J. Polym. Sci. Polym. Lett. Ed. 12* (1974) 281...6; A study of ozone attack on elastomer surfaces by attenuated total reflectance spectroscopy

P. Baranowski, D. Lupa, *Zesz. Nauk. — Akad. Ekon. Pznaniu Ser. 1 69* (1976) 59...62 (Pol.); *ATR-IR* spectroscopic methods for the analysis of coating materials

A. J. Barbetta, *Appl. Spectrosc. 38* (1984) 29...31; Polarized infrared attenuated total reflection spectra of powders

R. D. Blackledge, *J. Forensic Sci. 26* (1981) 554...6; Examination of automobile rubber bumper guards by attenuated total reflectance spectroscopy using a Fourier transform infrared spectrometer

E. J. Castillo, J. L. Koenig, J. M. Anderson, *Biomaterials 5* (1984) 186; Surface analysis of biomedical polymers by attenuated total reflectance-Fourier transform infrared spectroscopy

A. M. Dwivedi, D. S. Jayasuriya, *Polym. Mat. Sci. Eng. 54* (1986) 392...6; *FTIR* studies of poly(ethylene oxide) in aqueous solution using cylindrical internal reflection cell

J. A. Gardella, G. L. Grobe, W. L. Hopson, E. M. Eyring, *Anal. Chem. 56* (1984) 1169...77; Comparison of attenuated total reflectance and photoacoustic sampling for surface analysis of polymer mixtures by Fourier transform infrared spectroscopy

P. H. Gedam, P. S. Sampathkumaran, *Prog. Org. Coat. 11* (1983) 313...38; Attenuated total reflection *IR* spectroscopy (*FMIRS*): application on surface coating materials

G. Gidály, R. Kellner, *Mikrochim. Acta 1981 I*, 131...9; Simultaneous qualitative and quantitative *FT-IR-ATR*-spectroscopic analysis of submicrometre organic films and of the surface layer of bulk polymer samples

R. T. Graf, J. L. Koenig, H. Ishida, *ACS Polym. Prepr. 25/2* (1984) 188 f.; Comparison of *FTIR* transmission, specular reflectance, and attenuated total reflectance spectra of polymers

A. Hatta, *Mol. Cryst. Liq. Cryst. 62* (1980) 251...8; Application of infrared *ATR* spectroscopy to liquid crystals

J. P. Hobbs, S. Hill, C. S. Sung, K. Krishnan, *Soc. Plast. Eng. Techn. Pap. 28* (1982) 69...71; Three dimensional characterization of polymer surface structure by modified attentuated total reflection *IR* dichroism

J. P. Hobbs, C. S. P. Sung, K. Krishnan, S. Hill, *Macromolecules 16* (1983) 193...9; Characterization of surface structure and orientation in polypropylene and poly(ethylene terephthalate) films by modified attenuated total reflection *IR* dichroism studies

N. V. Ionina, *Zh. Prikl. Spektrosk. 35* (1981) 329...34 (Russ.); Study of the surface orientation of polymers by a method of polarization infrared spectroscopy of multiple attenuated total internal reflection

R. Iwamoto, K. Ohta, *Appl. Spectrosc. 38* (1984) 359...65; Quantitative surface analysis by Fourier transform attenuated total reflection infrared spectroscopy

R. Iwamoto, K. Ohta, T. Matsuda, K. Imachi, *J. Biomed. Mat. Res. 20* (1986) 507...20; Quantitative surface analysis of Cardiothane 51 by *FT-IR-ATR* spectroscopy

B. Jansen, H. Steinhauser, W. Prohaska, *Makromol. Chem. Macromol. Symp. 5* (1986) 237...44; Plasma treatment of the inner surface of polymer tubes for the improvement of their anticoagulant properties

T. S. Juscenko, A. V. Uvarov, R. M. Livsic, *Vysokomol. Soedin. A 24* (1982) 1999...2001 (Russ.); Methods of investigation of the photopolymerization of the lower layers of pigmented films

R. Kellner, G. Gidály, *Mikrochim. Acta 1981*, 119...29; Fourier-transform infrared versus conventional grating-infrared-attenuated total reflectance spectroscopic investigation of the adsorption of blood proteins on polymer surfaces

R. Kellner, G. Gidály, F. Unger, *Adv. Biomater. 3* (1982) 423...8; *FTIR-ATR* spectroscopic analysis of polyurethane-silicone blood-contact surfaces

R. Kellner, G. Götzinger, *Mikrochim. Acta 1984*, 61...74; *FTIR-ATR* spectroscopic analysis of the protein adsorption on polymer blood contact surfaces

R. Kellner, G. Götzinger, E. Pungor, K. Tóth, L. Polos, *Fresenius Z. analyt. Chem. 319* (1984) 839f.; *FTIR-ATR*-spectroscopic analysis of depth distribution of crown ethers on PVC-membrane surfaces

R. Kellner, G. Fischböck, G. Götzinger, E. Pungor, K. Tóth, L. Polos, E. Lindner, *Fresenius Z. analyt. Chem. 322* (1985) 151...6; *FTIR-ATR* spectroscopic analysis of *bis*-crown-ether based PVC-membrane surface

R. Kellner, In-situ *FTIR-ATR* spectroscopic studies of reactions in polymer surface areas, in W. E. Steger (ed.), *Progress in Polymer Spectroscopy*; Teubner, Leipzig 1986

E. W. Kinkelaar, J. T. Rozsa, L. J. Vavruska, *J. Paint Technol. 46* (1974) 63...8; Cure determination of coil coatings by the use of attenuated total reflectance (*ATR*) infrared techniques

V. Krentz, *Melliand Textilber. 5* (1969) 557...63; Ein Beitrag zur infrarotspektroskopischen Untersuchung von Textilien und Kunstledern nach dem *FMIR*-Verfahren

G. Leukroth, *Gummi Asbest Kunstst. 28* (1970) 1118, 1120, 1122, 1124; Mögliche Anwendung der *ATR*-Technik in der Analyse von polymeren Produkten

B. Liedberg, B. Ivarsson, J. Lundström, W. R. Salanek, *Progr. Coll. Polym. Sci. 70* (1985) 67...75; Fourier transform infrared reflection absorption spectroscopy (*FT-IRAS*) of some biologically important molecules adsorbed on metal surfaces

G. Menges, H. Schwesig, G. Hahn, *Org. Coat. Plast. Chem. 44* (1981) 229...33; Quantitative determination of reaction in PUR foam formation

F. M. Mirabella, *J. Polym. Sci. Polym. Phys. Ed. 20* (1982) 2309...15; Quantitative analysis of polymers by attenuated total reflectance Fourier-transform infrared spectroscopy. Vinyl acetate and methyl content of polyethylene

R. N. O'Brien, K. Hartman, *ACS Org. Coat. Plast. Chem. 28* (1968) 236...45; *ATR* (attenuated total reflectance) infrared spectroscopy study of the epoxy-cellulose interface

K. Ohta, R. Iwamoto, *Anal. Chem. 57* (1985) 2491...9; Lower limit of the thickness of the measurable surface layer by Fourier transform infrared attenuated total reflection spectrometry

K. Ohta, R. Iwamoto, *Appl. Spectrosc. 39* (1985) 418...25; Experimental proof of the relation between thickness of the probed surface layer and absorbance in *FT-IR/ATR* spectroscopy

A. Pirnia, C. S. Sung, *ACS Polym. Prepr. 28/1* (1987) 9f.; Three-dimensional orientation measurements in liquid crystalline polymers by *FT-IR ATR* dichroism

S. E. Polchlopek, *Appl. Spectrosc. 17* (1963) 112ff.; *ATR* effects with different prisms

K.-H. Reichert, *Farbe Lack 72* (1966) 13...21; Anwendung der *ATR*-Methode zur infrarotspektroskopischen Untersuchung von Mehrschicht-Anstrichfilmen

A. E. Rheineck, R. H. Peterson, G. M. Sastry, *J. Paint Technol. 39* (1967) 484...9; Attenuated total reflectance studies on drying oil films

E. Roggendorf et al., *Plaste Kautsch. 23* (1976) 586...9; Messungen der geschwächten *IR*-Totalreflexion zur Prüfung der Biostabilität von Plasten und Elasten

P. B. Roush, *Proc. SPIE-Int. Soc. Opt. Eng. 289* (1981) 124...6; Use of heated attenuated total reflectance (*ATR*) to monitor polymer transitions

D. A. Saucy, S. J. Simko, R. W. Linton, *Anal. Chem. 57* (1985) 871...5; Comparison of photoacoustic and attenuated total reflectance sampling depths in the infrared region

S. D. Stuchebryukov, A. A. Vavkushevsky, V. M. Rudoy, *Surface Interface Anal. 6* (1984) 29...33; Quantitative attenuated total reflection (*ATR*) spectroscopy of films with an absorption gradient

C. S. P. Sung, *Macromolecules 14* (1981) 591...4; Modified technique for measurement of orientation from polymer surfaces by attenuated total reflection infrared dichroism

C. S. P. Sung, J. P. Hobbs, *ACS Polym. Prepr. 25/2* (1984) 154f.; Recent development of *FT-IR* attenuated total internal reflection dichroism techniques for structural characterization of polymer surfaces

A. M. Tiefenthaler, W. M. Urban, *ACS Polym. Prepr. 28/1* (1987) 6; Application of circle *ATR FT-IR* spectroscopy to surface studies of polymer films and fibers

A. Trifonov, *Z. phys. Chemie (Leipzig) 254* (1973) 156...72; Anwendung der *ATR*-Spektroskopie bei der Untersuchung von polymeren Schichten und den darin ablaufenden Vorgängen

M. K. Tse, C. S. Sung, *Org. Coat. Plast. Chem. 42* (1980) 734...8; Comparison of crystallinity and molecular orientation between surface and bulk of some polymers by *FTIR-ATR* and transmission spectroscopy

A. E. Tshmel, V. I. Vettegren, V. M. Zolotarev, A. F. Ioffe, *J. Macromol. Sci. Physics B21* (1982) 243...64; Investigation of the molecular structure of polymer surfaces by *ATR* spectroscopy

V. I. Vettegren, A. E. Tshmel, *Vysokomol. Soedin. B18* (1976) 521...3 (Russ.); Intermolecular interactions of the surface of polymers

H. Wagner, L. Wuckel, *Plaste Kautsch. 18* (1971) 426...30; Infrarotspektroskopische Untersuchungen an Kunststoff-oberflächen mittels *ATR*

T. Zajicek, M. Camelot, C. Roques-Carmes, *Polym. Mat. Sci. Eng. 54* (1986) 386...91; Surface characterization of polymers by space oriented absorbance using *IR-ATR* spectroscopy

R. G. Zbankov, O. N. Tretinnikov, *Vysokomol. Soedin. A 27* (1985) 2200...5 (Russ.); Account of nonideal character of the contact between a sample and reflecting element in quantitative *ATR-IR*-spectroscopy of polymers

2.2.6 Reflectance absorption spectroscopy, diffuse reflectance, other methods of reflectance spectroscopy

D. L. Allara, A. Baca, C. A. Pryde, *Macromolecules 11* (1978) 1215...20; Distortions of band shapes in external reflection infrared spectra of thin polymer films on metal substrates

D. L. Allara, C. A. Pryde, *Org. Coat. Plast. Chem. 38* (1979) 638...45; The application of external reflection infrared spectroscopy to thermal reactions of ultra thin polymer films

D. L. Allara, *Polym. Sci. Technol. 12B* (1980) 751...6; Adsorption studies of polymers on metals by Fourier transform reflection infrared spectroscopy

R. L. Barbour, J. R. Mooney, M. Mehicic, R. J. Weinert, K. C. Benton, J. G. Grasselli, *Makromol. Chem. Macromol. Symp. 5* (1986) 49...59; Polymer coatings on steel substrates: an infrared spectroscopic study of temperature effects

C. S. Blackwell, P. J. Degen, F. D. Osterholtz, *Appl. Spectrosc. 32* (1978) 480...4; Internal reflectance spectroscopy of reacted surfaces: fluorinated polyethylene and polypropylene

F. J. Boerio, C. A. Gosselin, *Adv. Chem. Ser. 203* (1983) 541...58; *IR* spectra of polymers and coupling agents adsorbed onto oxidized aluminum

J. M. Chalmers et al., *Polym. Bull. 11* (1984) 433...5; Investigation of the crystallinity of poly(acryl ether ketones) by reflection spectroscopy

M. G. Chan, D. L. Allara, *Polym. Eng. Sci. 14* (1974) 12...5; Infrared reflection studies of metal-polymer interfaces

D. B. Chase, R. L. Amey, W. G. Holtje, *Appl. Spectrosc. 36* (1982) 155...7; Applications of diffuse reflectance *FT-IR* to pigment photodecomposition in paint

E. G. Chatzi, H. Ishida, J. L. Koenig, Application of diffuse reflectance *FT-IR* spectroscopy for the surface study of Kevlar fibers, in J. G. Grasselli, D. G. Cameron (eds.), *SPIE Symp. Proc. 553*; Washington, DC 1985

E. G. Chatzi, S. L. Tidrick, J. L. Koenig, *ACS Polym. Prepr. 28/1* (1987) 13f.; Characterization of the surface hydrolysis of Kevlar-49-fibers by diffuse reflectance *FT-IR* spectroscopy

S. R. Culler, H. Ishida, J. L. Koenig, *Appl. Spectrosc. 38* (1984) 1...7; Nondestructive *FT-IR* sampling techniques to study glass fiber composite interfaces

S. R. Culler, M. T. McKenzie, L. J. Fina, H. Ishida, J. L. Koenig, *Appl. Spectrosc. 38* (1984) 791; Fourier transform diffuse reflectance infrared study of polymer films and coatings; a method for studying polymer systems

S. Curran, S. Siggia, R. Porter, E. Otocka, *Org. Coat. Plast. Chem. 42* (1980) 760...6; Reflectance infrared analysis of polystyrene photooxidation

H. Dannenberg, J. W. Forbes, A. C. Jones, *Anal. Chem. 32* (1960) 365...70; Infrared spectroscopy of surface coatings in reflected light

J. A. Davies, A. Sood, *Makromol. Chem. 186* (1985) 1631...42; *DRIFT* study of functional group interconversions on modified silica surfaces

R. V. Flor, M. J. Prager, *J. Text. Inst. 73* (1982) 138...41; Monitoring by multiple-internal-reflection spectroscopy of the removal of scotchgard finishes from rayon-ramie blends

J. D. Frazee, *J. Oil Col. Chem. Assoc. 57* (1974) 300...9; Internal reflection spectroscopy: application to organic coatings and plastic sheeting

M. P. Fuller, P. R. Griffiths, *Anal. Chem. 50* (1978) 1906...10; Diffuse reflectance measurements by infrared Fourier transform spectrometry

A. Garton, *Polym. Composites 5* (1984) 258...63; A novel technique for the study of coupling agent phenomena

R. T. Graf, J. L. Koenig, H. Ishida, *ACS Polym. Prepr. 25/2* (1984) 159; *In-situ* studies of polymeric fibers by *FTIR* external reflectance spectroscopy

R. T. Graf, J. L. Koenig, H. Ishida, *Anal Chem. 56* (1984) 773...8; Characterization of silane-treated glass fibers by diffuse reflectance Fourier transform spectroscopy

W. G. Golden, *ACS Polym. Prepr. 25/2* (1984) 158...6; Fourier transform infrared reflection-absorption spectroscopy of monolayers and thin films adsorbed on low-area surfaces

P. R. Griffiths, *Am. Lab. 10/10* (1978) 69f.; Infrared analysis by diffuse reflectance spectrometry

N. J. Harrick, Transmission and reflection spectroscopy, nature of the spectra, in L.-H. Lee, *Characterization of Metal and Polymer Surfaces*, Vol. 2: *Polymer Surfaces*; Academic Press, New York etc. 1977

A. Hatta et al., *Chem. Lett. 7* (1983) 1077...80; Measurement of *IR*-reflection-absorption spectra from thin poly(vinyl acetate) films on silicon surfaces

T. Hattori, K. Shirai, M. Niwa, Y. Murakami, *Bull. Chem. Soc. Japan 54* (1981) 1964...7; Quantitative interpretation of infrared diffuse reflectance spectra over the whole concentration range

R. Hempel, H. Viola, *Acta Polymer. 30* (1979) 450...2; Anwendung der Reflexionsspektroskopie zur Ermittlung der Tautomeranteile *p*-substituierter 4-Phenylazo-1-naphthole in Polyamidgewebe

G. J. Higgerson, J. W. Marler, J. P. Connell, *J. Text. Inst. 76* (1985) 133...44; Calibrating near-infra-red reflectance instruments for wool base and wool content

C. A. Hill, *J. Appl. Polym. Sci. 27* (1982) 3313...27; Degradation studies of plasticized PVC. I. Multiple internal reflection infrared spectroscopy

M. Ito, J. R. Pereira, R. S. Porter, *J. Polym. Sci. Polym. Lett. Ed. 20* (1982) 61...7; Surface characterization of extrusion-drawn semicrystalline poly(ethylene terephthalate) by multiple internal reflection

M. A. Kaiser, D. B. Chase, *Anal. Chem. 52* (1980) 1849...51; Diffuse reflectance infrared spectrometric analysis of ultrathin Carbowax 20 M on Chromosorb W

R. Kellner, *Mikrochim. Acta* (Wien) *1974*, 921...6; Identifizierung geringster Mengen organischer Rückstände auf kleinen, stark konkaven Achatlagerschalen durch Infrarotreflexionsspektroskopie

E. H. Korte, A. Otto, *Appl. Spectrosc. 42* (1988) in print; Infrared diffuse reflectance accessory for local analysis on bulky samples

S. A. Larsen, *J. Text. Int. 70* (1979) 526...8; Examination of wool top by infra-red reflectance: A note on the influence of dyeing

H. Maulhardt, D. Kunath, *Appl. Spectrosc. 34* (1980) 383...5; A simple device for diffuse reflectance Fourier transform infrared spectroscopy

M. T. McKenzie, D. L. Koenig, *ACS Polym. Prepr. 25/2* (1984) 180...1; Fourier transform diffuse reflectance infrared study of fibers, polymer films and coatings

M. T. McKenzie, J. L. Koenig, *Appl. Spectrosc. 39* (1985) 408; Further developments in the methodology of surface analysis by *FT-IR*: quantitative aspects of diffuse reflectance methods

M. T. McKenzie, S. R. Culler, J. L. Koenig, *Appl. Spectrosc. 38* (1984) 786; Applications of diffuse reflectance *FT-IR* to the characterization of an E-glass fiber/gamma-APS coupling system

F. M. Mirabella, *J. Polym. Sci. Polym. Phys. Ed. 23* (1985) 861...71; Quantitative aspects of internal reflection spectroscopy: polymer surface composition measurement

K. Molt, *Fresenius Z. analyt. Chem. 319* (1984) 743...50; Die Infrarot-Spektroskopie als Methode zur chemischen Charakterisierung von dünnen Schichten auf Metallen

T. Nguyen, W. E. Byrd, *Polym. Mat. Sci. Eng. 53* (1985) 568...73; Reflection/absorption Fourier transform infrared spectroscopy studies of the degradation of organic protective coatings on steel

T. Nguyen, E. Byrd, A. Tsao, *J. Appl. Polym. Sci. 32* (1986) 6339...52; Characterization of epoxy coatings on steel by reflection/absorption and angle of incidence Fourier transform infrared spectroscopy. 1. Effects of film thickness

H. X. Nguyen, H. Ishida, *Makromol. Chem. Macromol. Symp. 5* (1986) 135...49; Molecular analysis of the interface of poly(ether-ether-ketone) and the basal plane of graphite single crystals

C. M. Paralusz, *J. Colloid Interface Sci. 47* (1974) 719...46; Internal reflection spectroscopy applied to the analysis of adhesive tapes

T. P. Schultz, M. C. Templeton, G. D. McGinnis, *Anal. Chem. 57* (1985) 2867...9; Rapid determination of lignocellulose by diffuse reflectance Fourier transform infrared spectrometry

M. W. Urban, J. L. Koenig, Surface studies of E-glass fiber composite interfaces using diffuse reflectance and photoacoustic *FT-IR* spectroscopy, in J. G. Grasselli, D. G. Cameron (eds.), *SPIE Symp. Proc. 553*; Washington, DC 1985

M. W. Urban, E. G. Chatzi, B. C. Perry, J. L. Koenig, *Appl. Spectrosc. 40* (1986) 1103; Phase transitions and surface characterization of poly(butylene terephthalate) fibers by photoacoustic and diffuse reflectance Fourier transform infrared spectroscopy

P. A. Wilks, *Am. Lab. 12* (1980) 92, 94, 98...102; Internal reflection spectroscopy

G. Xue, S. Jiang, C. Dui, W. Zhu, R. Seng, *Polym. Bull. 15* (1986) 363...8; Characterization of orientation at polyester fiber surface by modified infrared reflection technique

2.2.7 Photoacoustic *IR* spectrometry

E. G. Chatzi, M. W. Urban, J. L. Koenig, *Makromol. Chem. Macromol. Symp. 5* (1986) 99...104; Characterization of Kevlar fiber surfaces using a newly developed infrared photoacoustic technique

E. G. Chatzi, H. Ishida, J. L. Koenig, Application of a modified *FT-IR* photoacoustic technique for the surface characterization of Kevlar fibers, in H. Ishida, J. L. Koenig (eds.), *Composite Interfaces*; Elsevier Sci. Publ., New York 1986

E. G. Chatzi, M. W. Urban, H. Ishida, J. L. Koenig, *Polymer 27* (1986) 1850; Determination of the accessibility of N-H groups of Kevlar 49 fibres by photoacoustic *FT-IR* spectroscopy

R. W. Duerst, P. Mahmoodi, *ACS Polym. Prepr. 25/2* (1984) 194...5; *IR-PAS* chamber for signal-to-noise enhancement

J. A. Gardella, Jr., G. L. Grobe, W. L. Hopson, E. M. Eyring, *Anal. Chem. 56* (1984) 1169...77; Comparison of attenuated total reflectance and photoacoustic sampling for surface analysis of polymer mixtures by Fourier transform infrared spectroscopy

L. H. Lee, *Org. Coat. Plast. Chem. 40* (1979) 116...23; Photoacoustic spectroscopy for the study of adhesion and adsorption of dyes and polymers

C. H. Lochmueller, D. Wilder, *Anal. Chim. Acta 116* (1980) 19...24; Qualitative examination of chemically-modified silica surfaces by near-infrared photoacoustic spectroscopy

J. F. McClelland, *Anal. Chem. 55* (1983) 89 A...105 A; Photoacoustic spectroscopy

C. K. N. Patel, *Proc. Int. Conf. Infrared Phys. 2nd* (1979) 111...21; Infrared optoacoustic spectroscopy

F. A. Rasoul, A. Anani, A. Mobasher, *J. Appl. Polym. Sci. 29* (1984) 1491...7; Use of photoacoustic spectroscopy in studying the natural weathering of polyethylene films

S. M. Riseman, E. M. Eyring, *Spectrosc. Lett. 14* (1981) 163...85; Normalizing infrared *FT* photoacoustic spectra of solids

M. G. Rockley, *Ultrason. Symp. Proc. 2* (1980) 649...51; Fourier-transformed infrared photoacoustic spectroscopy, the technique and its applications

B. S. H. Royce, Y. C. Teng, J. Enns, *Ultrason. Symp. Proc. 2* (1980) 652...7; Fourier transform infrared photoacoustic spectroscopy of solids

S. Tanaka, *ACS Polym. Prepr. 25/2* (1984) 190f.; *FTIR*-photoacoustic spectroscopy of films

N. Teramae, M. Hiroguchi, S. Tanaka, *Bull. Chem. Soc. Jpn. 55* (1982) 2097...100; Fourier transform infrared photoacoustic spectroscopy of polymers

N. Teramae, S. Tanaka, *Appl. Spectrosc. 39* (1985) 797...9; Subsurface layer detection by Fourier transform infrared photoacoustic spectroscopy

M. W. Urban, J. L. Koenig, *Appl. Spectrosc. 40* (1986) 994; Depth-profiling studies of double-layer PVF_2-on-PET films by Fourier transform infrared photoacoustic spectroscopy

D. W. Vidrine, *Appl. Spectrosc. 34* (1980) 314...9; Photoacoustic Fourier transform infrared spectroscopy of solid samples

D. W. Vidrine, *ACS Polym. Prepr. 25/2* (1984) 147f.; Photoacoustic and reflection *FT-IR* spectrometry: photometric approximations for practical quantitative analysis

F. G. Will, R. S. MacDonald, R. D. Gleim, M. R. Winkle, *J. Chem. Phys. 78* (1983) 5847...52; Infrared photoacoustic spectroscopy of undoped polyacetylene

C. Q. Yang, T. J. Ellis, R. R. Bresee, W. G. Fateley, *Polym. Mat. Sci. Eng. 53* (1985) 169...75; Depth profiling of *FT-IR* photoacoustic spectroscopy and its applications for polymeric materials studies

C. Q. Yang, W. G. Fateley, *Polym. Mat. Sci. Eng. 54* (1986) 404...10; *FT-IR PAS* surface characterization of polymers

S. I. Yaniger, S. M. Riseman, T. Frigo, E. M. Eyring, *J. Chem. Phys. 76* (1982) 4298...9; Infrared photoacoustic spectroscopy of conducting polymers. II. P-doped polyacetylene

S. I. Yaniger, D. J. Rose, W. P. McKenna, E. M. Eyring, *Macromolecules 17* (1984) 2579...83; Photoacoustic infrared spectroscopy of doped and undoped poly(p-phenylene)

S. I. Yaniger, D. J. Rose, W. P. McKenna, E. M. Eyring, *Appl. Spectrosc. 38* (1984) 7...11; Infrared photoacoustic spectroscopy of conducting polymers. III. Poly-p-phenylene and its derivatives

2.2.8 Emission *IR* spectroscopy

D. L. Allara, D. Teicher, J. F. Durana, *Chem. Phys. Lett. 84* (1981) 20...4; Fourier transform infrared emission spectrum of a molecular monolayer at 300 K

D. B. Chase, *Appl. Spectrosc. 35* (1981) 77...81; The sensitivity and limitations of condensed phase infrared emission spectroscopy

K. Molt, *Fresenius Z. analyt. Chem. 308* (1981) 321...6; Aufnahme von Infrarot-Emissionsspektren dünner Schichten auf Metalloberflächen mit Hilfe eines rechnergekoppelten Gitterspektrometers

K. Wagatsume, K. Monma, W. Suetaka, *Appl. Surf. Sci. 7* (1981) 281...5; Infrared emission spectra of thin films on metal surfaces by a polarization modulation method

2.3 Spectroscopy in near and far infrared

2.3.1 *NIR* spectroscopy

A. Basch, T. Wasserman, M. Lewin, *J. Polym. Sci. Polym. Chem. Ed. 12* (1974) 1143...50; Near-infrared spectrum of cellulose: a new method for obtaining crystallinity ratios

K. H. Bassett, C. Y. Liang, R. H. Marchessault, *J. Polym. Sci. A-1* (1963) 1687...92; The infrared spectrum of crystalline polysaccharides. IX. The near infrared spectrum of cellulose

L. T. Black, G. E. Hammerstrand, W. F. Kwolek, *Rubber Chem. Techn. 58* (1985) 304...13; Analysis of rubber, resin, and moisture content of guayule by near infrared reflectance spectroscopy

R. M. Bly, P. E. Kiener, B. A. Fries, *Anal. Chem. 38* (1966) 217...20; Near-infrared method for analysis of block and random ethylene-propylene copolymers

M. Buback, H.-P. Vögele, H.-J. Winkels, *Makromol. Chem. Macromol. Symp. 5* (1986) 69...74; High-pressure absorption spectroscopy in polymerizing systems

G. Bucci, T. Simonazzi, *Chim. Ind. Milano 44* (1962) 262 (Ital.); Determination of the composition of ethylene-propylene copolymers by means of near-infrared spectroscopy

P. J. Corish, *Spectrochim. Acta 15* (1959) 598; Analysis of *cis*- and *trans*-1:4 contents of polyisoprenes by near infrared spectroscopy

E. W. Crandall, A. N. Jagtap, *J. Appl. Polym. Sci. 21* (1977) 449...54; The near-infrared spectra of polymers

H. Dannenberg, *SPE-Trans. 3/1* (1963) 78; Determination of functional groups in epoxy resins by near-infrared spectroscopy

H. V. Drushel, F. A. Iddings, *Anal. Chem. 35* (1963) 28...33; Infrared spectrophotometric analysis of ethylene-propylene copolymers

J. W. Ellis, J. Bath, *J. Am. Chem. Soc. 62* (1940) 2859...61; Hydrogen bridging in cellulose as shown by infrared absorption spectra

A. Evans, R. R. Hibbard, A. S. Powell, *Anal. Chem. 23* (1951) 1604...10; Determination of carbon-hydrogen groups in high molecular weight hydrocarbons

G. N. Foster, S. B. Row, R. G. Griskey, *J. Appl. Polym. Sci. 8* (1964) 1357...61; Infrared spectrometry of polymers in the overtone and combination regions

W. F. X. Frank, W. Strohmeyer, *Progr. Colloid Polym. Sci. 66* (1979) 205...12; A far infrared spectroscopic study of the problem of hard-segment clustering in poly(urethane)

A. Garton, D. J. Carlsson, D. M. Wiles, P. T. T. Wong, *J. Polym. Sci. Polym. Lett. Ed. 18* (1980) 85...8; Far-infrared spectroscopy of polyamide fibers and fabrics

R. F. Goddu, *Anal. Chem. 29* (1957) 1790...4; Determination of unsaturation by near-infrared spectrophotometry

R. F. Goddu, *Anal. Chem. 30* (1958) 2009...13; Determination of phenolic hydroxyl by near infrared spectrophotometry

R. F. Goddu, D. A. Delker, *Anal. Chem. 30* (1958) 2013...6; Determination of terminal epoxides by near-infrared spectrophotometry

R. F. Goddu, D. A. Delker, *Anal. Chem. 32* (1960) 140; Spectra-structure correlations for the near-infrared region

H. U. Hoppler, I. Tomka, *Kunststoffe 77* (1987) 162...6; Methode zur schnellen und berührungslosen Dickenbestimmung an geschmolzenen Kunststoffbändern

S. Iwanska, J. Urbanski, *Polimery (Warsaw) 29* (1984) 17f. (Pol.); The application of *NIR*-spectroscopy to the investigation of the reactions of epoxide compounds with amines. II. Investigation of the speed of reaction of the active diluents of epoxy resins with triethylenetetramine

S. Iwanska, J. Urbanski, *Polimery (Warsaw) 31* (1986) 126...9 (Pol.); Application of *NIR* spectroscopy to the investigation of the reactions of epoxide compounds with amines. III. Investigations of the curing rate of commercial epoxy resins with aromatic diamines

W. Kaye, *Spectrochim. Acta 6* (1954) 257...87; Near-infrared spectroscopy. I. Spectral identification and analytical applications

G. S. Kitukhina, V. V. Zharkov, *Plast. Massy 1976* (7) 74 (Russ.); Application of the *NIR* spectral region for the investigation of the curing of epoxy resins

S. A. Larsen, J. L. Kinnison, *Text. Res. J. 52* (1982) 25...31; Estimating quality components of natural fibers by near-infrared reflectance. Part II. Clean wool base and average wool fiber diameter

R. G. J. Miller, H. A. Willis, *J. Appl. Chem. (Lond.) 6* (1956) 385...91; Quantitative analysis in the 2 micron region applied to synthetic polymers

J. A. Mitchell, C. D. Bockman, A. V. Lee, *Anal. Chem. 29* (1957) 499...502; Determination of acetyl content of cellulose acetate by near infrared spectroscopy

S. Mizushima, T. Shimanouchi, M. Tsuboi, T. Arakawa, *J. Am. Chem. Soc. 79* (1957) 5357; Near infrared spectra of compounds with two peptide bonds and the configuration of a polypeptide chain. VI. Further evidence of the internal hydrogen bonding and an estimation of its energy

B. G. Osborne, *J. Food Technol. 16* (1981) 13...9; Principles and practice of near infrared (*NIR*) reflectance analysis

H. H. Ramey, *Text. Res. J. 52* (1982) 20...5; Estimating quality components of natural fibers by near-infrared reflectance. Part I. Cotton fiber cross-sectional area and specific surface

T. Takeuchi, S. Tsuge, Y. Yamaguchi, *J. Polym. Sci. A-1 6* (1968) 3415...7; Near-infrared spectrophotometric analysis of styrene-acrylonitrile copolymers

T. Takeuchi, S. Tsuge, Y. Sugimura, *Anal. Chem. 41* (1969) 184...6; Near-infrared spectrophotometric analysis of ethylene-propylene copolymers

C. Tosi, *Makromol. Chem. 112* (1968) 303...6; A near infrared study of ethylene-propylene copolymers

P. A. Turley, A. Pietrantonio, *J. Cellular Plast. 20* (1984) 274...8; Rapid hydroxyl number determination by near infrared reflectance analysis

A. Visapää, *Kemian Teollisuus 22* (1965) 487...503; The near-infrared spectra of common solvents

F. W. Wees, M. Buback, *Ber. Bunsenges. Phys. Chem. 80* (1976) 1017...23; Untersuchung der Hochdruckpolymerisation des Äthylens durch Spektroskopie im nahen Infrarot

D. L. Wetzel, *Anal. Chem. 55/12* (1983) 1165A...76A; Near-infrared reflectance analysis — sleeper among spectroscopic techniques

L. G. Weyer, *J. Appl. Polym. Sci. 31* (1986) 2417...31; Utilizing zero crossover points in the near infrared reflectance analysis of industrial polymers

K. B. Whetsel, *Appl. Spectrosc. 2* (1968) 1ff.; Near infrared spectroscopy

2.3.2 *FIR* spectroscopy

D. R. Beckett, J. M. Chalmers, M. W. Mackenzie, H. A. Willis, H. G. M. Edwards, J. S. Lees, D. A. Long, *Europ. Polym. J. 21* (1985) 849...52; The far-infra-red spectra of crystalline isotactic polypropylene polymorphs

F. F. Bentley, Far-infrared spectrometry, in H. A. Szymanski, *Progress in Infrared Spectroscopy*, Vol. 1, 99...113; Plenum Press, New York 1962

V. A. Bershtein, V. A. Ryzhov, *J. Macromol. Sci. Phys. B23* (1984) 271...87; Relationship between molecular characteristics of polymers and parameters of far-infrared spectra

J. W. Brasch, Y. Mikawa, R. J. Jacobsen, *Appl. Spectrosc. Rev. 2* (1968) 187 ff.; Far infrared spectroscopy

G. W. Chantry, J. W. Fleming, *Brit. Polym. J. 4* (1972) 279...90; Modern experimental methods for the observation of the *FIR* spectra of polymers

J. R. Durig, *NATO Adv. Study Inst. Ser. C 57* (1980) 333...60; Conformational analysis by far infrared *FT* spectroscopy

A. Finch, P. N. Gates, K. Radcliffe, F. N. Dickson, F. F. Bentley, *Chemical Applications of Far Infrared Spectroscopy*; Academic Press, New York 1970

W. F. X. Frank, H. Fiedler, W. Strohmeier, *Appl. Polym. Symp. (1978)* 75...87; Polymers containing benzene rings: Characteristics of the absorption spectra in the far infrared

W. F. X. Frank, W. Strohmeier, *Prog. Colloid Polym. Sci. 66* (1979) 205...12; A far infrared spectroscopic study of the problem of hard-segment clustering in polyurethane

W. F. X. Frank, H. Schmidt, B. Heise, G. W. Chantry, E. A. Nicol, H. A. Willis, M. E. A. Cudby, *Polymer 22* (1981) 17...9; A new far infra-red absorption band at 39 cm^{-1} in the spectrum of high pressure crystallized polyethylene

W. F. X. Frank, W. Strohmeier, M. L. Hallensleben, *Polymer 22* (1981) 615...8; Far infra-red absorption spectra of undeuterated and deuterated poly(ethylene terephthalate)

A. Garton, D. J. Carlsson, D. M. Wiles, P. T. T. Wong, *J. Polym. Sci. Polym. Lett. Ed. 18* (1980) 85...8; Far-infrared spectroscopy of polyamide fibers and fabrics

A. Hadni, *NATO Adv. Study Inst. Ser. C 57* (1980) 171...99; Some remarks on far infrared techniques for measuring absorption spectra

D. O. Hummel, *Kunststoffe 55* (1965) 102...12; Die Spektroskopie im fernen Infrarot bei der Analyse von Hochpolymeren, Harzen, Monomeren und Weichmachern

E. Knözinger, *Fresenius Z. analyt. Chem. 278* (1976) 177...90; Practical aspects of *FIR* Fourier spectroscopy in chemistry

E. Knözinger, *Angew. Chem. 88* (1976) 1...16; Ferninfrarot-Fourier-Spektroskopie als Methode zur Strukturaufklärung in der Chemie

M. Latour, A. Montaner, M. Galtier, G. Geneves, *J. Polym. Sci. Polym. Phys. Ed. 19* (1981) 1121...9; Structural study of conformation phases in poly(vinylidene fluoride) by far-infrared spectroscopy

M. Latour, H. A. Dorra, J. L. Galigné, *J. Polym. Sci. Polym. Phys. Ed. 22* (1984) 345...56; Far-infrared and *X*-ray studies on poled semicrystalline poly(vinylidene fluoride)

U. Leute, *Polym. Bull. 4* (1981) 89...96; High pressure *FIR*-spectroscopy on polyethylene at elevated temperature

U. Leute, *Polym. Bull. 4* (1981) 407...14; *FIR*-spectroscopy in the high pressure phase of polyethylene

W. Prettl, W. F. X. Frank, *Colloid Polym. Sci. 257* (1979) 920...6; Phonon mode coupling and Fano-type antiresonance in polyethylene

J. E. Stewart, F. J. Linnig, *J. Res. Natl. Bur. Stand. A 71* (1967) 19...23; Far infrared spectrum of vulcanized natural rubber

H. A. Willis, R. G. J. Miller, D. M. Adams, H. A. Gebbie, *Spectrochim. Acta 19* (1963) 1457...61; Synthetic resins as window materials for far infrared spectroscopy

P. T. Wong, A. Garton, D. J. Carlsson, D. M. Wiles, *J. Macromol. Sci. Phys. B 18* (1980) 313...24; Far-infrared spectrum of poly(*p*-phenylene terephthalamide)

H. R. Wyss, R. D. Werder, H. H. Günthard, *Spectrochim. Acta 20* (1964) 573...9; Far infrared spectra of twelve organic liquids

2.4 Combination of *IR* spectroscopy with other methods

2.4.1 *IR* spectroscopy and chromatographic methods

2.4.1.1 Liquid chromatography (gel permeation chromatography, *HPLC*) and *IR* spectroscopy

D. G. Anderson, K. E. Isakson, *ACS Div. Org. Coat. Plast. Chem. Pap. 30* (1970) 123...8; Determination of monomer distribution in copolymers using gel permeation chromatography and infrared spectroscopy

D. J. Belton, E. Sullivan, *J. Appl. Polym. Sci. 31* (1986) 1309...26; Infrared and liquid chromatographic characterization of epoxy cresol novolac-phenol formaldehyde novolac-tertiary amine resin systems

J. V. Dawkins, M. Hemming, *J. Appl. Polym. Sci. 19* (1975) 3107...18; Infrared detection of polymers in gel permeation chromatography

W. J. de Klein, *Z. analyt. Chem. 246* (1969) 294...7; Infrared spectroscopic identification of compounds separated by gas-liquid chromatography, using a potassium bromide micropellet technique

F. M. Mirabella, E. M. Barrall, J. F. Johnson, *J. Appl. Polym. Sci. 20* (1976) 959...65; The determination of copolymer composition as a function of molecular weight by preparative gel permeation chromatography and comparison to the rapid stop-and-go *GPC/IR* method

F. M. Mirabella, E. M. Barrall, J. F. Johnson, *Polymer 17* (1976) 17...20; A rapid technique for the qualitative analysis of polymers and additives using stop-and-go *GPC* and *IR*

G. Samay, A. Dankovics, *Müanyag Gumi 17* (1980) 150...3 (Hung.); Determination of molar mass distribution and chemical composition of copolymers by gel-permeation chromatography/*IR* spectroscopy

2.4.1.2 Gas chromatography and *IR* spectroscopy

R. F. Brady, *Anal. Chem. 47* (1975) 1425...8; Analysis of microgram quantities of organic vapors by combined capillary-column gas chromatography and vapor phase infrared spectrometry

I. L. Davies, *J. Oil Colour Chem. Ass. 68* (1985) 109...15; Instrumental analysis in the coatings industry

G. Dijkstra, *Lab. Instrum. 10* (1) (1974) 19...20, 23; Coupling of a gas chromatograph with an *IR* spectrometer (replacement of the mass spectrometer)

P. Friese, *Das Papier 36* (1982) 601...6; Celluloseether-Analytik mittels *GC* und *IR*

N. Grassie, M. A. Diab, A. Scotney, *Polym. Degrad. Stab. 16* (1986) 79...97; Thermal degradation of bromine-containing polymers. Part 7. Poly(2,3-dibromopropyl methacrylate) and poly(2,3-dibromopropyl acrylate); *ibid.* 361...82, Part 8. Copolymers of 2,3-dibromopropyl methacrylate and 2,3-dibromopropyl acrylate with methylacrylate

G. Guiochon, J. Henniker, *Brit. Plastics 37* (1964) 74; Complementary methods of polymer analysis by infrared spectroscopy and gas phase chromatography

J. Haslam, A. R. Jeffs, H. A. Willis, *Analyst 86* (1961) 44; Applications of gas-liquid chromatography. Collection of fractions from the gas chromatograph and their identification by infrared spectroscopy

T. Helmen, *Farbe Lack 80* (1974) 715...31; Einsatzmöglichkeiten von *IR*-Spektroskopie und Gaschromatographie in der Lackindustrie, beleuchtet durch einige ausgewählte Beispiele

A. B. Littlewood, *J. Gas Chromatogr. 6* (1968) 65...8; Informal symposium of the gas chromatography discussion group and the infrared discussion group. Instrumentation of gas chromatography and infrared spectroscopy linked

A. B. Littlewood, *Chromatographia 1* (1968) 223...30; The coupling of gas chromatography with methods of identification. III. Infrared spectrophotometry

F. D. Mercaldo, *Am. Lab. 6/3* (1974) 63...7; GC-IR system for the identification of multicomponent mixtures

T. H. Parliment, *Microchem. J. 20* (1975) 492...4; Procedure for preparing infrared spectra on gas chromatographic fractions

R. H. Shaps, W. Simons, A. Varano, *Am. Lab. 9/3* (1977) 95...101; A new analytical tool *GC/IR* and *GC/NMR*

R. H. Shaps, A. Varano, *Am. Lab. 7/11* (1975) 77...81; *GC/IR* as an accessory for an *IR* spectrometer

2.4.1.3 Pyrolysis gas chromatography and *IR* spectroscopy

S. Bădilescu et al., *Mater. Plast (Bucharest) 16* (1979) 145...7 (Rum.); Investigation of the composition of acrylonitrile-butadien-styrene copolymers by infrared spectroscopy and pyrolysis-gas chromatography

J. K. Gillham, S. Tamura, *Weekly Govt. Abstr. Chem. 99/33* (1977) 489; Pyrolysis-molecular weight chromatography-vapor phase infrared spectrophotometry: An on-line system for analysis of polymers. IV. Influence of *cis/trans* ratio on the thermal decomposition of 1,4-polybutadienes

J. K. Haken, *Pigment Resin Technol. 7* (1978) 4...7; Analysis of acetate-acrylate copolymer systems

T. L. Ivanova, V. M. Rjabikova, G. P. Malachova, A. N. Zigel, G. S. Popova, *Plast. Massy 1986* (9) 43...5 (Russ.); Identification of polystyrene materials from the products of thermal decomposition by *IR* spectroscopy and pyrolysis-gas liquid chromatography

S. S. Karaenev, G. Kostov, R. Milina, M. Kh. Mihailov, *Vysokomol. Soedin. A 16* (1974) 2162...5 (Russ.); Determination of the composition of terpolymers by *IR* spectroscopy and pyrolysis gas chromatography

E. Kiran, J. K. Gillham, *J. Appl. Polym. Sci. 20* (1976) 931...47; Pyrolysis-molecular weight chromatography-vapor phase infrared spectrophotometry: A new on-line system for analysis of polymers. I. Instrumentation

E. Kiran, J. K. Gillham, *J. Appl. Polym. Sci. 20* (1976) 2045...68; Pyrolysis-molecular weight chromatography: A new on-line system for analysis of polymers. II. Thermal decomposition of polyolefins: Polyethylene, polypropylene, polyisobutylene

E. Kiran, J. K. Gillham, E. Gipstein, *J. Appl. Polym. Sci. 21* (1977) 1159...76; Pyrolysis-molecular weight chromatography-vapor phase infrared spectrophotometry: An on-line system for analysis of polymers. III. Thermal decomposition of polysulfones and polystyrene

E. Kiran, J. K. Gillham, *Polym. Eng. Sci. 19* (1979) 699...708; Pyrolysis-molecular weight chromatography-vapor phase infrared spectrophotometry: An on-line system for analysis of polymers — a review

O. Kirret, E. Küllik, L. Lahe, *Eesti NSV Teaduste Akadeemia 23 Keemia* (1974) 187...91; Über die Identifizierung von Bikomponentfasern mittels der Infrarot-Spektroskopie und Pyrolyse-Gaschromatographie

H.-J. Kretzschmar, D. Gross, J. Kelm, Pyrolysis-gas chromatography and spectroscopic identification of fluorine polymers, in C. E. Roland Jones, C. A. Cramers (eds.), *Analytical Pyrolysis*; Elsevier, Amsterdam 1977

H. J. Kretschmar, J. Kelm, H. Tengicki, D. Gross, *Kautsch. Gummi Kunstst. 34* (1981) 846...50; Analyse von vulkanisierten EPDM/SBR Kautschuken durch Pyrolyse-Gas-Chromatographie und Spektrometrie

H. Mosimann, W. Weber, *Schweizer Archiv 36* (1970) 402...11; Methode zur Bestimmung der Ausgangsphenole in Phenol-, Kresol- und Xylenolharzen mit Hilfe der Pyrolysen-Gaschromatographie

A. K. Mukherji, M. A. Butler, D. L. Evans, *J. Appl. Polym. Sci. 25* (1980) 1145...55; Compositional determination of 2,6-dimethyl-1,4-phenylene oxide and styrene homopolymer blends by infrared spectrometry and pyrolysis gas chromatography

W. Noble, B. B. Wheals, M. J. Whitehouse, *J. Forens. Sci. 3* (1974) 163...74; The characterization of adhesives by pyrolysis gas chromatography and infrared spectroscopy

G. Oehme, H. Baudisch, H. Mix, *Makromol. Chem. 177* (1976) 2657...67; Analyse von Polystyrolharzen mit funktionellen Gruppen mittels *IR*-Spektroskopie und Pyrolyse-Gaschromatographie-Massenspektroskopie

J. R. Parrish, *Anal. Chem. 47* (1975) 1999...2003; Quantitative analysis of cation-exchange resins by infrared spectrophotometry and pyrolysis-gas chromatography

S. R. Tamura, J. K. Gillham, *J. Appl. Polym. Sci. 22* (1978) 1867...84; Pyrolysis-molecular weight chromatography-vapor infrared spectrophotometry: An on-line system for analysis of polymers. IV. Influence of *cis/trans* ratio on the thermal decomposition of 1,4-polybutadienes

A. N. Zigel, V. M. Rjabikova, G. P. Malachova, T. A. Fadeeva, *Plast. Massy 1986* (8) 37...9 (Russ.); Identification of rubber in high-impact polystyrene

2.4.2 *IR* spectroscopy and thermal analysis

H. Alaminov, R. Markova, *Eur. Polym. J. 12/8* (1976) 481...4; A study on modified polymers by means of *IR*-spectroscopy and thermal analysis

T. Anagnostou, E. Jaul, *J. Coat. Technol. 53* (1981) 35...45; Synthesis of blocked MDI adducts, their *DSC* evaluation and effect of pigmentation

V. A. Erä, J. J. Lindberg, A. Mattila, L. Vauhkonen, T. Linnahalme, *Angew. Makromol. Chem. 50* (1976) 43...52; Phenol-formaldehyde impregnant characterization by infrared spectroscopy and differential scanning calorimetry

V. S. Gupta, A. K. Chakravorty, P. K. Ghosh, B. K. Dutta, *Technology 8* (1971) 60...5; Epoxy resins. Their infrared spectrophotometric and thermogravimetric studies

V. Halip et al., *Mater. Plast. 3* (1975) 157...60; Structural characterization of spinnable polypropylene by infrared spectroscopy and differential thermal analysis

Z. H. Huang, L. H. Wang, *Makromol. Chem. Rapid Commun. 7* (1986) 255...9; Infrared studies of transesterification in poly(ethylene terephthalate)/polycarbonate blends

S. Igarashi, O. Yamamoto, H. Kambe, *Kolloid-Z. Z. Polym. 199* (1964) 97...104; Differential thermal and infrared analyses of oxidized polyethylene

E. Ito, K. Yamamoto, Y. Kobayashi, T. Hatakeyama, *Polymer 19* (1978) 39...42; Change of amorphous state of poly(ethylene terephthalate) by heat treatment below the glass transition temperature

A. V. Kiselev et al., *Colloid J. USSR 38* (1976) 519...22; *IR*-spectroscopic and thermogravimetric investigation of the curing of epoxide powder compositions and Zeolite-supported catalysts

K. Kishore, *J. Chem. Eng. Data 25* (1980) 92...4; Spectral and thermal data on poly(styrene peroxide)

A. V. Kostocko, G. A. Vasileva, L. N. Maklanova, V. N. Kuleznev, *Vysokomol. Soedin. A 29* (1987) 245...9; Study of the interaction in cellulose nitrate-urethane rubber systems

T. S. Long, J. J. Pisney, *Soc. Plast. Eng. Tech. Pap. 22* (1976) 398...403; Characterization of polyurethane using infrared and thermal analysis

S. Y. Pusatcioglu, M. A. Kubat, *Soc. Plast. Eng. Tech. Pap. 25* (1979) 750...3; An analytical approach to solving die stain problems

D. E. Smith, *Thermochim. Acta 14* (1976) 370...2; Characterization of blends and copolymers of ethylene and methyl methacrylate by combined thermogravimetric analysis-infrared spectroscopy

V. W. Srichatrapimuk, S. L. Cooper, *J. Macromol. Sci. Phys. B 15* (1978) 267...311; Infrared thermal analysis of polyurethane block polymers

M. Terano, T. Kataoka, *Makromol. Chem. Rapid Commun. 7* (1986) 725...31; Analysis of $MgCl_2$-supported high-yield catalysts by thermal analysis and infrared spectroscopy

J. Žurakowska-Orszagh et al., *Polimery 23* (1978) 255...8 (Pol.); Investigations of the structure and composition of N-*t*-butylacrylamide styrene copolymers

2.4.3 *IR*- and *NMR* spectroscopy

T. M. Abramova, S. G. Alekseeva, P. M. Valetskii, L. I. Golubenkova, I. M. Makarova, I. J. Slonim, J. T. Urman, A. N. Sabadas, *Vysokomol. Soedin. A 22* (1980) 1637...44 (Russ.); *IR*- and *NMR* spectroscopic investigations of oligomeric and cured phenolcarborane compositions

A. G. Altenau, L. M. Headley, C. O. Jones, H. C. Ransaw, *Anal. Chem. 42* (1970) 1280...2; Termonomer analysis in ethylene propylene terpolymers

D. H. Beebe, G. E. Gordon, R. W. Thudium, M. C. Throckmorton, T. L. Hanlon, *J. Polym. Sci. Polym. Chem. Ed. 16* (1978) 2285...301; Microstructure determination of poly(1,3-pentadiene) by a combination of infrared, 60-MHz *NMR*, 300-MHz *NMR*, and *X*-ray diffraction spectroscopy

D. Braun, G. Holzer, *Angew. Makromol. Chem. 116* (1983) 51...76; Polymerisation von Vinylchlorid bei Atmosphärendruck. 2. Mitt. Chemische und spektroskopische Methoden zur Charakterisierung von U-PVC

M. E. A. Cudby, A. Bunn, *Polymer 17* (1976) 345...7; Determination of chain branching in low density polyethylene by ^{13}C nuclear magnetic resonance and infra-red spectroscopy

J. Devaux, P. Godard, J. P. Mercier, R. Touillaux, J. M. Dereppe, *J. Polym. Sci. Polym. Phys. Ed. 20* (1982) 1881...94; Bisphenol-A polycarbonate-poly(butylene terephthalate) transesterification. II. Structure analysis of the reaction products by *IR* and ^1H and ^{13}C *NMR*

P. K. Dhal, *J. Macromol. Sci. Chem. A 23* (1986) 181...7; Spectroscopic methods for the determination of monomer reactivity ratios in glycidylmethacrylate-styrene copolymerization

D. Doskočilová, B. Schneider, E. Drahorádová, J. Štokr, M. Kolínský, *J. Polym. Sci. A-2 9* (1971) 2753...62; Structure of chlorinated poly(vinyl chloride). II. Distribution of Cl atoms in the polymer chain

D. Doskočilová, B. Schneider, J. Štokr, S. Ševčik, M. Přádný, L. Lochmann, *Makromol. Chem. 186* (1985) 1905...18; Model compounds of poly(methyl methacrylate). Conformational structure of the dimethyl esters of 2,2,4-trimethyl- and of 2-methoxymethyl-2,4-dimethylglutaric acid. ^{13}C *NMR*, ^1H *NMR* and vibrational spectroscopic study

J. Dybal, J. Spevaček, B. Schneider, *J. Polym. Sci. Polym. Phys. Ed. 24* (1986) 657...74; Ordered structures of syndiotactic poly(methyl methacrylates) studied by a combination of infrared, Raman, and *NMR* spectroscopy

A. Entezami, B. Kämpf, F. Schué, J. Sledz, C. Tanielian, *Bull. Soc. Chim. France 1972*, 1520...9; Etude de la microstructure de quelques polypentadiènes-1,3 stéréoréguliers par spectrometrie de résonance magnétique nucléaire et spectrophotometrie infrarouge

H. S. Fochler, J. R. Mooney, L. E. Ball, R. D. Boyer, J. G. Grasselli, *Spectrochim. Acta 41 A* (1985) 271...8; Infrared and *NMR* spectroscopic studies of the thermal degradation of polyacrylonitrile

H. Guéniffey, E. Klesper, H. Kämmerer, *Makromol. Chem. 162* (1972) 199...204; Structure des poly(méthacrylates de *p*-tolyl) déterminée par infrarouge et *RMN*

L. W. Jelinski, J. J. Dumais, J. P. Luongo, A. L. Cholli, *Macromolecules 17* (1984) 1650...5; Thermal oxidation and its analysis at low levels in polyethylene

M. E. Johnson-Plaumann, H. P. Plaumann, S. E. Keeler, *Rubber Chem. Technol. 59* (1986) 580...91; Analysis of EPM elastomers by infrared and *NMR* methods

K. Kishore, H. K. Pandey, *Progr. Polym. Sci. 12* (1986) 155...78; Spectral studies on plant rubbers

Yu. V. Kissin, V. I. Tsvetkova, N. M. Chirkov, *Eur. Polym. J. 8* (1972) 529...46; The stereoregularity of polypropylene from *IR* and *NMR* data

J. P. Kistler, G. Friedmann, B. Kämpf, *Bull. Soc. Chim. Fr. 1967*, 4759...64 (Fr.); Determination of the microstructure of polyisoprenes by nuclear magnetic resonance and infrared spectroscopy

Yu. I. Kotov, E. M. Murashova, N. M. Pavlova, F. A. Galil-Ogly, *Kauch. Rezina 10* (1975) 8...10 (Russ.); *NMR*- and *IR* spectroscopy for the investigation of the microstructure of isoprene rubbers

M. LeClerc, R. E. Prud'Homme, A. Soum, M. Fontanille, *J. Polym. Sci. Polym. Phys. Ed. 23* (1985) 2031...41; Determination of the geometric structure of three substituted polyacetylenes. Polymethylacetylene, polypentylacetylene, and poly(*t*-butylacetylene)

R. Lukáš, M. Kolínský, *J. Polym. Sci. Polym. Chem. Ed. 14* (1976) 403...8; Structure of chlorinated poly(vinyl chloride). III. Preparation of poly(vinyl chloride)-β,β-d_2 as a model for the study of the mechanism of chlorination and of the chlorinated poly(vinyl chloride) structure

C. L. McCormick et al., *J. Appl. Polym. Sci. 27* (1982) 3103...20; Water-soluble copolymers. 5. Determination of the composition of statistical copolymers of acrylamide with sulfonated comonomers by *IR* and ^{13}C-*NMR* spectroscopy

W. F. Maddams, *J. Vinyl Techn. 7* (1985) 65...72; Spectroscopic studies on the characterization of defects in the molecular structure of poly(vinyl chloride)

E. Mertzel, J. L. Koenig, *Adv. Polym. Sci. 75* (1986) 73...112; Application of *FT-IR* and *NMR* to epoxy resins

S. Nagarajan, Z. H. Stachurski, *J. Polym. Sci. Polym. Phys. Ed. 20* (1982) 989...1000; A study of the PE-PTFE system. I. *IR* and *NMR* measurements

J. R. Paxson, J. C. Randall, *Anal. Chem. 50* (1978) 1777...80; Quantitative measurement of ethylene incorporation into propylene copolymers by carbon-13 nuclear magnetic resonance and infrared spectrometry

Q. T. Pham, J. Vialle, J. Guillot, *Quad. Ricerca Sci. 84* (1973) 42...51; The microstructure of polybutadiene sequences in (acrylonitrile-butadiene) copolymers studied by *IR* and *NMR*

E. L. Saier, L. Petrakis, L. R. Cousins, W. J. Heilman, J. F. Itzel, *J. Appl. Polym. Sci. 12* (1968) 2191...2200; Infrared and nuclear magnetic resonance of maleic anhydride copolymers and their half esters

R. Schmolke, W. Kimmer, W. Sauer, *Acta Polymer. 30* (1979) 432...8; Die Anwendung der modernen Analytik zur Identifizierung von Polymeren

B. Schneider, J. Špeváček, *NMR* and vibrational spectra of aggregates of stereoregular poly(methyl-methacrylate)s, in W. E. Steger (ed.), *Progress in Polymer Spectroscopy*; Teubner, Leipzig 1986

H. Sobue, T. Uryu, K. Matsuzaki, Y. Tabata, *J. Polym. Sci. A 2* (1964) 3333...8; Stereoregularity of polymethacrylonitrile

W. T. Stevenson, A. Garten, J. A. Ripmeester, D. M. Wiles, *Polym. Degrad. Stab. 15* (1986) 125...41; A spectroscopic study of the carbonization of poly(acrylonitrile) and poly-(acrylonitrile-*co*-acrylic acid)

J. Štokr, B. Schneider, D. Doskočilová, J. Loevy, P. Sedláček, *Polymer 23* (1982) 714...21; Conformational structure of poly(ethylene terephthalate). Infra-red, Raman and n.m.r. spectra

Y. Tanaka, Y. Takeuchi, M. Kobayashi, H. Tadokoro, *J. Polymer Sci. A-2 9* (1971) 43...57; Characterization of diene polymers. I. Infrared and *NMR* studies: Nonadditive behaviour of characteristic infrared bands

Y. Tanaka et al., *Rubber Chem. Technol. 51* (1978) 168...79; Sequence distribution of 1,4-polybutadienes

I. M. Ward, *Adv. Polym. Sci. 66* (1985) 81...115; Determination of molecular orientation by spectroscopic techniques

L. Zetta, A. De Marco, G. Casiraghi, M. Cornia, R. Kaptein, *Macromolecules 18* (1985) 1095...1100; Exposure of hydroxyl groups in phenolacetaldehyde oligomers, as investigated by photo-*CIDNP*: ^{1}H *NMR* and infrared spectroscopy

2.4.4 *IR* spectroscopy and mass spectrometry

P. Burke, C. J. Curry, L. M. Davies, D. R. Cousins, *Forensic Sci. Int. 28* (1985) 201...19; A comparison of pyrolysis mass spectrometry, pyrolysis gas chromatography and infrared spectroscopy for the analysis of paint resins

D. O. Hummel, I. Holland-Moritz, J. Kolb, H.-J. Düssel, *Acta Polymer. 32* (1981) 512...23; Kombination von Infrarotspektroskopie und Pyro-Feldionenmassenspektrometrie für die Analyse und Charakterisierung von thermostabilen, heterocyclischen Polymeren

K. Neru, *Rev. Gen. Caoutch. Plast. 46* (1969) 999ff. (Fr.); Stability of EPDM and its behaviour at high temperatures

G. Oehme, H. Baudisch, H. Mix, *Makromol. Chem. 177* (1976) 2657...87; Analyse von Polystyrolharzen mit funktionellen Gruppen mittels *IR*-Spektroskopie und Pyrolyse-Gaschromatographie-Massenspektroskopie

G. J. Sutton, B. J. Tighe, *J. Polym. Sci. Polym. Chem. Ed. 11* (1973) 1069...77; Poly-α-ester degradation studies. I. Introduction. Design and construction of equipment

2.4.5 *IR* spectroscopy and X-ray diffraction

C. Baker, W. F. Maddams, J. E. Preedy, *J. Polym. Sci. Polym. Phys. Ed. 15* (1977) 1041...54; X-ray diffraction and infrared studies on annealed highly syndiotactic poly-(vinyl chloride)

R. Biais, C. Geny, C. Mordini, M. Carrega, *Brit. Polym. J. 12* (1980) 179...84; X-ray and infrared investigation of the supramolecular structure of PVC

B. D'Alo, G. Coppola, B. Pallesi, *Polymer 15* (1974) 130...2; Studies of crystalline forms of nylon-6 by X-ray and *IR* spectrophotometry

C. Garbuglio, M. Ragazzini, O. Pilati, D. Carcano, Gb. Cevidalli, *Eur. Polym. J. 3* (1967) 137...44; Copolymerization of ethylene and chlorotrifluoroethylene by trialkylboron catalysts. II. Physico-chemical characterization of the copolymers

A. S. Gomes, F. B. Coutinho, E. M. Macchi, *J. Polym. Sci. Polym. Chem. Ed. 20* (1982) 2345...8; Conformation studies of poly-β-amide by infrared spectroscopy and X-ray diffraction

H. Hendus, G. Schnell, *Kunststoffe 51* (1961) 69...74; Röntgenographische und *IR*-spektroskopische Kristallinitätsbestimmung an Polyäthylen

K. H. Illers, H. Haberkorn, P. Simak, *Makromol. Chem. 158* (1972) 285...311; Untersuchungen über die γ-Struktur in unverstrecktem und verstrecktem 6-Polyamid

T. Ishikawa, S. Nagai, N. Kasai, *J. Polym. Sci. Polym. Phys. Ed. 18* (1980) 291...9; Effect of casting conditions on polymorphism of Nylon-12

S. Kobayashi, H. Tadokoro, Y. Chatani, *Makromol. Chem. 112* (1968) 225...41; Structural studies on polyethers, $[-(CH_2)_m-O-]_n$. VI. The higher members with $m = 6-10, 12$

M. Kobayashi, T. Uesaka, H. Tadokoro, *Rep. Progr. Polym. Phys. Japan 18* (1975) 189...92; Molecular vibrations of polytetrahydrofuran (PTHF) and linear polyethers with the PTHF type molecular packing

M. Ragazzini, C. Garbuglio, D. Carcano, B. Minasso, Gb. Cevidalli, *Eur. Polym. J. 3* (1967) 129...36; Copolymerization of ethylene and chlorotrifluoroethylene by trialkylboron catalysts. I. Polymerization and reactivity ratios

C. Votteler, V. Hoffmann, G. Trafara, *Makromol. Chem. 185* (1984) 1953...77; Untersuchungen zu Modifikationen von Polyamid-6 und Polyamid-4 mit eingelagerten Alkalihalogeniden

2.4.6 Combination with other methods

N. S. Allen, J. P. Binkley, B. J. Parsons, N. H. Tennent, G. O. Phillips, *Polymer Photochem. 2* (1982) 97...107; Spectroscopic properties and photosensitivity of epoxy resins

T. Asakura, A. Kuzuhara, R. Tabeta, H. Saito, *Macromolecules 18* (1985) 1841...5; Conformation characterization of Bombyx mori silk fibroin in the solid state by high-frequency ^{13}C cross polarization-magic angle spinning *NMR*, X-ray diffraction, and infrared spectroscopy

D. H. Beebe, C. E. Gordon, R. N. Thudium, M. C. Throckmorton, T. L. Hanlon, *J. Polym. Sci. Polym. Chem. Ed. 16* (1978) 2285...301; Determination of the microstructure of poly-1,3-pentadiene by a combination of infrared, 60-MHz *NMR*, 300-MHz *NMR* spectroscopy and X-ray diffraction

B. H. Chang et al., *J. Polym. Sci. Polym. Phys. Ed. 22* (1984) 255...63; Mechanism of chlorination of polyethylene single crystals

J. F. Dacher, J. P. Guenier, B. Herve-Bazin, O. Moulut, *Chromatographia 8* (1975) 228...33 (Fr.); Investigating aromatic amines in vulcanized rubber by extraction and concentration, followed by a series of methods of physical analysis. Chromatography in the gas phase and on thin-layers, *IR*, and *UV* absorption spectroscopy

E. Gruber, W. L. Knell, *Makromol. Chem. 179* (1978) 733...46; Bestimmung der chemischen Heterogenität statistischer Copolymere anhand von Untersuchungen an

Poly(styrol-*co*-butylacrylat) und Poly(styrol-*co*-butyl-methacrylat)

H. Hendus, K.-H. Illers, E. Ropte, *Kolloid-Z. Z. Polym. 216...7* (1967) 110...9; Strukturuntersuchungen an Styrol-Butadien-Styrol-Blockcopolymeren

T. Y. Hu, *Wear 82* (1982) 369...76; Characterization of the crystallinity of polytetrafluoroethylene by *X*-ray and *IR* spectroscopy, differential scanning calorimetry, viscoelastic spectroscopy and the use of a density gradient tube

N. Inagaki, K. Katsuura, *J. Macromol. Sci. Chem. A 18* (1982) 661...72; Glow discharge polymerization of CF_4/CH_4 mixture investigated by infrared spectroscopy and *ESCA*

N. Inagaki, A. Kishi, *J. Polym. Sci. Polym. Chem. Ed. 21* (1983) 1847...52; Glow discharge polymerization of tetramethylsilane investigated by infrared spectroscopy and *ESCA*

K. Janicka, *Handb. Anal. Synth. Polym. Plast.* (1977) 64...100; Ellis Horwood Ltd., Chichester, Engl.; Infrared and ultraviolet absorption spectroscopy (applied to polymers)

G. Kämpf, Untersuchung der Abbauvorgänge bei der Bewitterung von Polymeren mit physikalischen Methoden, XVIIth *FATIPEC* Congress, Lugano 1984, Switzerland. Verein. Lack- und Farbenchemiker

R. P. Lattimer, E. R. Hooser, H. E. Diem, C. K. Rhee, *Rubber Chem. Technol. 55* (1982) 442...55; Analytical characterization of tackifying resins

J. B. Lear, *J. Coat. Techn. 53* (1981) 51...7, *ibid.* 63...5; Analysis of paint films

A. I. Malysev, M. A. Motorina, A. V. Pavlov, Ju. I. Kotov, V. E. Markovic, *Plast. Massy 1980/6* 44...6 (Russ.); Methods of analytical control during the manufacture of polycarbonates

T. Masuoka, H. Yasuda, *Kobunshi Ronbunshu 38* (1981) 687...92 (Japan.); Estimation of reproducibility of plasma polymerization by infrared and *X*-ray photoelectron spectroscopy

F. Mersch, R. Zimmer, *Kautsch. Gummi Kunstst. 39* (1986) 427...32; Analysis of rubber vulcanizates by advanced chemical techniques

R. D. Miller, D. Hofer, J. Rabolt, G. N. Fickes, *ACS Polym. Mat. Sci. Eng. 52* (1985) 216...9; Conformationally locked organosilane high polymers

H. K. R. Nielsen, *SPPRI Report T* (1981) 13...81; Forensic examination and analysis of paints

C. V. Oprea, M. Popa, *Angew. Makromol. Chem. 92* (1980) 73...88; Mechanochemically initiated polymerizations. Characterization of poly(acrylonitrile) mechanochemically synthesized by vibratory grinding

S. Ozasa, N. Hatada, Y. Fujioka, E. Ibuki, *Bull. Chem. Soc. Jap. 53* (1980) 2610...7; Studies of polyphenyls and polyphenylenes. II. The synthesis and physical properties of polyphenyls containing *p*-linkages

J. B. Pausch, *Anal. Chem. 54* (1982) 89...90 *A*, 92 *A*, 95...6 *A*; Analysis of rubber and plastic chemicals by *LC*/spectroscopy

A. V. Pebalk, I. E. Kardas, N. V. Kozlova, E. L. Zajceva, Ju. A. Kozlow, A. N. Pravednikov, *Vysokomol. Soedin. A 22* (1980) 972...6 (Russ.); Structure and polymerization of α,α,α,α-tetrafluoro-*p*-xylylene by means of *UV* and *IR* spectroscopy

A. V. Pebalk, N. N. Baraskov, Ju. A. Kozlov, I. E. Kardas, A. N. Pravednikov, *Vysokomol. Soedin. A 23* (1981) 2705...12 (Russ.); Investigation of the composition and polymerization of 9,10-anthraquinodimethane by means of *UV* and *IR* spectroscopy

M. Sabliovschi, G. Grigoriu, *J. Thermal Anal. 26* (1983) 23...30; Compatibility of binary systems of poly(methyl methacrylate)-poly(vinyl chloride) and poly(vinyl acetate). I. Thermogravimetric, infrared spectroscopic and microscopic studies

V. N. Vatulev et al., *Vysokomol. Soedin. A 20* (1978) 663...71 (Russ.); Investigation of the domain structure of segmented poly(ether amidourethane) by *IR* spectroscopy and optical microscopy

B. Wandelt, J. Jachowicz, M. Kryszewski, *Acta Polymer. 32* (1981) 637...42; Some aspects of the photooxidation mechanism of poly(2,6-dimethyl-1,4-phenylene oxide)

2.5 Raman spectroscopy

2.5.1 Fundamentals, general investigations of polymers

M. E. Andersen, *Org. Coat. Appl. Polym. Sci. Proc. 44* (1981) 545...7; *MOLE*, a micro Raman instrument for polymer analysis in conjunction with electron microscopy

Y. Cho, M. Kobayashi, H. Tadokoro, *J. Chem. Phys. 84* (1986) 4643...50; Theory of reorientational motional broadening of vibrational spectral bands in solid state

M. M. Coleman, D. J. Skrovanek, P. C. Painter, *Appl. Spectrosc. 38* (1984) 448...50; A simple method for determining the lower critical solution temperature of polymer blends using a Raman spectrometer

S. W. Cornell, J. L. Koenig, *Macromolecules 2* (1969) 540...5; The Raman spectra of polybutadiene rubbers

S. W. Cornell, J. L. Koenig, *Macromolecules 2* (1969) 546...9; Raman spectra of polyisoprene rubbers

M. E. A. Cudby, H. A. Willis, P. J. Hendra, C. J. Peacock, *Chem. Ind. 15* (1971) 531...8; Laser Raman spectroscopy in the polymer industry

D. L. Gerrard, *Chem. Br. 20* (1984) 715...9, 728; Raman spectroscopy and polymer analysis

J. G. Grasselli, M. Mehicic, J. R. Mooney, *Fresenius Z. analyt. Chem. 324* (1986) 537...43; Application of infrared and Raman spectroscopy in industry

C. E. Hathaway, J. R. Nielsen, *Spectrochim. Acta 23 A* (1967) 881; A Raman irradiation system for powders and polymers

P. J. Hendra, *Adv. Polym. Sci., Fortschr. Hochpolym.-Forsch. 6* (1969) 151 ff.; Laser-Raman spectra of polymers

P. J. Hendra, Raman spectroscopy, in D. O. Hummel (ed.) *Polymer Spectroscopy*; Verlag Chemie, Weinheim 1974

W. Kiefer, *Appl. Spectrosc. 27* (1973) 253...7; Raman difference spectroscopy with the rotating cell

J. J. Kim, J. McLeish, A. J. Hyde, R. T. Bailey, *Chem. Phys. Lett. 22* (1973) 503...6; Librational Raman scattering from solid polymers

M. Kobayashi, Low-frequency Raman and Brillouin scattering of long-chain compounds, in W. E. Steger (ed.), *Progress in Polymer Spectroscopy*; Teubner, Leipzig 1986

E. Koglin, J.-M. Sequaris, P. Lewinsky, P. Valenta, H. W. Nürnberg, *Fresenius Z. analyt. Chem. 321* (1985) 638f.; Oberflächenverstärkte Raman-Spektroskopie (*SERS*) von Biopolymeren

J. C. Marino, J. M. Pastor, J. A. de Saja, *Polymer 26* (1985) 383...6; Variable temperature and stretching cell for Raman spectroscopy studies of polymers

J. R. Nielsen, *J. Polym. Sci. C 7* (1964) 19...35; Raman spectra of polymers

G. D. Patterson, *Macromolecules 15* (1982) 204...6; On the applicability of Raman scattering to the study of reorientational motions in polymers

A. Peterlin, *J. Polym. Sci. Polym. Phys. Ed. 20* (1982) 2329...56; Accordion-type Laser-Raman scattering by polymers

R. F. Schaufele, *J. Polym. Sci. D4* (1970) 67...90; Laser-vibrational scattering by polymers

R. Signer, I. Weiler, *Helv. Chim. Acta 15* (1932) 649; Raman-Spektrum und Konstitution hochmolekularer Stoffe; 62. Mitteilung über hochpolymere Verbindungen

A. Simon, M. Mücklich, D. Kunath, G. Heintz, *J. Polym. Sci. 30* (1958) 201ff.; Über Raman- und ultrarotspektroskopische Untersuchungen an Hochpolymeren

H. J. Sloane, *ACS Org. Coat. Plast. Chem. Pap. 30* (1970) 27...42; Use of group frequencies of structural analysis in the Raman compared to the infrared

R. G. Snyder, *J. Chem. Phys. 76* (1982) 3921...7; The structure of chain molecules in the liquid state: low-frequency Raman spectra of *n*-alkanes and perfluoro-*n*-alkanes

R. G. Snyder, J. R. Scherer, D. H. Reneker, J. P. Colson, *Polymer 23* (1982) 1286...94; Distribution of straight-chain lengths in unannealed and annealed solution-crystallized polyethylene by Raman spectroscopy

R. G. Snyder, S. L. Wunder, *Macromolecules 19* (1986) 496...8; Long-range conformational structure and low-frequency isotropic Raman spectra of some highly disordered chain molecules

G. R. Strobl, *Colloid Polym. Sci. 257* (1979) 584...90; Einige polymerspezifische Anwendungen der Schwingungsspektroskopie

G. R. Strobl, R. Eckel, *Colloid Polym. Sci. 258* (1980) 570...7; Analysis of the intensities of the longitudinal acoustic vibrations in *n*-alkanes and polyethylene

J. D. Swalen, N. E. Schlotter, R. Santo, J. F. Rabolt, *J. Adhesion 13* (1981) 189...94; Raman spectroscopy of laminated polymer films by integrated optical techniques

2.5.2 CH polymers

2.5.2.1 Polyacetylene (polyvinylene) and poly(diacetylene)

D. N. Batchelder, D. Bloor, *J. Polym. Sci. Polym. Phys. Ed. 17* (1979) 569...81; Strain dependence of the vibrational modes of a diacetylene crystal

D. N. Batchelder, R. J. Kennedy, D. Bloor, R. J. Young, *J. Polym. Sci. Polym. Phys. Ed. 19* (1981) 677...88; Morphology and structure of heavily deformed single crystals of a polydiacetylene. II. Resonance Raman and optical spectroscopy

D. N. Batchelder, D. Bloor, *Adv. Infrared Raman Spectrosc. 11* (1984) 133...209; Resonance Raman spectroscopy of conjugated macromolecules

D. Bloor, F. H. Preston, D. J. Ando, D. N. Batchelder, Resonant Raman scattering from diacetylene polymers, in K. J. Ivin (ed.), *Structural Studies of Macromolecules by Spectroscopic Methods*; Wiley, London 1976

Y. Furukawa, T. Arakawa, H. Takeuchi, I. Harada, *J. Chem. Phys. 81* (1984) 2907...14; Vibrational spectroscopic study on partly hydrogenated *trans*-polyacetylenes

S. L. Hsu, A. J. Signorelli, G. P. Pez, R. H. Baughman, *J. Chem. Phys. 69* (1978) 106...11; Highly conducting iodine derivatives of polyacetylene: Raman, *XPS*, and *X*-ray diffraction studies

S. Lefrant, E. Faulques, S. Krichene, G. Sagon, *Polym. Commun. 24* (1983) 361...3; Raman study of *trans*-polyacetylene and poly-*p*-phenylene with excitation in the u. v. range

L. S. Lichtmann, E. A. Imhoff, A. Sarhangi, D. B. Fitchen, *J. Chem. Phys. 81* (1984) 168...184; Resonance Raman spectra of *cis*(CH)$_x$ and (CD)$_x$

I. R. Lyall, D. N. Batchelder, *Brit. Polym. J. 17* (1985) 372...6; Resonance Raman spectroscopy of polydiacetylene Langmuir-Blodgett films

E. Mulazzi, *Springer Ser. Solid-State Sci. 63* (1985) 128...32; Resonant Raman scattering from *cis* and *trans*-polyacetylene

E. Mulazzi, *Solid State Commun. 55* (1985) 807...10; Polarized resonant Raman scattering spectra from stretched *trans*-polyacetylene. Theory

F. B. Schuegerl, H. Kuzmany, *J. Chem. Phys. 74* (1981) 953...8; Optical modes of *trans*-polyacetylene

W. Siebrand, M. Z. Zgierski, *J. Chem. Phys. 81* (1984) 185...90; Analysis of Raman excitation profiles for *cis*-(CH)$_x$ and -(CD)$_x$ polymers

2.5.2.2 Polyethylene

R. Alamo, L. Mandelkern, *J. Polym. Sci. Polym. Phys. Ed. 24* (1986) 2087...2105; Origin of endothermic peaks in differential scanning calorimetry

G. Capaccio, I. M. Ward, M. A. Wilding, G. W. Longman, *J. Macromol. Sci. Phys. B15* (1978) 381...407; Morphology of bulk crystallized linear polyethylene: Study by small-angle *X*-ray scattering, Raman spectroscopy, and gel permeation chromatography

G. Capaccio, I. M. Ward, M. A. Wilding, *IUPAC 26. Int. Symp. Macromolecules, Mainz 3* (1979) 1194...7; Morphological memory in the plastic deformation of linear polyethylene; study by Raman spectroscopy

G. Capaccio, M. A. Wilding, I. M. Ward, *J. Polym. Sci. Polym. Phys. Ed. 19* (1981) 1489...504; Morphology of oriented linear polyethylene: A study by Raman spectroscopy

C. Chang, S. Krimm, *J. Polym. Sci. Polym. Phys. Ed. 17* (1979) 2163...70; Longitudinal acoustic mode in polymers. V. Nature of perturbing forces in *n*-paraffins and polymers

C. Chang, S. Krimm, *J. Polym. Sci. Polym. Phys. Ed. 22* (1984) 1871...84; Longitudinal acoustic mode in polymers. VII. Surface structure from swelling studies of freeze-dried polyethylene single crystals

Y. Cho, M. Kobayashi, H. Tadokoro, *J. Chem. Phys. 84* (1986) 4636...42; Raman band profiles and mobility of polymethylene chains

R. Eckel, H. Schwickert, M. Buback, G. R. Strobl, *Polym. Bull. 6* (1982) 559...64; Raman spectrum of the high pressure phase of polyethylene

M. Glotin, L. Mandelkern, *Colloid Polym. Sci. 260* (1982) 182...92; A Raman spectroscopic study of the morphological structure of the polyethylenes

M. Glotin, L. Mandelkern, *J. Polym. Sci. Polym. Phys. Ed. 21* (1983) 29...43; On the use of Raman-active longitudinal acoustic modes in the study of polyethylene lamellar structures

M. Glotin, L. Mandelkern, *J. Polym. Sci. Polym. Lett. Ed. 21* (1983) 807...11; On the use of the Raman-active longitudinal acoustic mode in the study of crystallite size distribution in polyethylene

L. Mandelkern, R. Alamo, W. L. Mattice, R. G. Snyder, *Macromolecules 19* (1986) 2404...8; Observation of the Raman *D-LAM* band in ethylene copolymers: Hydrogenated polybutadiene

A. Peterlin, R. G. Snyder, *J. Polym. Sci. Polym. Phys. Ed. 19* (1981) 1727...37; Accordion-type laser-Raman-scattering by drawn linear polyethylene

J. F. Rabolt, C.-H. Wang, *Macromolecules 16* (1983) 1698...1700; Morphological characterization of high-pressure crystallized polyethylene by Raman and Brillouin scattering

J. Runt, I. R. Harrison, *J. Macromol. Sci. Phys. B18* (1980) 83...91; Effect of mass perturbations on the *LA* mode only polymers: Surface bromination of polyethylene crystals

R. G. Snyder, J. R. Scherer, A. Peterlin, *Macromolecules 14* (1981) 77...82; Low-frequency Raman study of drawn polyethylene

R. G. Snyder, N. E. Schlotter, R. Alamo, L. Mandelkern, *Macromolecules 19* (1986) 621...6; Observation of a conformationally liquidlike component in crystalline polyethylene by Raman spectroscopy

E. Steger, U. Steger, S. Kulpe, I. Seidel, K. Szulzewsky, Disputed assignments of polyethylene vibrational bands clarified further by single crystal Raman spectra of α, ω-dibromoalkynes, in W. E. Steger (ed.), *Progress in Polymer Spectroscopy*; Teubner, Leipzig 1986

G. R. Strobl, R. Eckel, *J. Polym. Sci. Polym. Phys. Ed. 14* (1976) 913...20; A Raman spectroscopic determination of the interlamellar forces in crystalline *n*-alkanes and of the limiting elastic modulus E_c of polyethylene

G. R. Strobl, *Colloid Polym. Sci. 257* (1979) 584...90; Einige polymerspezifische Anwendungen der Schwingungsspektroskopie

Y. K. Wang, D. A. Waldman, J. E. Lasch, R. S. Stein, S. L. Hsu, *Macromolecules 15* (1982) 1452...4; Raman spectroscopic study of highly deformed polyethylene

Y. K. Wang, D. A. Waldman, R. S. Stein, S. L. Hsu, *J. Appl. Phys. 53* (1982) 6591...8; Raman spectroscopic study of ultraoriented solid state extruded polyethylene

S. L. Wunder, *Macromolecules 14* (1981) 1024...30; Raman spectroscopic study of the high-pressure phase of polyethylene

S. L. Wunder, M. I. Bell, G. Zerbi, *J. Chem. Phys. 85* (1986) 3827...39; Band broadening of CH_2-vibrations in the Raman spectra of polymethylene chains

2.5.2.3 Polypropylene, polybutene-1

R. T. Bailey, A. J. Hyde, J. J. Kim, *Adv. Raman Spectrosc. 1* (1972) 296...302; The Raman spectra of oriented isotactic polypropylene

L. D. Cambon, L. D. Vinh, *J. Raman Spectrosc. 14* (1983) 291...6; Raman effect study on uniaxially stretched isotactic polypropylene: new results

S. W. Cornell, J. L. Koenig, *J. Polym. Sci. A-2 7* (1969) 1965...82; Laser-excited Raman scattering in polybutene-1

M. I. Ize-Iyamu, *Polym. Bull. 12* (1984) 487...90; Raman study of chain deformation in polypropylene

G. Masetti, F. Cabassi, G. Zerbi, *Polymer 21* (1980) 143...52; Vibrational spectrum of syndiotactic polypropylene. Raman tacticity bands and local structures of iso- and syndiotactic polypropylenes

S. D. Merajver, S. L. Wunder, W. Wallace, *J. Polym. Sci. Polym. Phys. Ed. 23* (1985) 2043...57; Spectroscopic study of α- and β-phase isotactic polypropylene and of atactic polypropylene in solution

V. N. Nikitin, L. I. Maklakov, *Opt. Spektrosk. 13* (1962) 603 (Russ.); Raman spectrum of isotactic polypropylene

S. K. Satija, C. H. Wang, *J. Chem. Phys. 69* (1978) 2739...44; Polarized Raman scattering studies of chain orientation in hydrostatically extruded polypropylene

2.5.2.4 Polystyrene

S. W. Cornell, J. L. Koenig, *J. Appl. Phys. 39* (1968) 4883...90; Laser-excited Raman scattering in polystyrene

B. Jasse, R. S. Chao, J. L. Koenig, *J. Polym. Sci. Polym. Phys. Ed. 16* (1978) 2157...69; Laser Raman scattering in uniaxially oriented atactic polystyrene

B. Jasse, J. L. Koenig, *J. Polym. Sci. Polym. Phys. Ed. 18* (1980) 731...3; Polarized Raman study of molecular orientation in uniaxially stretched atactic polystyrene

S. J. Spells, I. W. Shepherd, C. J. Wright, *Polymer 18* (1977) 905...12; Raman, infra-red and neutron studies of low frequency vibrations in some substituted polystyrenes

H. Takezoe, A. Fukuda, E. Kuze, K. Era, *J. Polymer Sci. Polym. Lett. Ed. 17* (1979) 415...9; Raman circular polarization difference spectra (I+)-(I−) excited by circularly polarized laser radiation in atactic polystyrene

2.5.3 CHal and CHHal polymers

A. Baruya, D. L. Gerrard, W. F. Maddams, *Macromolecules 16* (1983) 578...80; Resonance Raman spectrum of degraded poly(vinyl chloride). 4. Determination of conjugated polyene sequence lengths

H. J. Bowley, D. L. Gerrard, W. F. Maddams, *Polym. Commun. 27* (1986) 43f.; The low frequency Raman spectra of some poly(vinyl chloride) gels

H. J. Bowley, D. L. Gerrard, W. F. Maddams, *Makromol. Chem. 188* (1987) 899...906; Resonance Raman spectroscopic studies on dehydrochlorinated stretched poly(vinyl chloride)

D. L. Gerrard, W. F. Maddams, *Macromolecules 14* (1981) 1356...62; Resonance Raman spectrum of degraded poly(vinyl chloride). 3. Background studies

J. Green, J. F. Rabolt, *Macromolecules 20* (1987) 456f.; Identification of a Curie transition in vinylidene fluoride/tetrafluoroethylene random copolymers by spectroscopic methods

C. E. Hathaway, J. R. Nielsen, *J. Chem. Phys. 41* (1964) 2203; Raman spectrum of polytetrafluoroethylene

J. King, D. I. Bower, W. F. Maddams, *Soc. Plast. Eng. Techn. Pap. 29* (1983) 345...8; Raman spectroscopic orientation studies on plasticised and unplasticised poly(vinyl chloride) sheets

J. L. Koenig, D. Druesedow, *J. Polym. Sci. A-2 7* (1969) 1075...84; Raman spectra of extended-chain syndiotactic poly(vinyl chloride)

J. L. Koenig, F. J. Boerio, *J. Chem. Phys. 52* (1970) 4170f.; Raman scattering and thermal defects in polytetrafluoroethylene

H. J. Kretzschmar, D. Groß, J. Kelm, *Kunststoffe 69* (1979) 154...7; Zur Analyse von Fluorkunststoffen

H. Kriegsmann, *Z. Elektrochem. 64* (1960) 541; Die Raman- und *IR*-Spektren linearer Methylpolysiloxane

M. Meeks, J. L. Koenig, *J. Polym. Sci. A-2 9* (1971) 717...29; Laser-Raman spectra of vinyl chloride − vinylidene chloride copolymers

G. Minoni, G. Zerbi, *J. Polym. Sci. Polym. Lett. Ed. 22* (1984) 533...7; Calculation of longitudinal acoustical modes (*LAM*) for semifluorinated *n*-alkanes

G. Peitscher, W. Holtrup, *Angew. Makromol. Chem. 47* (1975) 111...28; Nachweis von Polyensequenzen in thermisch gealtertem Polyvinylchlorid durch Resonanz-Ramanspektroskopie

J. F. Rabolt, G. Piermarini, S. Block, *J. Chem. Phys. 69* (1978) 2872...6; Raman spectroscopic evidence for conformational deformation in the high pressure phase of polytetrafluoroethylene

M. E. R. Robinson, D. I. Bower, B. P. Maddams, *J. Polym. Sci. Polym. Phys. Ed. 16* (1978) 2115...38; Molecular orientation in poly(vinyl chloride) studied by Raman spectroscopy and birefringence measurements

H. Schwickert, G. R. Strobl, R. Eckel, *Colloid Polym. Sci. 260* (1982) 588...93; Pressure induced changes in the Raman spectra of liquid *n*-alkanes and perfluoro-*n*-alkanes

K. Tashiro, Y. Itoh, M. Kobayashi, H. Tadokoro, *Macromolecules 18* (1985) 2600...6; Polarized Raman spectra and *LO-TO* splitting of poly(vinylidene fluoride) crystal form *I*

K. Zabel, N. E. Schlotter, J. F. Rabolt, *Macromolecules 16* (1983) 446...52; Structural characterization of an ethylene-tetrafluoroethylene alternating copolymer by polarized Raman scattering

2.5.4 CHO polymers

F. Adar, H. Moether, *Polymer 26* (1985) 1935...43; Raman microprobe spectra of spinoriented and drawn filaments of poly(ethylene terephthalate)

R. H. Atalla, R. E. Whitmore, C. J. Heimbach, *Macromolecules 13* (1980) 1717...9; Raman spectral evidence for molecular orientation in native cellulosic fibers

B. J. Bulkin, M. Lewin, F. J. DeBlase, *Macromolecules 18* (1985) 2587...94; Conformational change, chain orientation, and crystallinity in poly(ethylene terephthalate) yarns: Raman spectroscopic study

B. J. Bulkin, M. Lewin, F. J. DeBlase, J. Kim, *Polym. Mat. Sci. Eng. 54* (1986) 397...403; Crystallization kinetics of polymers studied by vibrational spectroscopy: poly(ethylene terephthalate) and poly(propylene terephthalate)

R. Burzynski, P. N. Prasad, J. Biegajski, D. A. Cadenhead, *Macromolecules 19* (1986) 1059...62; Laser-Raman optical wave-guide study of mono- and multi-layer Langmuir-Blodgett films of poly(diacetylenes) containing a carboxylic acid group

C. Chang, Y. K. Wang, D. A. Waldman, S. L. Hsu, *J. Polym. Sci. Polym. Phys. Ed. 22* (1984) 2185...94; Analysis of the longitudinal acoustic mode in linear aliphatic polyesters

F. J. DeBlase, M. L. McKelvy, M. Lewin, B. J. Bulkin, *J. Polym. Sci. Polym. Lett. Ed. 23* (1985) 109...15; Low-frequency Raman spectra of poly(ethylene terephthalate)

J. Derouault, M. J. Gall, P. J. Hendra, V. Ellis, M. E. A. Cudby, H. A. Willis, *Quad. Ricerca Sci. 84* (1973) 85...95; The laser-Raman spectrum of polyethylene terephthalate

E. Gulari, K. McKeigue, K. Y. S. Ng, *Macromolecules 17* (1984) 1822...5; Raman and *FTIR* spectroscopy of polymerization: bulk polymerization of methyl methacrylate and styrene

D. A. Jarvis et al., *Polymer 21* (1980) 41...54; Characterization of the biaxial orientation of poly(ethylene terephthalate) by measurements of the refractive index and by Raman and *IR* spectroscopy

J. S. Kim, M. Lewin, B. J. Bulkin, *J. Polym. Sci. Polym. Phys. Ed. 24* (1986) 1783...9; Conformational reorganization viewed by the Raman spectrum of aromatic polyesters

Y. Matsui, T. Kubota, H. Tadokoro, T. Yoshihara, *J. Polym. Sci. A 3* (1965) 2275; Raman spectra of polyethers

M. B. Moran, G. C. Martin, *J. Macromol. Sci. Chem. A 19* (1983) The laser Raman spectrum of poly(ethylene glycol dimethacrylate)

M. B. Moran, G. C. Martin, *ACS Polym. Prepr. 24/2* (1983) 141; The laser Raman spectra of dimethacrylate networks

L. Penn, F. Milanovich, *Polymer 20* (1979) 31...6; Raman spectroscopy of Kevlar 49 fibre

H. Tadokoro, A. Kobayashi, Y. Kawaguchi, S. Sobajima, S. Murahashi, Y. Matsui, *J. Chem. Phys. 35* (1961) 369...70; Normal vibrations and Raman spectrum of polyoxymethylene

K. Tashiro, M. Kobayashi, H. Tadokoro, *Polym. Bull. 1* (1978) 61...6; Polarized Raman spectra of doubly oriented poly(vinyl alcohol)

G. M. Venkatesh, P. J. Bose, A. H. Khan, J. P. Sibilia, S. L. Hsu, *J. Appl. Polym. Sci. 26* (1981) 223...30; Vibrational spectroscopic study of poly(ethylene terephthalate) crystallized by annealing in the oriented state

F. Viras, T. A. King, *Polymer 25* (1984) 899...905; Low-frequency excitations in amorphous acrylic polymers

F. Viras, T. A. King, *Polymer 25* (1984) 1411...4; Low frequency excitations in amorphous polycarbonate studied by Raman spectroscopy

2.5.5 CHN and CHNO polymers

J. M. Delabar, W. Guschlbauer, *Biopolymers 18* (1979) 2073...89; Raman spectroscopic study of ^{2}H- and ^{15}N-substituted guanosines: Monomers, gels, and polymers

C. Galiotis, I. M. Robinson, R. J. Young, B. J. Smith, D. N. Batchelder, *Polym. Commun. 26* (1985) 354f.; Strain dependence of the Raman frequencies of a Kevlar 49 fibre

M. K. Gupta, R. Bansil, *J. Polym. Sci. Polym. Phys. Ed. 19* (1981) 353...60; Laser Raman spectroscopy of polyacrylamide

M. K. Gupta, R. Bansil, *J. Polym. Sci. Polym. Lett. Ed. 21* (1983) 969...77; Raman spectroscopy and thermal investigations on polyacrylamide gels with varying monomer-comonomer ratios

Y. S. Huang, J. L. Koenig, *Appl. Spectrosc. 25* (1971) 620...2; Raman spectra of polyacrylonitrile

K. Itoh, M. Oya, *Polym. J. 18* (1986) 837...42; Raman spectra and conformation of polypeptides containing glycine, L-alanine, and L-phenylalanine residues

J. L. Koenig, P. L. Sutton, *Biopolymers 8* (1969) 167...71; Raman spectrum of the right-handed α-helix of poly-L-alanine

V. Renugopalakrishnan, T. W. Collette, L. A. Carreira, R. S. Bhatnagar, *Macromolecules 18* (1985) 1786...8; Low-frequency Raman spectra as a conformational probe for polypeptides and proteins

2.5.6 Resins, other binders

E. M. Allen, *Ind. Eng. Chem. Prod. Res. Dev. 24* (1985) 493...5; Laser Raman method for the study of the homogeneity of epoxy-amine coatings

C. Galiotis, R. J. Young, D. N. Batchelder, *J. Mater. Sci. Lett. 2* (1983) 263...6; A resonance Raman spectroscopic study of the strength of the bonding between an epoxy resin and a polydiacetylene fiber

C. G. Hill, A. M. Hedren, J. A. Koutsky, G. E. Meyers, *J. Appl. Polym. Sci. 29* (1984) 2749...62; Raman spectroscopy of urea-formaldehyde resins and model compounds

J. L. Koenig, P. T. K. Shih, *J. Polym. Sci. A-2 10* (1972) 721...40; Structure of unsaturated polyester resins crosslinked with styrene as studied by Raman spectroscopy

C. S. Lu, J. L. Koenig, *ACS Org. Coat. Plast. Chem. 32* (1972) 112...16; Raman spectra of epoxy resins

L. A. O'Neill, N. A. R. Falla, *Chem. Ind. (London) 47* (1971) 1349...51; Laser Raman spectra of drying oils and alkyd resins

2.5.7 Miscellaneous polymers, pyrolysates

M. Alden, J. Bromqvist, H. Edner, H. Lundberg, *Fire Mater. 7* (1983) 32...7; Raman spectroscopy in the analysis of fire gases

P. Dobud, D. Sutton, D. G. Tuck, *Can. J. Chem. 48* (1970) 2290...2; Use of Raman spectroscopy in the study of anion exchange of complex anions

J. Friedrich, J. F. Rabolt, *Macromolecules 20* (1987) 1975...9; Structural studies of phase transitions in poly(di-*n*-alkylsiloxanes). 1. Poly(dimethylsiloxane) and poly(diethylsiloxane)

H. Ishida, J. L. Koenig, *Appl. Spectrosc. 32* (1978) 469...79; Vibrational assignments of organosilanetriols. II. Crystalline phenylsilanetriol and phenylsilanetriol-d_3

H. Ishida, J. L. Koenig, M. E. Kenney, *Proc. Ann. Conf. Reinf. Plast. Comp. Inst. 34* (1979) 17 B, 1...5; The detection of a new potential silane coupling agent in thickness copy of less than a monolayer on glass surfaces *UV* resonance Raman spectroscopy

H. Ishida, J. L. Koenig, B. Asumoto, M. E. Kenney, *Polym. Composites 2* (1981) 75...80; Application of *UV* resonance Raman spectroscopy to the detection of monolayers of silane coupling agent on glass surfaces

J. L. Koenig, P. T. K. Shih, *J. Colloid Interface Sci. 36* (1971) 247...53; Raman studies of the glass fiber-silane resin interface

Y. Sasaki, Y. Nishina, M. Sato, K. Okamura, *J. Mater Sci. 22* (1987) 443...8; Raman study of SiC fibers made from polycarbosilane

K. Suckocka-Galas, *Polimery (Warsaw) 28* (1983) 260...3 (Pol.); Concerning the employment of broad-range Raman spectroscopy and *IR* spectroscopy for the characterization of ion aggregates in styrene ionomers

Y. Tsujita, S. L. Hsu, W. J. Macknight, *Macromolecules 14* (1981) 1824...6; Low-frequency Raman spectroscopic study of ionomers

2.5.8 Time-dependent processes

D. Bloor, D. N. Batchelder, R. J. Kennedy, D. J. Ando, *IUPAC 26. Int. Symp. Macromolecules, Mainz 1* (1979) 312...5; Resonant Raman scattering studies of the solid-state polymerization of diacetylenes

D. Bloor, R. J. Kennedy, D. N. Batchelder, *J. Polym. Sci. Polym. Phys. Ed. 17* (1979) 1355...66; Raman spectroscopic studies of the solid-state polymerization of diacetylenes. I. Thermal polymerization of 1,6-di-*p*-toluenesulfonyloxy-2,4-hexadiyne

B. J. Bulkin, M. Verbeke, M. Lewin, *Polym. Mat. Sci. Eng. 50* (1984) 189...93; Crystallization kinetics and mechanisms by rapid scanning Raman spectroscopy

B. J. Bulkin, M. Lewin, M. L. McKelvy, *Spectrochim. Acta 41 A* (1985) 251...61; Crystallization kinetics of poly-(ethylene terephthalate) studied by rapid scanning Raman spectroscopy

B. J. Bulkin, M. Lewin, J. Kim, *Macromolecules 20* (1987) 830...5; Crystallization kinetics of poly(propylene terephthalate) studied by rapid scanning Raman spectroscopy and *FT-IR* spectroscopy

S. Chow, Y. L. Chow, *J. Appl. Polym. Sci. 18* (1974) 735...44; Laser Raman spectral study of resol formation

B. Chu, G. Fytas, G. Zalczer, *Macromolecules 14* (1981) 395...7; Study of thermal polymerization of styrene by Raman scattering

M. M. Coleman, J. R. Shelton, J. L. Koenig, *Rubber Chem. Technol. 45* (1972) 173...81; Raman spectroscopic studies of the vulcanization of rubbers. III. Studies of vulcanization systems based on 2-mercaptobenzothiazole

R. Eckel, M. Buback, G. R. Strobl, *Colloid Polym. Sci. 259* (1981) 326...34; Untersuchung der druckinduzierten Kristallisation von Polyethylen mit Hilfe einer neuen Raman-Hochdruckzelle

E. Gulari, K. McKeigue, K. Y. S. Ng, *Macromolecules 17* (1984) 1822...5; Raman and *FTIR* spectroscopy of polymerization: Bulk polymerization of methyl methacrylate and styrene

J. L. Koenig, M. M. Coleman, J. R. Shelton, *Rubber Chem. Technol. 44* (1971) 71...86; Raman spectrographic studies of the vulcanization of rubbers. I. Raman spectra of vulcanized rubbers

D.-C. Lee, J. R. Ford, G. Fytas, B. Chu, G. L. Hagnauer, *Macromolecules 19* (1986) 1586...92, 1592...1603; Application of Raman and laser light scattering to the melt polymerization of hexachlorocyclotriphosphazene, 1 + 2

S. Lefrant, E. Rzepka, P. Bernier, M. Rolland, M. Aldissi, *Polymer 21* (1980) 1235...7; Raman study of oxygen induced isomerization of $(CH)_x$ films

S. Lefrant, M. Aldissi, *J. Phys. 44* (1984) 235...9; The thermal isomerization of polyacetylene studied by Raman scattering

J. H. O'Donnell, P. W. O'Sullivan, *Polym. Bull. 5* (1981) 103...10; A kinetic study of crosslinking vinyl polymerization by laser Raman spectroscopy. Free radical polymerization of diethylene glycol *bis*(allyl carbonate)

W. M. Sears, J. L. Hunt, J. R. Stevens, *J. Chem. Phys. 75* (1981) 1589...98; Raman scattering from polymerizing styrene. I. Vibrational mode analysis

W. M. Sears, J. L. Hunt, J. R. Stevens, *J. Chem. Phys. 75* (1981) 1599...602; Raman scattering from polymerizing styrene. II. Intensity changes as a function of conversion

J. R. Shelton, J. L. Koenig, M. M. Coleman, *Rubber Chem. Technol. 44* (1971) 904...13; Raman spectroscopic studies of the vulcanization of rubbers. II. Raman spectroscopic studies as a function of cure time

B. Tieke, D. Bloor, *Makromol. Chem. 180* (1979) 2275...8; Raman spectroscopic studies of the solid-state polymerization of diacetylenes. 3. *UV*-polymerization of diacetylene Langmuir-Blodgett multilayers

2.5.9 Quantitative investigations

D. I. Bower, I. M. Ward, *Polymer 23* (1982) 645...9; Quantitative characterization of orientation in PET fibres by Raman spectroscopy

D. L. Gerrard, W. F. Maddams, K. P. Williams, *Polym. Commun. 25* (1984) 182...4; The Raman spectra of some branched polyethylenes

M. Glotin, R. Domszy, L. Mandelkern, *J. Polym. Sci. Polym. Phys. Ed. 21* (1983) 285...94; A Raman spectroscopic study of solution-crystallized polyethylenes

J. D. Louden, *Polym. Commun. 27* (1986) 82...4; Crystallinity in poly(aryl ether ketone) films studied by Raman spectroscopy

A. Neppel, I. S. Butler, N. Brockman, A. Eisenberg, *J. Macromol. Sci. Phys. B19* (1981) 61...73; Vibrational spectra of polymers. III. Raman evidence for ion clustering in styrene/sodium p-styrene carboxylate copolymers

J. Štokr, B. Schneider, A. Frydrichova, J. Coupek, *J. Appl. Polym. Sci. 23* (1979) 3553...61; Composition analysis of cross-linked styrene-ethylene dimethacrylate and styrene-divinylbenzene copolymers by Raman spectroscopy

G. R. Strobl, W. Hagedorn, *J. Polym. Sci. Polym. Phys. Ed. 16* (1978) 1181...93; Raman spectroscopic method for determining the crystallinity of polyethylene

3 Vibrational spectroscopy of macromolecular systems

3.1 Fundamentals

J. de Abajo, D. O. Hummel, C. Votteler, *Revista Plást. Modernos 351* (1985) 303...12; Aplicación de la espectroscopía *IR* asistida por ordenador al análisis de polímeros y mezclas poliméricas

G. W. Chantry, *Proc. Int. Conf. Infrared Phys. 2nd* (1979) 122...7; Infrared and submillimeter-wave spectroscopy of liquids and polymers

N. B. Colthup, *Appl. Spectrosc. 30* (1976) 589...93; The calculation of some CH wag group frequencies in substituted benzenes, naphthalenes, and acetylenes

H. Günzler, H. Kienitz, E. Neuhaus, *Naturwissenschaften 43* (1956) 299; Eine spezifische Ultrarot-Absorptionsbande der Olefine vom Typ des Tetraalkyläthylens

P. W. Higgs, *Proc. Roy. Soc. (London) 220 A* (1953) 472; The vibration spectra of helical molecules: Infrared and Raman selection rules, intensities, and approximate frequencies

D. O. Hummel, *Kunststoffe 46* (1956) 442; Über die Identifizierung von Kunststoffen und Harzen sowie ihren Erzeugnissen durch ihre Infrarot-Spektren

D. O. Hummel, *Pure Appl. Chem. 11* (1965) 497...533; Fortschritte bei der infrarotspektroskopischen Analyse makromolekularer Systeme

D. O. Hummel, Applied infrared spectroscopy, in D. O. Hummel (ed.), *Polymer Spectroscopy*; Verlag Chemie, Weinheim 1974

S. Krimm, *Fortschr. Hochpolymeren-Forsch. 2* (1960) 66; Infrared spectra of high polymers

S. Krimm, *J. Polym. Sci. C7* (1965) 3; Recent developments in the vibrational spectroscopy of high polymers

C. Y. Liang, S. Krimm, G. B. B. M. Sutherland, *J. Chem. Phys. 25* (1956) 543...8; Infrared spectra of high polymers. I. Experimental methods and general theory

C. Y. Liang, *J. Molec. Spectrosc. 1* (1957) 61...8; Selection rules for the vibrational spectra of high polymers

J. P. Luongo, *Anal. Chem. 33* (1961) 1816...23; Chemical structure by absorption spectroscopy

R. Schmolke, W. Kimmer, W. Sauer, *Acta Polymer. 30* (1979) 432...8; Die Anwendung der modernen Analytik zur Identifizierung von Polymeren

N. Sheppard, G. B. B. M. Sutherland, *Proc. Roy. Soc. A196* (1949) 195; Vibration spectra of hydrocarbon molecules. I. Frequencies due to deformation vibrations of hydrogen atoms attached to a double bond

T. Shimanouchi, *Pure Appl. Chem. 36* (1973) 93...107; Local and overall vibrations of polymer chains

H. J. Sloane, *ACS Org. Coat. Plast. Chem. 30* (1970) 27...42; Use of group frequencies of structural analysis in the Raman compared to the infrared

G. R. Strobl, *Colloid. Polym. Sci. 257*/16 (1979) 584...90; Einige polymerspezifische Anwendungen der Schwingungsspektroskopie

H. Tadokoro, *J. Chem. Phys. 33* (1960) 1558; Normal vibrations of the polymer molecules of helical configuration

H. Tadokoro, *J. Chem. Phys. 35* (1961) 1050...4; Normal vibrations of the polymer molecules of helical configuration. II. A simple method of factoring of the secular equation

H. Tadokoro, M. Kobayashi, K. Yasufuku, S. Murahashi, *J. Chem. Phys. 42* (1965) 1432; Normal vibrations of the polymer molecules of helical conformations. V. Isotactic polypropylene and its deuteroderivatives

H. Tadokoro, M. Kobayashi, Vibrational spectroscopy, in D. O. Hummel (ed.), *Polymer Spectroscopy*; Verlag Chemie, Weinheim 1974

H. A. Willis, M. E. A. Cudby, *Z. analyt. Chem. 263* (1963) 291...7; Recent developments in the molecular spectroscopy of polymers

3.2 Defined natural and synthetic macromolecules

3.2.1 CH polymers

F. Ciampelli, C. Tosi, *Spectrochim. Acta 24 A* (1968) 2157...63; Correlations in vibrational spectra of hydrocarbons and their application to macromolecular systems

M. C. Harvey, A. D. Ketley, *J. Appl. Polym. Sci. 5* (1961) 247...50; The infrared identification of short-chain branches in polyolefins

H. Luther, H. H. Oelert, *Z. analyt. Chem. 183* (1961) 161; Zur molekülspektroskopischen Gruppenanalyse gesättigter Kohlenwasserstoffe

S. E. Wiberley, S. C. Bunce, W. H. Bauer, *Anal. Chem. 32* (1960) 217; Carbon-hydrogen stretching frequencies

3.2.1.1 Polyacetylene and poly(diacetylen)e

C. Chang, S. L. Hsu, *Makromol. Chem. 186* (1985) 2557...67; An infrared spectroscopic investigation of the phase behaviour of a polydiacetylene. The case of polydiacetylene with side groups containing a urethane function

J. C. W. Chien, *Polyacetylene*; Academic Press, Orlando etc. 1984. Chapter 6: Spectroscopic, physical, and mechanical properties

T. C. Clarke, J. F. Rabolt, G. B. Street, *ACS Polym. Prepr. 23* (1982) 92f.; Infrared study of doped polyacetylene

M. Galtier et al., *Polymer 25* (1984) 1253...57; *IR*-absorption of oriented polyacetylene

M. Gussoni, C. Castiglioni, M. Miragoli, G. Lugli, G. Zerbi, *Spectrochim. Acta 41 A* (1985) 371...80; Derivation of charge distribution from infrared intensities: the case of polyacetylene

H. Haberkorn, H. Naarmann, K. Penzien, J. Schlag, P. Simak, *Synthetic Metals 5* (1982) 51...71; Structure and conductivity of poly(acetylene)

V. I. Kasatochkin et al., *Dokl. Akad. Nauk. SSSR 153*/2 (1963) 346...9 (Russ.); *IR* spectra of poly-ynes

I. Kmínek, J. Trekoval, *Makromol. Chem. Rapid Commun. 7* (1986) 53...7; Formation of polyacetylene films on the catalyst titanium tetrabutoxide/ethylmagnesium bromide

M. Palpacuer, O. Bernard, C. Deloupy, M. Rolland, J. M. Abadie, *Comptes Rendus C 295* (1982) 779...82; Etude par transmission infrarouge du polyacétylène fortement dopé

K. R. Popov, L. V. Smirnov, *Optics and Spectroscopy 14* (1963) 417; A spectroscopic study of polyvinylene

Z. Shen, M. Yang, Y. Cai, M. Shi, *Scientia Sinica B 26* (1983) 785...98; Stereospecific polymerization of acetylene by rare-earth coordination catalysts

H. Shirakawa, S. Ikeda, *Polym. J. 2* (1971) 231...44; Infrared spectra of polyacetylene

H. Takeuchi, Y. Furukawa, I. Harada, H. Shirakawa, *J. Chem. Phys. 84* (1986) 2882...90; Vibrational analysis of polyacetylene and copoly(acetylene and acetylene-d$_2$). In-plane vibrations of *trans* polyene chains

M. Tanaka, A. Watanabe, J. Tanaka, *Bull. Chem. Soc. Jap. 53* (1980) 645...7; Absorption spectra of the polyacetylene films doped with BF$_3$

3.2.1.2 Polyethylene

M. Ashida, E. Ikada, Y. Ueda, H. Aizawa, *J. Polym. Sci. Polym. Chem. Ed. 20* (1982) 3107...14; Properties of low-molecular-weight polyethylene treated with gas plasma

C. Baker, W. F. Maddams, *Makromol. Chem. 177* (1976) 437...48; Infrared spectroscopic studies on polyethylene. 1. The measurement of low levels of chain branching

C. Baker, P. David, W. F. Maddams, *Makromol. Chem. 180* (1979) 975...87; Infrared spectroscopic studies on polyethylene. 5. The measurement of chain branching on powder polyethylene specimens

F. J. Baltá-Calleja, A. Hidalgo, *Kolloid-Z. Z. Polym. 229* (1969) 21...3; The short chain branching of low molecular weight polyethylene crystallized from solution

E. Cernia, C. Mancini, G. Montaudo, *J. Polym. Sci. B1* (1963) 371...7; Contribution to the investigation of polyethylene by infrared techniques

E. M. Cernia, C. Mancini, *J. Polym. Sci. B3* (1965) 1097...1100; *IR* investigation of polyethylene initiated by alkylperoxycarbonates

M. E. A. Cudby, *J. Polym. Sci. B3* (1965) 73...76; *cis*-Vinylene unsaturation in polyethylene

A. Dahme, J. Dechant, *Acta Polymer. 33* (1982) 490...4; Zur Temperaturabhängigkeit des *IR*-Spektrums von Polymeren. Part 1. Deutung der Temperaturabhängigkeit der *IR*-Banden von Polyethylen

A. Dahme, J. Dechant, *Acta Polymer. 33* (1982) 546...9; Zur Temperaturabhängigkeit des *IR*-Spektrums von Polymeren. Part 2. Einfluß des Ordnungszustandes von Polyethylen auf die Temperaturabhängigkeit einiger *IR*-Banden

W. Glenz, A. Peterlin, *Makromol. Chem. 150* (1971) 163...77; *IR*-Studies on drawn polyethylene. Part III. The orientation of vinyl and methyl end groups

C. Groeneveld, P. P. Wittgen, H. P. Swinnen, A. Wernsen, G. C. Schuit, *J. Catalysis 83* (1983) 346...61; Hydrogenation of olefins and polymerization of ethylene over chromium oxide/silica catalysts. V. In situ infrared measurements and investigation of the polymer

M. C. Harvey, A. D. Ketley, *J. Appl. Polym. Sci. 5* (1961) 247...50; The infrared identification of short-chain branches in polyolefins

P. J. Hendra, E. P. Marsden, *Polymer 18* (1977) 414f.; About structural transitions in polyethylene

S. Igarashi, O. Yamamoto, H. Kambe, *Kolloid-Z. Z. Polymere 199* (1964) 97; Differential thermal and infrared analysis of oxidized polyethylene

R. J. de Kock, P. A. H. M. Hol, H. Bos, *Z. analyt. Chem. 205* (1964) 371...81; Infrared determination of unsaturated bonds in polyethylene

S. Krimm, J. H. C. Ching, V. L. Folt, *Macromolecules 7* (1974) 537...8; Mixed-crystal infrared study of chain organization in polyethylene crystallized under orientation and pressure

S. Krimm, J. Jakeš, *Macromolecules 4* (1971) 605...9; Vibrational spectrum of cyclic C$_{34}$H$_{68}$ and chain folding in polyethylene single crystals

S. Krimm, C. Y. Liang, G. B. B. M. Sutherland, *J. Chem. Phys. 25* (1956) 549...62; Infrared spectra of high polymers. II. Polyethylene

J. N. Lomonte, G. A. Tirpak, *J. Polym. Sci. A2* (1964) 705...9; Detection of ethylene homopolymer in ethylene propylene block copolymers

W. F. Maddams, J. Woolmington, *Makromol. Chem. 186* (1985) 1665...70; Infrared spectroscopic studies on polyethylene. 6. Linear low density polymers

W. F. Maddams, S. F. Parker, *Makromol. Chem. 189* (1988) 333...9; Infrared spectroscopic studies of polyethylene. 7. The use of the methyl deformation band for branch characterization

M. A. McRae, W. F. Maddams, *Makromol. Chem. 177* (1976) 449...459; Infrared spectroscopic studies on polyethylene. 2. The characterisation of specific types of alkyl branches in low-branched polymers and copolymers

J. R. Nielsen, A. H. Woollett, *J. Chem. Phys. 26* (1957) 1391...1400; Vibrational spectra of polyethylenes and related substances

J. R. Rasmussen, E. R. Sledronski, G. M. Whitesides, *J. Am. Chem. Soc. 99* (1977) 4736...45; Introduction, modification, and characterization of functional groups on the surface of low-density polyethylene film

D. R. Rueda, E. Cagiao, F. J. Baltá-Calleja, *Makromol. Chem. 182* (1981) 2705...13; Degradation of bulk polyethylene by nitric acid. 1. *IR* study of oxidized groups

F. M. Rugg, J. J. Smith, L. H. Wartman, *J. Polym. Sci. 11* (1953) 1...20; Infrared spectrophotometric studies on polyethylene. I. Structure

F. M. Rugg, J. J. Smith, R. C. Bacon, *J. Polym. Sci. 13* (1954) 535...47; Infrared spectrophotometric studies on polyethylene. II. Oxidation

Y. Sato, M. Hoshino, F. Ebisawa, *J. Appl. Polym. Sci. 26* (1981) 2053...60; A study on hydroxyl groups in polyethylene

D. C. Smith, *Ind. Eng. Chem. 48* (1956) 1161; Molecular structure of Marlex polymers

G. A. Tirpak, *J. Polym. Sci. B3* (1965) 371...374; Position of ethyl branches in conventional polyethylene made by the free radical process

A. H. Willbourn, *J. Polym. Sci. 36* (1959) 569...97; Polymethylene and the structure of polyethylene: Study of short-chain branching, its nature and effects

3.2.1.3 Polypropylene

I. J. Grant, I. M. Ward, *Polymer 6* (1965) 223; The infra-red spectrum of syndiotactic polypropylene

E. H. Immergut, G. Kollmann, A. Malatesta, *J. Polym. Sci. 51* (1961) 57; *IR* spectrum of cationically produced polypropylene

J. L. Koenig, A. van Roggen, *J. Appl. Polym. Sci. 9* (1965) 359; Integrated infrared band intensity measurement of stereoregularity in polypropylene

C. Y. Liang, W. R. Watt, *J. Polym. Sci. 51* (1961) 14; Infrared spectrum of polypropylene prepared by a nonstereospecific catalyst

M. P. McDonald, I. M. Ward, *Polymer 2* (1961) 341; The assignment of the infra-red absorption bands and the measurement of tacticity in polypropylene

R. L. Miller, *J. Polym. Sci. 57* (1962) 975; On the characterization of stereoregular polymers. IV. Application to polypropylene

T. Miyazawa, K. Fukushima, Y. Ideguchi, *J. Polym. Sci. B1* (1963) 385; Far infrared spectra and their vibrational assignments of isotactic polypropylene

T. Miyazawa, *J. Polym. Sci. B2* (1964) 847; Infrared spectra and chemical structure of polypropylene

T. Miyazawa, *J. Chem. Phys. 43* (1965) 4030; Molecular vibrations and infrared absorption of the helical form of syndiotactic polypropylene

M. Peraldo, M. Cambini, *Spectrochim. Acta 21* (1965) 1509; Infra-red spectra of syndiotactic polypropylene

J. P. Sibilia, R. C. Wincklhofer, *J. Appl. Polym. Sci. 6* (1962) 56; Determination of isotacticity in polypropylene

R. G. Snyder, J. H. Schachtschneider, *Spectrochim. Acta 20* (1964) 853; Valence force calculation of the vibrational spectra of crystalline isotactic polypropylene and some deuterated polypropylenes

M. C. Tobin, *J. Phys. Chem. 64* (1960) 216; The *IR*-spectra of polymers. III. The *IR* and Raman spectra of isotactic polypropylene

G. Zerbi, M. Gussoni, F. Ciampelli, *Spectrochim. Acta 23 A* (1967) 301...11; Structure of liquid isotactic polypropylene from its vibrational spectrum

3.2.1.4 Higher poly(alkylethylene)s

S. M. Gabbay, S. S. Stivala, *Polymer 17* (1976) 121...4; Infrared investigations of poly-l-pentene and poly(4-methyl-1-pentene)

K. Holland-Moritz, I. Modríc, K.-U. Heinen, D. O. Hummel, *Kolloid-Z. Z. Polymere 251* (1973) 913...8; Raman- und Infrarotspektren der höheren, isotaktischen Poly-α-olefine. I. Der Einfluß der Temperatur auf das Schwingungsspektrum

K. Holland-Moritz, P. Djudovic, D. O. Hummel, *Progr. Colloid Polym. Sci. 57* (1975) 206...11; Raman- und Infrarotspektren isotaktischer Poly-α-olefine. II. Polyocten-1, Polydecen-1

K. Holland-Moritz, *Colloid Polym. Sci. 253* (1975) 922...8; Raman- und Infrarotspektren isotaktischer Poly-α-olefine. III. Polydodecen-1, Polytetradecen-1, Polyhexadecen-1, Polyoctadecen-1

K. Holland-Moritz, *J. Appl. Polym. Sci. Appl. Polym. Symp. 34* (1978) 49...74; Raman and infrared spectroscopic studies on the state of order in isotactic poly(alkyl ethylene)s: a review

K. Holland-Moritz, E. Sausen, *J. Polym. Sci. Polym. Phys. Ed. 17* (1979) 1...23; Vibrational spectra and normal coordinate analysis of isotactic poly(alkyl ethylene)s. I. Modification I of poly(ethyl ethylene) and its deuterated derivatives

K. Holland-Moritz, E. Sausen, P. Djudovic, M. M. Coleman, P. C. Painter, *J. Polym. Sci. Polym. Phys. Ed. 17* (1979) 25...43; Vibrational spectra and normal coordinate analysis of isotactic poly(alkyl ethylene)s. II. Modification I of poly(propylethylene) and its deuterated derivatives

I. Modríc, K. Holland-Moritz, D. O. Hummel, *Colloid Polym. Sci. 254* (1976) 342...7; Raman- und Infrarot-Spektren isotaktischer Polyalkyläthylene. V. Der Wellenzahlbereich unterhalb 700 cm^{-1}

M. Ukita, *Bull. Chem. Soc. Japan 39* (1966) 742; The vibrational spectra and vibrational assignments of isotactic polybutene-1

3.2.1.5 Polybutadienes

J. L. Binder, *J. Polym. Sci. A1* (1963) 47; The infrared spectra and structures of polybutadienes

J. L. Binder, *J. Polym. Sci. A3* (1965) 1587; Infrared spectra of polybutadienes

J. K. Clark, H. J. Chen, *J. Polym. Sci. Polym. Chem. Ed. 12* (1974) 925...8; Proposed method for determining the sequence distributions of the configurations in high 1,4-polybutadienes by infrared spectroscopy

M. M. Coleman, D. L. Tabb, B. L. Farmer, J. L. Koenig, *J. Polym. Sci. Polym. Phys. Ed. 12* (1974) 445...54; Normal coordinate analysis of *cis*-1,4-polybutadiene

M. A. Golub, *ACS Polym. Prepr. 21/2* (1980) 152f.; Thermal rearrangements of polybutadienes with different vinyl content

W. Kimmer, E. O. Schmalz, *Kautschuk Gummi Kunststoffe 16* (1963) 606; Die quantitative infrarotspektroskopische Bestimmung der Isomeren in Polybutadien und Butadien-Styrol-Copolymerisaten

V. N. Nikitin, L. A. Mikhailova, Yu. G. Baklagina, *Vysokomol. Soedin. 1* (1959) 1094 (Russ.); Two crystalline modifications of 1,4-*trans*-polybutadiene

B. Tieke, G. Wegner, *Makromol. Chem. Rapid Commun. 2* (1981) 543...9; Solid-state polymerization of 1,4-substituted *trans,trans*-butadienes in Perovskite-type layer structures

3.2.1.6 Polyisoprenes

J. L. Binder, H. C. Ransaw, *Anal. Chem. 29* (1957) 503; Analysis of polyisoprenes by infrared spectroscopy

J. L. Binder, *J. Polym. Sci. A1* (1963) 37; The infrared spectra and structures of polyisoprenes

F. Ciampelli, D. Morero, M. Cambini, *Makromol. Chem. 61* (1963) 250; Some remarks on the infrared analysis of polyisoprenes

D. W. Fraga, *J. Polym. Sci. 41* (1959) 522; Absence of 3,4-structure in natural polyisoprenes

E. O. Schmalz, G. Geiseler, *Z. analyt. Chem. 191* (1962) 1; Beitrag zur Isomerenanalyse des Kautschuks. II. Polyisoprene

P. Šimák, G. Fahrbach, *Angew. Makromol. Chem. 16/17* (1971) 309...24; Spektroskopische Untersuchung der Mikrostruktur von Polyisopren, Polybutadien und Isopren-Butadien-Copolymeren

M. Štolka, J. Vodehnal, I. Kössler, *Coll. Czechoslov. Chem. Commun. 28* (1963) 1535; Preparation of 3,4-polyisoprene and its infra-red spectrum

J. Vodehnal, I. Kössler, *Coll. Czechoslov. Chem. Commun. 29* (1964) 2428; Infrared analysis of polyisoprene. II. Insoluble samples

J. Vodehnal, I. Kössler, *Coll. Czechoslov. Chem. Commun. 29* (1964) 2859; Infrared analysis of polyisoprene. III. 3,4-Polyisoprene

3.2.1.7 Other unsaturated polyhydrocarbons, derivatives of polyenes

N. B. Colthup, *Appl. Spectrosc. 25* (1971) 368...71; The interpretation of the infrared spectra of conjugated polyenes in the 1000...900 cm^{-1} region

I. V. Ikonickij, N. A. Buzina, B. D. Babickij, V. A. Kormer, *Vysokomol. Soedin. A21* (1979) 2360...5 (Russ.); Determination of the isomeric states of polyalkenamers by means of infrared spectroscopy

I. Kössler, J. Vodehnal, M. Štolka, *J. Polym. Sci. A3* (1965) 2081; Cyclo- und cyclized polyisoprenes

N. Neto, M. Muniz-Miranda, E. Benedetti, F. Garruto, M. Aglietto, *Macromolecules 13* (1980) 1295...1301; Vibrational analysis of *trans*-1,4-polypentadiene. 1. Single-chain model

Z. Shen, M. F. Farona, *J. Polym. Sci. Polym. Chem. Ed. 22* (1984) 1009...15; Polymerization of terminal alkynes by a new Ziegler-Natta catalyst system: scandium naphthenate/trialkylaluminium

V. Štěpán, J. Vodehnal, I. Kössler, N. G. Gaylord, *Coll. Czechoslov. Chem. Commun. 31* (1966) 2878; Cyclo- and cyclized diene polymers. VI. Infrared spectra of cyclopoly-cyclopentadiene and polycyclopentadienes

M. Štolka, J. Vodehnal, I. Kössler, *J. Polym. Sci. A 2* (1964) 3987; Cyclo- and cyclized diene polymers. II. Infrared study of the cyclization of *cis*-1,4, *trans*-1,4, and 3,4-poly-isoprenes

C. Tosi, F. Ciampelli, G. Dall'Asta, *J. Polym. Sci. Polym. Phys. Ed. 11* (1973) 529...38; Spectroscopic method for analysis of polyalkenamers

3.2.1.8 Aliphatic-aromatic and aromatic polyhydrocarbons, miscellaneous polyhydrocarbons

F. Eckhardt, H.-O. Heinze, *Z. analyt. Chemie 170* (1959) 166; Beiträge zur Struktur und Chemie der Cumaronharze unter Berücksichtigung der *IR*-Spektroskopie und der Gaschromatographie

R. Fourme, D. André, L. Bosio, B. Jasse, *J. Molec. Struct. 71* (1981) 245...52; Crystal and molecular structure of syndiotactic 2,4,6-triphenylheptane, a polystyrene model molecule

C. Y. Liang, S. Krimm, *J. Polym. Sci. 27* (1958) 241; Infrared spectra of high polymers. VI. Polystyrene

F. M. Mirabella, *J. Appl. Polym. Sci. 25* (1980) 2265...71; Investigation of the dependence of the infrared absorptivity of a functional moiety on the molecular weight of a homopolymer

S. J. Spells, I. W. Shepherd, C. J. Wright, *Polymer 18* (1977) 905...12; Raman, infrared and neutron studies of low frequency vibrations in some substituted polystyrenes

3.2.2 Fluorine-containing polymers

F. J. Boerio, J. L. Koenig, *J. Polym. Sci. A-2 9* (1971) 1517...23; Vibrational analysis of poly(vinylidene fluoride)

G. W. Chantry, E. A. Nicol, R. G. Jones, H. A. Willis, M. E. A. Cudby, *Polymer 18* (1977) 37...41; On the vibrational assignment problem for polytetrafluoroethylene. 1. The far infra-red spectrum

G. Dube, H. Kriegsmann, *Z. Chem. 5* (1965) 421 f.; Infrarotspektroskopische Untersuchungen an Polytetrafluoräthylenen

G. Dube, *Infrarotspektroskopische Untersuchungen an Polytetrafluoräthylen*; Thesis, Math. Nat. Sci. Faculty, Humboldt University, Berlin 1966

M. Friedrich, D. Hinze, *Plaste Kautsch. 31* (1984) 448...9; Infrarotanalyse glimmpolymerisierter Fluorkohlenstoffschichten

D. Hinze, *Faserforsch. Textiltech. 27* (1976) 307...11; Ein Beispiel für das Infrarot-Absorptionsspektrum vollständig amorpher Polymere: Glimmpolymerisiertes Tetrafluoräthylen

S. L. Hsu, J. P. Sibilia, K. P. O'Brien, R. G. Snyder, *Macromolecules 11* (1978) 990...5; A spectroscopic analysis of the structure of a hexafluoroisobutylene-vinylidene fluoride copolymer

W. Y. Hsu, *Macromolecules 16* (1983) 745...9; Infrared study of helix reversal in "Nafion" perfluorinated membranes and precursors

C. Y. Liang, S. Krimm, *J. Chem. Phys. 25* (1956) 563...71; Infrared spectra of high polymers. III. Poly(tetrafluoroethylene) and poly(chlorotrifluoroethylene)

H. Matsuo, *J. Polym. Sci. 21* (1956) 331; Effect of crystallinity on the infrared band of poly(chlorotrifluoroethylene) at 490 cm^{-1}

M. Matsuo, *J. Polym. Sci. 25* (1957) 234; Measurement of the degree of crystallinity of poly(chlorotrifluoroethylene) by infrared method

R. E. Moynihan, *J. Am. Chem. Soc. 81* (1959) 1045; The molecular structure of perfluorocarbon polymers. Infrared studies of poly(tetrafluoroethylene)

J. P. Sibilia, A. R. Paterson, *J. Polym. Sci. C8* (1965) 41...57; Application of infrared spectrometry to the study of some polymer problems

H. W. Starkweather, R. C. Ferguson, D. B. Chase, J. M. Minor, *Macromolecules 18* (1985) 1684...6; Infrared spectra of amorphous and crystalline poly(tetrafluoroethylene)

K. Tashiro, K. Takano, M. Kobayashi, Y. Chatan, H. Tadokoro, *Polymer 25* (1984) 195...208; Structure and ferroelectric phase transition of vinylidene fluoride-trifluoroethylene copolymers. 2. VDF 55% copolymer

3.2.3 CCl and CHCl polymers, miscellaneous poly(halohydrocarbons)

I. A. Abu-Isa, M. E. Myers, *J. Polym. Sci. Polym. Chem. Ed. 11* (1973) 225...31; Chlorinated polyethylene. II. Chlorine distribution on the polymer chains

M. Ballester, J. Castañer, J. Riera, *J. Am. Chem. Soc. 88* (1966) 957...63; Synthesis, structure and configuration of some macromolecular chlorocarbons of high thermal and chemical stability

V. G. Boitsov, Yu. Ya. Gotlib, *Opt. Spectrosc. USSR Suppl. 2* (1966) 65; Normal vibrations of poly(vinyl chloride)

P. B. Checkland, W. H. T. Davison, *Trans. Faraday Soc. 52* (1956) 151; Infrared spectrum of rubber hydrochloride

M. M. Coleman, R. J. Petcavich, P. C. Painter, *Polymer 19* (1978) 1243...8; Application of infra-red digital subtraction techniques to the microstructure of polychloroprenes. 1. Accentuation and assignment of bands due to structural irregularities

M. M. Coleman, M. S. Wu, I. R. Harrison, P. C. Painter, *J. Macromol. Sci. Phys. B15* (1978) 463...80; Vibrational spectra and conformation of poly(vinylidene chloride)

M. M. Coleman, D. F. Varnell, B. A. Brozoski, P. C. Painter, *Polymer 22* (1981) 762...4; On the vibrational spectra of poly-1,1,2,2-tetrachlorobutane. A model for head-to-head poly(vinylidene chloride)

A. Crugnola, F. Danusso, *J. Polym. Sci. B6* (1968) 535...7; Association phenomena in dilute solutions of crystalline (low temperature) vinyl chloride polymers

N. H. Faizi, A. I. Kurilenko, *Vysokomol. Soedin. B13* (1971) 216...20 (Russ.); *IR* spectroscopic investigation with polarized light of the structure of poly(vinylidene chloride), grafted onto orientating synthetic fibers

R. C. Ferguson, *J. Polym. Sci. A 2* (1964) 1735; Infrared and nuclear magnetic resonance studies of the microstructures of polychloroprenes

O. Fredriksen, J. A. Crowo, *Makromol. Chem. 100* (1967) 231; Strukturuntersuchungen an nachchloriertem Polyvinylchlorid

W. Fuchs, D. Louis, *Makromol. Chem. 22* (1957) 1; Die Struktur chlorierter Polyvinylchloride (Struktur und *IR*-Spektrum)

H. Germar, *Makromol. Chem. 86* (1965) 89; Die Mikrostruktur chlorierter Polyvinylchloride aus dem Ultrarotspektrum

P. Hildenbrand, W. Ahrens, F. Brandstetter, P. Simak, *J. Macromol. Sci. Chem. A 17* (1982) 1093...1106; The formation of terminal double bonds in vinyl chloride polymerization

B. L. Joss, R. S. Bretzlaff, R. P. Wool, *Polym. Eng. Sci. 24* (1984) 1130...7; Spectroscopic observations on nonequilibrium glassy poly(vinyl chloride) and polystyrene

W. Kimmer, R. Schmolke, *Plaste Kautsch. 32* (1985) 145...8; Zur Analyse von PVC-Compounds

M. Kolínský, D. Doskočilová, B. Schneider, J. Štokr, E. Drahorádová, V. Kuška, *J. Polym. Sci. A-1 9* (1971) 791...800; Structure of chlorinated poly(vinyl chloride). I. Determination of the mechanism of chlorination from infrared and *NMR* spectra

S. Krimm, C. Y. Liang, *J. Polym. Sci. 22* (1956) 95; Infrared spectra of high polymers. IV. Poly(vinyl chloride), poly(vinylidene chloride) and copolymers

S. Krimm, V. L. Folt, J. J. Shipman, A. R. Berens, *J. Polym. Sci. A 1* (1963) 2621; Infrared spectra and assignments for poly(vinyl chloride) and deuterated analogs

S. Krimm, S. Enomoto, *J. Polym. Sci. A 2* (1964) 669; Infrared studies of conformational changes in poly(vinyl chloride)

S. Krimm, J. J. Shipman, V. L. Folt, A. R. Berens, *J. Polym. Sci. B 3* (1965) 275; Infrared evidence for solid state constrain on chain conformations in poly(vinyl chloride)

S. Krimm, *Pure Appl. Chem. 16* (1986) 369; Normal vibrations of poly(vinyl chloride)

J. J. Lindberg, F. Stenman, I. Laipio, *J. Polym. Sci. Symp. 42* (1973) 925...9; Raman and infrared spectra of chlorinated polyethylenes

J. P. Luongo, R. Salovey, *J. Polym. Sci. A 3* (1965) 2759...66; Absorption spectra of poly-*p*-iodostyrene

T. Miyazawa, Y. Ideguchi, *J. Polym. Sci. B 3* (1965) 541...3; Chain conformation and infrared frequencies of poly(vinylidene chloride)

S. J. Mizushima, T. Shimanouchi, K. Nakamura, M. Hayashi, S. Tsuchiya, *J. Chem. Phys. 26* (1957) 970; C-Cl stretching frequencies in relation to rotational isomerism

E. E. C. Monteiro, E. B. Mano, *J. Polym. Sci. Polym. Chem. Ed. 22* (1984) 533...45; Infrared study on the interaction of poly(vinyl chloride) and ketones. I. PVC-MEK film system

W. H. Moore, S. Krimm, *Makromol. Chem. Suppl. 1* (1975) 491...506; The vibrational spectrum of crystalline syndiotactic poly(vinyl chloride)

K. Nambu, *J. Appl. Polym. Sci. 4* (1960) 69; Studies on chlorinated polyethylenes. I. Infrared spectra of chlorinated polyethylenes

S. Narita, S. Ichinohe, S. Enomoto, *J. Polym. Sci. 36* (1959) 389; Infrared spectra of vinylidene chloride-vinyl chloride copolymer

S. Narita, S. Ichinohe, S. Enomoto, *J. Polym. Sci. 37* (1959) 251...61, 263...71; Infrared spectrum of polyvinylidene chloride I, II

N. V. Platonova, I. B. Klimenko, V. I. Gracev, L. V. Smirnov, *Vysokomol. Soedin. A 22* (1980) 2464...71 (Russ.); Spectroscopic investigation of the oxidative thermal degradation of polyacrylnitrite

H. U. Pohl, D. O. Hummel, *Makromol. Chem. 113* (1968) 190...214; Quantitative *IR*-spektroskopische Untersuchungen zur Temperaturabhängigkeit der CCl-Streckschwingungen von Polyvinylchlorid

B.-M. Quenum, *Polym. J. 7* (1975) 277...86; Chlorinated polyethylene. I. Infrared study

G. Salomon, A. C. van der Schee, *J. Polym. Sci. 14* (1954) 287...94; Infrared analysis of some chlorinated natural rubbers

T. Shimanouchi, M. Tasumi, *Bull. Chem. Soc. Japan 34* (1961) 359; Normal vibrations of poly(vinyl chloride)

P. Simak, *J. Macromol. Sci. Chem. A 17* (1982) 923...33; *IR* investigations of the structure of PVC

D. L. Tabb, J. L. Koenig, *J. Polym. Sci. Polym. Phys. Ed. 13* (1975) 1159...66; A normal coordinate analysis of *trans*-1,4-polychloroprene

M. Tasumi, T. Shimanouchi, *Polym. J. 2* (1971) 62; Normal vibrations of poly(vinyl chloride)

K. Volka, Z. Vymazal, T. Zajicek, Z. Vymazalova, *Eur. Polym. J. 17* (1981) 1189...91; Effect of stabilizers in the thermal treatment of PVC. X. An *IR* spectroscopic study of PVC with basic cadmium stearate

M. S. Wu, P. C. Painter, M. M. Coleman, *J. Polym. Sci. Polym. Phys. Ed. 18* (1980) 95...110; Further studies of the preferred chain conformation of crystalline poly(vinylidene chloride)

M. S. Wu, P. C. Painter, M. M. Coleman, *J. Polym. Sci. Polym. Phys. Ed. 18* (1980) 111...20; Normal vibrational analysis of poly(vinylidene chloride)

3.2.4 CHN polymers

F. Beck, H. Leitner, *Angew. Makromol. Chem. 2* (1968) 51...63; Elektrochemisch initiierte Polymerisation von Acrylnitril

A. Bernas, R. Bensasson, I. Rossi, P. Barchewitz, *J. Chim. physique physico-chim. biol. 59* (1962) 442; Infrared spectroscopic analysis of some samples of polyacrylonitrile

C. Y. Liang, S. Krimm, *J. Polym. Sci. 31* (1958) 513; Infrared spectra of high polymers. VIII. Polyacrylonitrile

J. L. Lippert, J. A. Robertson, J. R. Havens, J. S. Tan, *Macromolecules 18* (1985) 63...7; Structural studies of poly(N-vinyl-imidazole) complexes by infrared and Raman spectroscopy

I. Matsubara, *Bull. Chem. Soc. Japan 33* (1960) 1624; Detection of end-groups in polyacrylonitrile by differential spectroscopy

C. Ruscher, R. Schmolke, *Faserforsch. u. Textiltechn. 14* (1963) 340; Ultrarotdichroismus hitzegeschädigter Polyacrylnitril-Folien

C. Ruscher, R. Schmolke, *Faserforsch. u. Textiltechn. 14* (1963) 459; Ultrarotdichroitische und röntgenographische Untersuchungen an Copolymeren des Acrylnitrils

C. Schneider, J. Herz, *Makromol. Chem. 73* (1964) 128; Die strahlenchemische Bildung von Keteniminogruppen bei der Tieftemperaturpolymerisation des Acrylnitrils

H. Sobue, T. Uryu, K. Matsuzaki, Y. Tabata, *J. Polym. Sci. A 2* (1964) 3333...8; Stereoregularity of polymethacrylonitrile

S. I. Stupp, S. H. Carr, *J. Polym. Sci. Polym. Phys. Ed. 16* (1978) 13...28; Spectroscopic analysis of electrically polarized polyacrylonitrile

R. Yamadera, H. Tadokoro, S. Murahashi, *J. Chem. Phys. 41* (1964) 1233; Normal vibrations of polyacrylonitrile and deuterated polyacrylonitrile

3.2.5 CHO polymers

3.2.5.1 Polymeric alcohols, phenols and ethers

M. Arnaudov, S. Hadjistoianova, P. Novakov, *J. Mat. Sci. 21* (1986) 3135...8; Infrared spectral study of diphenylether polymers

N. V. Chukanov et al., *Vysokomol. Soedin. A 18* (1976) 1793...8 (Russ.); *IR* spectroscopic investigation of homo and copolymers of ethylene oxide and propylene oxide

R. T. Conley, J. F. Bieron, *J. Appl. Polym. Sci. 7* (1963) 103; A study of the oxidative degradation of phenol-formaldehyde polycondensates using infrared spectroscopy

R. T. Conley, I. Metil, *J. Appl. Polym. Sci. 7* (1963) 37; An investigation of the structure of furfuryl alcohol polycondensates with infrared spectroscopy

R. T. Conley, J. F. Bieron, *J. Appl. Polym. Sci. 7* (1963) 171; A kinetic study of the oxidative degradation of phenol-formaldehyde polycondensates, using infrared spectroscopy

P. Friese, *Fresenius Z. analyt. Chem. 305* (1981) 337...46; Analytical characterization of polysaccharide-based thickeners. III. Identification by infrared spectroscopy

K. Fujii, J. Ukida, *Makromol. Chem. 65* (1963) 74; Observations on the infrared absorption band of poly(vinyl alcohol) at 916 cm^{-1}

R. J. Grisenthwaite, R. F. Hunter, *J. Appl. Chem. 6* (1956) 324; The infrared absorption spectra of some novolak and resole molecules

R. J. Grisenthwaite, R. F. Hunter, *Chem. Ind. 16* (1957) 196; The infrared absorption spectra of some novolak and resole molecules (discussion)

H. C. Haas, *J. Polym. Sci. 26* (1957) 391; A note on the infrared absorption spectrum of poly(vinyl alcohol)

G. Habermehl, *Angew. Chem. 76* (1964) 271; *IR*-spektroskopische Unterscheidung primärer, sekundärer und tertiärer Alkohole

J. F. Heil, J. M. Prausnitz, *J. Chem. Phys. 44* (1966) 737; Infrared study of hydrogen bonding between polymers and methanol: Poly(propylene oxide) and poly(propylene glycol)

D. O. Hummel, G. Ellinghorst, A. Khatchatryan, H. D. Stenzenberger, *Angew. Makromol. Chem. 82* (1979) 129...48; Segmented copolyethers with urethane and urea or semicarbazide links for blood circulation systems. II. Infrared-spectroscopic investigations

L. A. Igonin, M. M. Mirakhmedov, K. I. Turchaninova, A. N. Shabalin, *Dokl. Akad. Nauk SSSR 141* (1961) 1366 (Russ.); Investigation of the infrared absorption spectra during hardening of resolic phenolformaldehyde resin

K. Imada, T. Miyakawa, Y. Chatani, H. Tadokoro, S. Murahashi, *Makromol. Chem. 83* (1965) 113; Structural studies of [-(CH$_2$)$_m$-O-]$_n$

A. Kawasaki, J. Furukawa, T. Tsuruta, T. Saegusa, G. Kakogawa, R. Sakata, *Polymer 1* (1960) 315; Infra-red spectra of polyethers. I. Poly(alkylene oxide)s

G. S. Kituchina, V. V. Zarkov, *Plast. Massy 1981* (6) 57 (Russ.); Infrared spectroscopy of epoxidized polyoxypropylenepolyols

S. Krimm, C. Y. Liang, G. B. B. M. Sutherland, *J. Polym. Sci. 22* (1956) 227; Infrared spectra of high polymers. V. Poly(vinyl alcohol)

G. P. Lorenzi, E. Benedetti, E. Chiellini, *Chimica e Industria 46* (1964) 1474...84; Polimeri vinilici otticamente attivi. XIII. Polimerizzazione stereospecifica del (1-metil-propil)-vinil etere e del (2-metil-butil)-vinil etere otticamente attivi e racemi con sistemi catalitici diversi

K. Machida, T. Miyazawa, *Spectrochim. Acta 20* (1964) 1865; Infrared and Raman spectra of polyethyleneglycol dimethylethers in the liquid state

A. Miyake, *J. Am. Chem. Soc. 82* (1960) 3040; CH$_2$ rocking frequencies of ethylene glycol and its derivatives in relation to the configuration of polyethylene glycol

T. Miyazawa, K. Fukushima, Y. Ideguchi, *J. Chem. Phys. 37* (1962) 2764; Molecular vibrations and structure of high polymers. III. Polarized infrared spectra, normal vibrations, and helical conformation of polyethylene glycol

S. Murahashi, H. Yuki, T. Sano, U. Yonemura, H. Tadokoro, Y. Chatani, *J. Polym. Sci. 62* (1962) 77; Isotactic poly(vinyl alcohol)s

Y. Nakamura, *J. Chem. Soc. Japan, Ind. Chem. Sect. 60* (1957) 785; Infrared-spectra of phenolic resins. Cause of discoloration and preparation of colorless resins

A. Novak, E. Whalley, *Trans. Faraday Soc. 55* (1959) 1484; Infra-red spectra and structure of polyaldehydes

A. Novak, E. Whalley, *Can. J. Chem. 37* (1959) 1718; Infra-red spectra and structure of polyaldehydes. IV. Higher polyaldehydes

A. Novak, E. Whalley, *Can. J. Chem. 37* (1959) 1722; Infra-red spectra and structure of polyaldehydes. V. Polymonochloroacetaldehyde and polychloroacetaldehyde

R. E. Richards, H. W. Thompson, *J. Chem. Soc. 1947*, 1260; Vibrational spectra of phenolic derivatives and phenolic resins

S. Sasaki, Y. Takahashi, H. Tadokoro, *Polymer J. 4* (1973) 172...82; Structural studies of polyformals, $[-OCH_2O-(CH_2)_m-]_n$. I. Poly(1,3-dioxepane)

P. J. Secrest, *Off. Digest. Federat. Soc. Paint Technol. 37* (2) (1965) 187; Infrared studies of phenolic resins

R. Soda, *Bull. Chem. Soc. Japan 35* (1962) 152; On the structures of *p-t*-butylphenol and α-naphthol resins. III. Infrared absorption spectra of *p-t*-butylphenol and α-naphthol resins

H. Tadokoro, S. Seki, I. Nitta, *J. Chem. Phys. 23* (1955) 1351; Infrared absorption spectrum of deuterated poly(vinyl alcohol) film

H. Tadokoro, S. Seki, I. Nitta, *J. Polym. Sci. 22* (1956) 563; Some information on the infrared absorption spectrum of poly(vinyl alcohol) from deuteration and pleochroism

H. Tadokoro, M. Kobayashi, S. Murahashi, A. Mitsuishi, H. Yoshinaga, *Bull. Chem. Soc. Japan 35* (1962) 1429; Far infrared spectra and torsional vibrations of polyoxymethylene

Y. Tanaka, H. Kakiuchi, *J. Polym. Sci. A-1,4* (1966) 109; Epoxy compounds. VIII. Stereoregular and stereorandom polymerization of phenyl glycidyl ether with tertiary amines, and infrared spectra of poly(phenyl glycidyl ether)

L. Terlemezyan, M. Mihailov, P. Schmidt, B. Schneider, *Makromol. Chem. 179* (1978) 2315...22; Die Untersuchung temperaturbedingter Strukturänderungen in Polyoxymethylenen mit Hilfe der Infrarotspektroskopie

L. Terlemezyan, M. Mihailov, *Makromol. Chem. 179* (1978) 2807...10; Isotherme Veränderungen von konformationsempfindlichen Banden in den Infrarot-Spektren von Poly(oxymethylen) bei erhöhten Temperaturen

H. W. Thompson, P. Torkington, *Trans. Faraday Soc. 41* (1945) 246; The infrared spectra of compounds of high molecular weight

R. G. Žbankov, V. P. Komar, M. I. Rodinova, P. V. Kozlov, *Vysokomol. Soedin. 8* (1966) 157 (Russ.); Characteristics of the infrared spectra of cellulose ethers and esters in the crystalline state

3.2.5.2 Polymeric esters

F. G. Baddar, M. H. Nosseir, N. N. Messia, N. E. Ikladious, *Europ. Polym. J. 12* (1976) 63...40; Polyesters. Part IV. Structural elucidation of γ-phenylitaconic polyesters by joint application of *IR*, *UV* and *NMR* spectroscopy

U. Bartels, H. Hoyne, *Faserforsch. Textiltechn. 11* (1960) 503; Zur Analyse von Celluloseacetobutyraten

U. Baumann, H. Schreiber, K. Tessmar, *Makromol. Chem. 36* (1960) 81; *IR*-spektroskopische Untersuchungen zur Taktizität von PMMA

C. A. Boye, *J. Polym. Sci. 55* (1961) 263; Infrared spectra of *cis* and *trans* isomers of poly(1,4-cyclohexylene-dimethylene terephthalate)

W. W. Daniels, R. E. Kitson, *J. Polym. Sci. 33* (1958) 161...70; Infrared spectroscopy of polyethylene terephthalate

R. Danz, J. Dechant, C. Ruscher, *Faserforsch. Textiltech. 21* (1970) 503...8; Berechnung der Normalschwingungen eines ebenen Modells von Polyäthylenterephthalat

S. K. Dirlikov, J. L. Koenig, *Appl. Spectrosc. 33* (1979) 551...4; Infrared spectra of poly(methyl methacrylate) labeled with oxygen-18

S. K. Dirlikov, J. L. Koenig, *Appl. Spectrosc. 33* (1979) 555...61; Assigment of the carbon-hydrogen stretching and bending vibrations of poly(methyl methacrylate) by selective deuteration

J. Dybal, J. Štokr, B. Schneider, *Polymer 24* (1983) 971...80; Vibrational spectra and structure of stereoregular poly-(methyl methacrylates) and of the stereocomplex

W. Frank, D. Knaupp, *Ber. Bunsenges. Phys. Chem. 79* (1975) 1041...4; Die Absorptionsspektren von Polyäthylenterephthalat im Bereich des Fernen Infrarot. Ein Modell zur Interpretation

P. C. Gilette, S. D. Dirlikov, J. L. Koenig, J. B. Lando, *Polymer 23* (1982) 1759...64; An infrared study of model compounds of poly(tetramethylene terephthalate)

D. Grime, I. M. Ward, *Trans. Faraday Soc. 54* (1958) 959; The assignment of infra-red absorptions and rotational isomerism in polyethylene terephthalate and related compounds

J. K. Haken, R. L. Werner, *Br. Polym. J. 3* (1971) 157...62; Infrared spectra of polyvinyl acetate and poly(α,α′,β-trideuterovinyl acetate)

J. K. Haken, R. L. Werner, *Br. Polym. J. 3* (1971) 263...5; Infrared spectrum of polymethyl acrylate

J. K. Haken, R. L. Werner, *Spectrochim. Acta 27 A* (1971) 343...51; The infrared spectrum of polyvinyl formate

J. K. Haken, R. L. Werner, *Br. Polym. J. 4* (1972) 147...51; A temperature-sensitive band in the spectrum of polyvinyl acetate

D. O. Hummel, C. Schneider, *Kunststoffe 50* (1960) 427; Block- und Pfropfpolymerisationen an Polymethylmethacrylat unter dem Einfluß von ^{60}Co-γ-Strahlung

M. Ishibashi, *J. Polym. Sci. B1* (1963) 529; *Polymer 5* (1964) 305; Infrared spectra of polyethylene oxybenzoate

Y. Iwakura, F. Toda, T. Ito, K. Aoshima, *Makromol. Chem. 104* (1967) 26; Tacticities of poly(glycidyl methacrylate) obtained by radical polymerization

A. Kawasaki, J. Furukawa, T. Tsuruta, S. Inoue, K. Ito, *Makromol. Chem. 36* (1960) 260; Crystalline PMMA

A. Kawasaki, J. Furukawa, T. Tsuruta, G. Wasai, T. Makimoto, *Makromol. Chem. 49* (1961) 76; *IR* spectra of poly-(butyl acrylates)

F. Lalau-Keraly, *C. R. hebd. Séances Acad. Sci. 253* (1961) 2975; Étude des polymères de l'isophthalate et du téréphthalate diallylique par spectrométrie infrarouge

C. Y. Liang, S. Krimm, *J. Molec. Spectrosc. 3* (1959) 554; Infrared spectra of high polymers. Part IX. Polyethylene terephthalate

I. Lipschitz, *Polym. Plast. Technol. 19* (1982) 53...106; The vibrational spectrum of poly(methyl methacrylate). A review

I. Lipschitz, J. M. Gray, *ACS Polym. Prepr. 25/1* (1984) 199f.; The α-methyl and ester bends of PMMA

T. R. Manley, D. A. Williams, *Polymer 10* (1969) 339...84; Structure of terephthalate polymers. I. Infra-red spectra and molecular structure of poly(ethylene terephthalate)

A. Miyake, *J. Polym. Sci. 38* (1959) 497...512; The infrared spectrum of polyethylene terephthalate. II. Polyethylene-d_4 terephthalate

H. Nagai, H. Watanabe, A. Nishioka, *J. Polym. Sci. 62* (1962) 595...598; Infrared spectra of deuterated polymethyl methacrylates

H. Nagai, *J. Appl. Polym. Sci. 7* (1963) 1697; Infrared spectra of stereoregular polymethyl methacrylate

S. Okamura, T. Higashimura, A. Tanaka, R. Kato, Y. Kikuchi, *Makromol. Chem. 54* (1962) 226...9; Infrared absorption spectrum of poly-β-propiolactone obtained by two kinds of ionic polymerization

I. Ouchi, M. Hosoi, S. Shimotsuma, *J. Appl. Polym. Sci. 21* (1977) 3445...56; Infrared spectra of poly(ethylene 2,6-naphthalate) and some related polyesters

B. V. Ozerkovskii et al., *Vysokomol. Soedin. A25* (1983) 1816...22 (Russ.); The structure of cross-linked polymers of dimethacrylates and oligo *n*-methacrylates (I)

E. T. Reaville, W. F. Fallwell, *Off. Digest Federat. Soc. Paint Technol. 36* (1964) 625; Copolymers of alkyl maleates and fumarates, with vinyl acetate

G. Salomon, C. J. Schooneveldt, van der Kloes, J. H. L. Zwiers, *Recueil Trav. chim. Pay-Bas 79* (1960) 313; Infrared spectra of some methacrylic esters and their polymers

P. G. Schmidt, F. P. Gay, *Angew. Chem. 74* (1962) 638; Physikalische Charakterisierung von Poly(äthylenglykolterephthalat)

B. Schneider, J. Štokr, P. Schmidt, M. Mihailov, S. Dirlikov, u. a. *Polymer 20* (1979) 705...12; Stretching and deformation vibrations of CH_2, $C(CH_3)$ and $O(CH_3)$ groups of poly(methyl methacrylate)

R. A. Spurr, B. M. Hanking, J. W. Rowen, *J. Polym. Sci. 37* (1959) 431...40; The polymerization of diallyl phthalate, an investigation by infrared spectroscopy

J. Štokr, B. Schneider, *Collect. Czechoslov. Chem. Commun. 28* (1963) 1946; Vibration spectra of polyvinyl acetate and some model substances

A. Szilágyi, S. I. Vancsóné, V. Izvekov, *Magyar Kémiai Folyóirat 87* (1981) 209...13 (Hung.); Metal-containing coordination polymers. VIII. Investigation of the reaction of a polymer with ZnO by means of infrared spectroscopy

H. Tadokoro, K. Tatsuka, S. Murahashi, *J. Polym. Sci. 59* (1962) 413...23; Infrared absorption and structure of polyethylene terephthalate

M. C. Tobin, *J. Phys. Chem. 61* (1957) 1392; The infrared spectra of polyethylene terephthalate

F. Viras, T. A. King, *Polymer 25* (1984) 1411...4; Low frequency excitations in amorphous polycarbonate studied by Raman spectroscopy

I. M. Ward, M. A. Wilding, *Polymer 18* (1977) 327...35; Infrared and Raman spectra of poly(*m*-methylene terephthalate) polymers

3.2.5.3 Miscellaneous CHO polymers, carbons

M. Bartholin, *Makromol. Chem. 182* (1981) 2075...85; Styrene-divinylbenzene copolymers. 3. Revisited *IR* analysis

E. Benedetti, A. D'Alessio, P. Vergamini, A. Pennacchi, P. Ghetti, G. Ghelardi, *Riv. Combust. 34* (1980) 394...402; Characterization of coals by infrared spectroscopy

H. H. Oelert, *Erdöl, Kohle, Erdgas, Petrochemie 18* (1965) 876...80; Zur quantitativen Ultrarotspektroskopie an Steinkohlen

P. C. Painter et al., *Energy Res. Abstr. 9* (1984) 5690; Data base for the analysis of compositional characteristics of coal seams and macerals. Pt. 5: Recent *FT-IR* and ^{13}C *NMR* studies of coal structure

T. V. Verheyen, R. B. Johns, R. J. Esdaile, *Geochim. Cosmochim. Acta 47* (1983) 1579...87; Structural investigations of Australian coals. IV. A characterization of the variation in rank of bituminous coal fractions by elemental analysis and *IR* spectroscopy

H. Zweifel, T. Völker, *Makromol. Chem. 170* (1973) 141...53; On the mechanism of anionic polymerization of maleic anhydride. 2.

3.2.6 CHNO polymers

M. Bauer, J. Bauer, G. Kühn, *Acta Polymer. 37* (1986) 218...20; Analytik von Prepolymeren und Polymeren aromatischer Cyansäureester. 1. *IR*-Spektroskopie

M. Beer, H. B. Kessler, G. B. B. M. Sutherland, *J. Chem. Phys. 29* (1958) 1097; Spectra of homologous series of monosubstituted amides

E. G. Bendit, C. G. Cannon, B. C. Stace, *Nature 196* (1962) 436; Infrared absorption bands of the peptide group

E. M. Bradbury, A. Elliot, *Polymer 4* (1963) 47; Infra-red spectra and chain arrangement in some polyamides, polypeptides, and fibrous proteins

R. E. Camargo, C. W. Macosko, M. Tirrel, S. T. Wellinghoff, *Polym. Commun. 24* (1983) 314f.; Hydrogen bonding in segmented polyurethanes. Band assignment for the carbonyl region

C. G. Cannon, *Mikrochim. Acta [Wien] 1955,* 555; The interactions and structure of the −CONH− group in amides and polyamides

C. G. Cannon, *J. Chem. Phys. 24* (1956) 491; Infrared frequency shifts and amide group interactions

C. G. Cannon, *Spectrochim. Acta 16* (1960) 302; The infrared spectra and molecular configurations of polyamides

Ju. N. Chirgadze, *Biofizika 7* (1962) 523 (Russ.); Analysis of the peptide group vibrations

Ju. N. Chirgadze, *Biofizika 7* (1962) 657 (Russ.); The amide vibrations I and II of the peptide group as a function of the conformation

G. Cynkowska, P. Penczek, E. Wardzinska, *Polymery (Warsaw) 27* (1982) 253...6 (Pol.); Spectrophotometric investigation of the chemical composition of polyimides

J. Dechant, C. Ruscher, *Faserforsch. Textiltechn. 16* (1965) 180...5; Über die Feinstruktur der Polyamide. V. Dichroismus und Zuordnung des Ultrarotspektrums von Polycaprolactam

D. Doskočilová, H. Pivcová, B. Schneider, P. Čefelín, *Coll. Czechoslov. Chem. Commun. 28* (1963) 1867; On the structure and properties of polyamides. IV. Infrared spectra of polymethylcaprolactam and of amorphous polycaprolactam

K. Frigge, I. Dechant, *Faserforsch. Textiltechn. 26* (1975) 547...50; Über die Feinstruktur der Polyamide. 15th report. Infrarotspektroskopische Untersuchungen an Polycaproamid bei erhöhten Temperaturen

R. L. Gajduk, V. N. Vatulev, Ju. S. Lipatov, Ju. Ju. Kerca, *Vysokomol. Soedin. B26* (1984) 566...9 (Russ.); Anomalous temperature dependence in the range of carbonyl absorption of segmented polyurethanes

G. Heidemann, H.-J. Nettelbeck, *Faserforsch. Textiltechn. 18* (1967) 183...9; Infrarotspektroskopische Untersuchungen an Nylon 6 und seinen cyclischen Oligomeren

J. Hocker, *J. Appl. Polym. Sci. 25* (1980) 2879...89; Structural investigation of polyurethanes: Infrared spectroscopic investigations of monomeric and polymeric N,N'-diaryl ureas

D. O. Hummel, G. Ellinghorst, A. Khatchatryan, H.-D. Stenzenberger, *Angew. Makromol. Chem. 82* (1979) 129...48; Segmented copolyethers with urethane and urea or semicarbazide links for blood circulation systems. II. Infrared-spectroscopic investigations

H. Hummel, R. Bonart, *Macromol. Chem. 184* (1983) 2693...704; *IR*-Bandenstrukturanalyse der Amidstreckschwingungen von N-Methylacetamid als Modellsubstanz für Makromoleküle mit Peptidbindungen

H. Ishida, S. T. Wellinghoff, E. Baer, J. L. Koenig, *Macromolecules 13* (1980) 826...34; Spectroscopic studies of poly[N,N'-*bis*(phenoxyphenyl)pyromellitimide]. 1. Structure of the polyimide and three model compounds

H. Ishihara, I. Kimura, K. Saito, H. Ono, *J. Macromol. Sci. Phys. B10* (1974) 591...618; Infrared studies on segmented polyurethane-urea elastomers

D. Joel, M. Weiler, K. Wagner, *Plaste Kautsch. 29* (1982) 22...6; Biuretstrukturen in Polyurethan-Weichschaumstoffen

J. Jokl, *Coll. Czechoslov. Chem. Commun. 28* (1963) 3305; On the structure and properties of polyamides. VII. Near infrared spectra of polycaprolactam

E. P. Kaluckaja, S. S. Gusev, A. V. Kostocko, T. M. Berdnikova, *Vysokomol. Soedin. A23* (1981) 1487...93 (Russ.); *IR* spectroscopic investigation of the hydration of cellulose nitrate

S. Krimm, C. Y. Liang, *J. Appl. Phys. 29* (1958) 1407; Infrared spectra of high polymers. VIII. Polyvinyl nitrate

G. D. Litovčenko, T. N. Komogorova, N. P. Okromčedlidze, A. B. Raskina, A. S. Semenova, A. V. Volochina, M. V. Sablygin, *Vysokomol. Soedin. B21* (1979) 129...32 (Russ.); Investigation of the infrared spectra of copolymeric polyphenylene-1,3,4-oxadiazolene

L. I. Maklakov, V. L. Furer, A. L. Furer, *Vysokomol. Soedin. B25* (1983) 162...5 (Russ.); On the multiplicity of absorption bands in *IR* spectra of urethanes and polyurethanes

I. Maklakov, Infrared studies of oligourethane systems, in W. E. Steger (ed.), *Progress in Polymer Spectroscopy;* Teubner, Leipzig 1986

I. Matsubara, Y. Itoh, M. Shinomiya, *J. Polym. Sci. B4* (1966) 47; Lower-frequency infrared spectra (800...200 cm^{-1}) and structures of polyamides

N. V. Mikhailova et al., *Vysokomol. Soedin. B18* (1976) 631...4 (Russ.); The spectroscopic investigation of the volume and surface properties of polyimide films

T. Miyazawa, T. Shimanouchi, S. Mizushima, *J. Chem. Phys. 24* (1956) 408; Characteristic infrared bands of monosubstituted amides

W. H. Moore, S. Krimm, *Biopolymers 15* (1976) 2439...64; Vibrational analysis of peptides, polypeptides, and proteins. I. Polyglycine I

T. A. Romanova, L. M. Levitec, M. V. Sablygin, M. N. Bogdanov, G. I. Kudrjavcev, *Khim. Volokna 1980* (2) 27...31 (Russ.); Infrared spectroscopic characteristics of thermally stable fiber-forming polymers

I. D. Salabaeva et al., *Vysokomol. Soedin. B24* (1982) 653...6 (Russ.); Comparative *IR* spectroscopic investigation of aromatic polyamido acids of varying compositions

P. Schmidt, B. Schneider, *Coll. Czechoslov. Chem. Commun. 31* (1966) 1896; On the structure and properties of polyamides. XXV. Infrared study of deuterium exchange of amide hydrogen in polycaprolactam

B. Schneider, P. Schmidt, O. Wichterle, *Coll. Czechoslov. Chem. Commun.* 27 (1962) 1749; On the structure and properties of polyamides. I. Infrared spectra of polycaprolactam

S. V. Serchenkova et al., *Vysokomol. Soedin. A 18* (1976) 1863...9 (Russ.); *IR* spectroscopic investigations of compounds of benzimide-amido carboxylic acids

S. W. Shalaby, E. L. McCaffery, *Anal. Chem. 40* (1968) 823...5; Infrared determination of noncyclic imides and polyimides

P. Simak, *Makromol. Chem. 178* (1977) 2927...37; Polymorphie, Kristallinität und Schmelzwärme von Poly(ε-caprolactam). 1st report

D. K. Singh, K. K. Patidar, *Paintindia 28* (1978) 24...7; Identification of poly(ester imide) resins by *IR* spectroscopy

P. Subramanian, K. Venkatarao, *Macromol. Chem. Rapid Commun. 2* (1981) 179...82; Synthesis and characterization of a new polyamide containing azomethine groups in the polymer backbone

L. Sztraka, J. Varga, K. Belina, *Magyar Kémiai Folyóirat 87* (1981) 529...32 (Hung.); Investigation of polyimides. IV. Infrared spectra of polyimides, polyamido acid and of model compounds

D. S. Trifan, J. F. Terenzi, *J. Polym. Sci. 28* (1958) 443; Extents of hydrogen bonding in polyamides and polyurethanes

G. M. Venkatesh, D. Y. Shen, S. L. Hsu, *J. Polym. Sci. Polym. Phys. Ed. 19* (1981) 1475...88; Spectroscopic study of rigid-rod polymers. I. Structures of model compounds

V. I. Vettegren et al., *Faserforsch. Textiltechn. 28* (1977) 335...8; Zur Festigkeit von Polyimid-Makromolekülen

S. T. Wellinghoff, H. Ishida, J. L. Koenig, E. Baer, *Macromolecules 13* (1980) 834...9; Spectroscopic studies of poly[N,N'-bis-(phenoxyphenyl)pyromellitimide]. 2. Structural changes of polyimide upon yielding

F. Wood, K. King, *J. Textile Inst. 54* (1963) T111...T122; An infra-red spectroscopic investigation of the NHCO group in keratin, silk and nylon

V. V. Zarkov, L. I. Kopusov, T. V. Kozlova, *Plast. Massy 1981* (12) 41...5 (Russ.); Infrared spectroscopic investigation of the synthesis and the structure of polyurethanes

3.2.7 Organosilicon polymers

D. R. Anderson, *Chem. Anal. (N.Y.) 41* (1974) 247...86; Infrared, Raman and ultraviolet spectroscopy (of organosilicon compounds)

M. C. Harvey, W. H. Nebergall, *Appl. Spectrosc. 16* (1962) 12; The silicon-phenyl asymmetrical stretching vibration

J. Knizek, M. Horak, V. Chvalovsky, *Coll. Czechoslov. Chem. Commun. 28* (1963) 3079; Organosilicon compounds. XXXI. Spectroscopic behaviour of the vinyl group in silylolefins

H. Kriegsmann, *Z. Elektrochem. 64* (1960) 541; Spektroskopische Untersuchung an Siliciumverbindungen. XI. Die Raman- und *IR*-Spektren linearer Methylpolysiloxane

H. Kriegsmann, *Z. Elektrochem. 64* (1960) 848; Die Schwingungsspektren kettenförmiger Methylhydrogenpolysiloxane

H. Kriegsmann, *Z. Elektrochem. 65* (1961) 336; Die Schwingungsspektren einiger verzweigter und vernetzter Methyl- und Methylhydrogenpolysiloxane

H. Kriegsmann, *Z. Elektrochem. 65* (1961) 342; Spektroskopische Untersuchungen an Siliciumverbindungen. XVI.

Die Schwingungsspektren der Methyl- und Methyl-Wasserstoff-Polysiloxane

N. Neto, G. Sbrana, M. Muniz-Miranda, S. Dobos, B. Zelei, L. Harsányi, *J. Polym. Sci. Polym. Chem. Ed. 21* (1983) 3389...402; Spectroscopic investigation of organosilicon polymers. I. Vibrational analysis of poly(tetramethyl-*p*-silphenylene-siloxane)

R. E. Richards, H. W. Thompson, *J. Chem. Soc. [London] 1949*, 124; Infrared spectra of compounds of high molecular weight. IV. Silicones and related compounds

E. R. Shull, *Anal. Chem. 32* (1960) 1627; Estimation of hydroxyl, methyl, and phenyl in dimethyldiphenyl silicone resins by infrared spectrophotometry

A. L. Smith, J. A. McHard, *Anal. Chem. 31* (1959) 1174; Spectroscopic techniques for identification of organosilicon compounds

A. L. Smith, *Spectrochim. Acta 19* (1963) 849; Infrared spectra of organosilicon compounds in the CsBr region

E. Wojtynska, *Polimery 24* (1979) 238...41 (Pol.); Detection of silanol groups in polyphenylsiloxanes. Infrared spectroscopic investigation

N. Wright, M. J. Hunter, *J. Am. Chem. Soc. 69* (1947) 803; Organosiliconpolymers. III. Infrared spectra of the methylpolysiloxanes

C. W. Young, P. C. Servais, C. C. Currie, M. J. Hunter, *J. Am. Chem. Soc. 70* (1948) 3758; Organosilicon polymers. IV. Infrared studies on cyclic disubstituted siloxanes

3.2.8 Miscellaneous polymers

J. N. Baxter, J. Cymerman-Craig, J. B. Willis, *J. Chem. Soc. [London] 1955*, 669; The infrared spectra of some sulfonamides

D. Bloor, D. N. Batchelder, D. J. Ando, R. T. Tread, R. J. Young, *J. Polym. Sci. Polym. Phys. Ed. 19* (1981) 321...34; Spectroscopic studies of solutions, suspensions, and precipitates of poly(1,6-di-*p*-toluene sulfonyloxy-2,4-hexadiyne)

C. Chang, S. L. Hsu, *J. Polym. Sci. Polym. Phys. Ed. 23* (1985) 2307...17; Spectroscopic analysis of poly(*p*-phenylene benzobisthiazole) films

J. S. Gethner, *Org. Coat. Plast. Chem. 43* (1980) 413...8; Optical spectroscopy of coal

T. Hamaide, L. Germanaud, P. Le Perchec, *Makromol. Chem. 187* (1986) 1097...1107; New polymeric phosphonato-, phosphinato- and carboxybetaines. 1. Syntheses and characterization by *IR* spectroscopy

C. Heitner-Wirguin, *Polymer 20* (1979) 371...4; Infra-red spectra of perfluorinated cation-exchanged membrane

T. R. Manley, D. A. Williams, *Polymer 10* (1969) 307...18; Infrared spectrum and vibrational assignments of poly-(phosphonitrilic chloride)

J. Pielichowski, J. Obrzut, *Makromol. Chem. 181* (1980) 1209...13; Hypochromism of polyhalogenvinylcarbazoles

T. A. Starostina, A. B. Gilman, R. R. Sifrina, L. F. Rybakova, V. M. Kolotyrkin, *Vysokomol. Soedin. B 22* (1980) 548...52 (Russ.); Structure of the polymer of α,β-fluor-β-chlorovinylthiophene, which is obtained in glow discharge

S. H. Yu, *Polym. Mat. Sci. Eng. 50* (1984) 512...7; Characterization of hydroxyl-terminated liquid polymers of epichlorohydrin

G. Zundel, H. Noller, G.-M. Schwab, *Z. Naturforsch. 16 b* (1961) 716; Folien aus Polystyrolsulfonsäure und ihren Salzen. I. Herstellung und *IR*-Spektren mit Zuordnung

G. Zundel, H. Noller, G.-M. Schwab, *Z. Elektrochem. 66* (1962) 122; Folien aus Polystyrolsulfonsäure und ihren Salzen. II. *IR*-Untersuchungen über Hydratation

3.3 Natural and synthetic fibers

3.3.1 Fundamentals, reviews (also conventional methods)

G. Balbach, *Infrarotspektroskopische Untersuchungen zur Analyse beschichteter Gewebe sowie zur Chemie der Hochveredelung von Cellulosefasern*; Thesis, Stuttgart 1964

D. J. Bringardner, P. P. Pritulsky, *Textile World*, Dec. 1961, 47...59, 162; Latest word on identifying today's fibers

B. Cleverley, R. Herrmann, *J. Appl. Chem. 11* (1961) 344; Infrared spectra of textile materials: Identification of fibers and pure fabrics

M. Draghici, S. Badilescu, G. E. Baiulescu, *Spectrosc. Lett. 18* (1982) 583...95; Identification of paper by infrared spectrometry

J. E. Ford, W. J. Roff, *J. Textile Inst., Trans. 45* (1954) *T* 580...*T* 611; Identification of textile and related fibres

D. O. Hummel, *Melliand Textilchem. 1* (1965) 108...21, 139...45; Zur infrarot-spektroskopischen Identifizierung von Fasern und Geweben

D. O. Hummel, H. W. Siesler, E. Zoschke, I. Vierling, U. Morlock, T. Stadtländer, *Melliand Textilber. 54* (1973) 1340...6; *IR*-spektroskopische Untersuchungen an hochtemperaturbeständigen Fasern und Geweben mit der *ATR*-Technik. II.

O. Kirret, L. Lahe, G. Rajalo, E. Kirjanen, *Eesti NSV Teaduste Akadeemia 32 Keemia* (1983) 119...23; Characterization and identification of chemical fibres by infrared spectrometric method and computer

O. Kirret, P.-A. Koch, L. Lahe, G. Rajalo, E. Kirjanen, *Eesti NSV Teaduste Akadeemia 32 Keemia* (1983) 163...70; Characterization and identification of chemical and natural fibres by infrared spectroscopic method and computer

O. Kirret, L. Lahe, E. Kirjanen, Characterization and identification of nitrogen-containing chemical fibres and wool by infrared spectrometric method and computation, in W. E. Steger (ed.), *Progress in Polymer Spectroscopy*; Teubner, Leipzig 1986

N. W. Mikhailov, M. W. Shablygin, *Vysokomol. Soedin. 4* (1962) 1155 (Russ.); On the methods of recording and analyzing the *IR* absorption spectra of fiber materials in polarized light

K. D. Pohl, M.-L. Bumiller, *Chemiker-Ztg. 98* (1974) 364...70; Naturwissenschaftlich-kriminalistische Faseranalytik

J. H. Rau, *Melliand Textilber. 44* (1963) 1098...1102, 1197...1200, 1317...80; *ibid. 45* (1964) 224...6; Die Infrarot-Spektren der Textilfasern

C. Ruscher, R. Schmolke, *Faserforsch. Textiltechn. 11* (1960) 383...90; Zur Ultrarotspektroskopie an faserbildenden Hochpolymeren

K. W. Smalldon, *J. Forensic Sci. 18* (1973) 69...81; Identification of acrylic fibers by polymer composition as determined by infrared spectroscopy and physical characteristics

M. Stratmann, *Chemiker-Ztg. 98* (1974) 358...64; Qualitative und quantitative Faseranalysen

T. Szentpály, R. Szentpály, A. Stark, *Faserforsch. Textiltechn. 11* (1960) 189...95; Analysis of fiber mixtures

G. A. Tirpak, J. P. Sibilia, *J. Appl. Polym. Sci. 17* (1973) 643...8; New fiber-sampling technique for infrared spectroscopy as applied to Nylon 6 and poly(ethylene terephthalate)

K. Vogler, *Textil-Rdsch. 17* (1962) 547...59; Über den derzeitigen Stand der qualitativen und quantitativen Faseranalyse

R. G. Žbankov, *Zavodskaya Laboratoriya (Moscow) 29* (1963) 1438 (Russ.); *IR* spectroscopic methods for the investigation of fibers

3.3.2 Cellulose, cellulose derivatives, other polysaccharides

J. Blackwell, *ACS Symp. Ser. 48* (1977) 206...18; Infrared and Raman spectroscopy of cellulose

J. Dechant, *Faserforsch. Textiltechn. 18* (1967) 239...44; Ultrarotspektroskopische Zugänglichkeitsmessungen an Cellulose

J. Dechant, *Faserforsch. Textiltech. 19* (1968) 491...9; Die Interpretation des *UR*-Spektrums der Cellulose unter Verwendung von CD-deuterierten Proben

H. F. Higgins, C. M. Steward, K. J. Harrington, *J. Polym. Sci. 51* (1961) 59...84; Infrared spectra of cellulose and related polysaccharides

J. F. Hurtubise, H. Krässig, *Anal. Chem. 32* (1960) 177...81; Classification of fine structural characteristics in cellulose by infrared spectroscopy. Use of potassium bromide pellet technique

G. Jayme, P. K. Tio, *Papier 21* (1967) 883...6; Vergleichende infrarotspektroskopische Untersuchung von Cellulose und nativen Stärken

G. Jayme, P. K. Tio, *Papier 22* (1968) 322...8; Infrarotspektroskopische Untersuchungen an Polysacchariden und ihren Derivaten

A. A. Konkin, D. N. Šhigorin, L. I. Novikova, *Faserforsch. Textiltechn. 8* (1957) 85...90; *IR*-Absorptionsspektren der Mono- und Polysaccharide

C. Y. Liang, R. H. Marchessault, *J. Polym. Sci. 37* (1959) 385...95; Infrared spectra of crystalline polysaccharides. I. Hydrogen bonds in native cellulose

C. Y. Liang, R. H. Marchessault, *J. Polym. Sci. 39* (1959) 269...78; Infrared spectra of crystalline polysaccharides. II. Native celluloses in the region from 640 to 1700 cm^{-1}

J. Mann, H. J. Marrinan, *J. Polym. Sci. 32* (1958) 357; Crystalline modifications of cellulose. Part II. A study with plane-polarized infrared radiation

R. H. Marchessault, C. Y. Liang, *J. Polym. Sci. 43* (1960) 71...84; Infrared spectra of crystalline polysaccharides. III. Mercerized cellulose

H. J. Marrinan, J. Mann, *J. Polym. Sci. 21* (1956) 301; Infrared spectra of the crystalline modification of cellulose

E. R. McCall, S. H. Miles, V. W. Tripp, R. T. O'Connor, *Appl. Spectrosc. 18* (1964) 81...4; Differential infrared spectroscopy of chemically modified cottons

M. L. Nelson, R. T. O'Connor, *J. Appl. Polym. Sci. 8* (1964) 1311...24; Relation of certain infrared bands to cellulose crystallinity and crystal lattice type. Part I. Spectra of lattice types *I, II, III* and of amorphous cellulose

V. N. Nikitin, I. Ju. Levdik, *Ž. Prikl. Chim. 38* (1965) 2366...90 (Russ.); On the infrared absorption of cellulose at 900 cm^{-1}

R. T. O'Connor, E. F. DuPré, E. R. McCall, *Anal. Chem. 29* (1957) 998...1005; Infrared spectrophotometric procedure for analysis of cellulose and modified cellulose

R. T. O'Connor, E. F. DuPré, D. Mitcham, *Textile Res. J. 28* (1958) 382...92; Applications of infrared absorption spectroscopy to investigations of cotton and modified cottons. Part I. Physical and crystalline modifications and oxidation

J. Polcin, *Appl. Spectrosc. 28* (1974) 588...90; Preparation of samples for infrared spectrophotometric measurements of fibrous cellulose materials

C. Quivoron, J. Neel, *J. Chim. Phys. Physicochim. 63* (1966) 1210...22; Structure secondaire des polysaccharides. II. Etude, par spectroscopie infrarouge, des liaisons hydrogène dans quelques acetalalcools

B. D. Saksena, K. C. Agarwal, G. S. Jauhri, *J. Polym. Sci. 62* (1962) 347...57; Infrared spectrum of cellulose *I* in relation to its structure

B. Schneider, J. Vodňanský, *Coll. Czechoslov. Chem. Commun. 28* (1963) 2080...8; A study of the relation between the infrared spectra and the crystalline structure of cellulose

H. W. Siesler, H. Krässig, F. Grass, K. Kratzl, J. Derkosch, *Angew. Makromol. Chem. 42* (1975) 139...65; Strukturuntersuchungen an Cellulosefasern verschiedenen Verstreckungsgrades mittels *IR*-Reflexionsspektroskopie und Deuteriumaustausch

M. Slabina, B. Schneider, J. Jakeš, *Faserforsch. Textiltechn. 25* (1974) 525...8; Einige Probleme bei der Benutzung und Auswertung von Infrarot-Spektren in der Cellulose-Analytik

A. A. Vecher, V. M. Es'kov, T. N. Zhuikova, S. G. Zaichikov, V. S. Zak, G. I. Kurnevich, *Zh. Prikl. Spektrosk. 38* (1983) 803...7 (Russ.); *IR* spectroscopic investigation of thermal degradation of viscose rayon fibers in the presence of various additives

J. Vodňanský, M. Slabina, B. Schneider, *Coll. Czechoslov. Commun. 28* (1963) 3245...56; Investigation of the changes in composition and structure of cellulose and wood by infrared spectroscopy

3.3.3 Polyester fibers

B. v. Falkai, W. Giessler, F. Schultze-Gebhardt, G. Spilgies, *Angew. Makromol. Chem. 108* (1982) 9...39; Comparison of the structures of high-speed spun polyester filament yarns from poly(ethylene terephthalate) and from poly[1,4-*bis*(hydroxymethyl) cyclohexane terephthalate]

A. Garton, D. J. Carlsson, D. M. Wiles, *Text. Res. J. 51* (1981) 28...34; Infrared spectroscopy of polyethylene terephthalate fibers: uses and limitations

R. T. Graf, J. L. Koenig, H. Ishida, *ACS Polym. Prepr. 25/2* (1984) 159f.; In-situ studies of polymeric fibers by *FTIR* external reflectance spectroscopy

H. M. Heuvel, R. Huisman, *J. Appl. Polym. Sci. 30* (1985) 3069...93; Infrared spectra of poly(ethylene terephthalate) yarns. Fitting of spectra, evaluation of parameters, and applications

G. W. Urbanczyk, *Faserforsch. Textiltech. 27* (1976) 183...7; *IR*-spektroskopische Untersuchung der durch Verstreckung hervorgerufenen Orientierung in Poly(ethylentherephthalat)-Fasern

3.3.4 CHN and CHNO fibers

G. Heidemann, *Chemiefasern 20* (1970) 204...9; *IR*-spektroskopischer Nachweis einer Kern-Mantel-Struktur bei Polyamiden

O. Kirret, P.-A. Koch, L. Lahe, *Eesti NSV Teaduste Akad. Toimet, Keemia 31* (1982); Characterization and identification of polyacrylonitrile fibers and their modifications and modacrylic fibers by infrared spectrometric method

M. D. Kumanova, A. Spassov, *J. Polym. Sci. Polym. Lett. Ed. 24* (1986) 339...41; *IR*-study of the acrylic fiber shrinkage

R. B. Mathur, D. Gupta, O. P. Bahl, T. L. Dhami, *Fibre Sci. Technol. 20* (1984) 227...34; Infrared spectral studies of preoxidized PAN fibers incorporated with cuprous chloride additive

D. Minkwitz, H. Zimmer, *Melliand Textilber. 55* (1974) 909f.; Analyse von Polyacrylnitril- und Modacrylfasern

H. W. Siesler, *Makromol. Chem. 176* (1975) 2451...8; Orientierungsmessungen an uniaxial verstreckten Polyacrylnitrilfilmen

A. Strasheim, K. Buijs, *Spectrochim. Acta 16* (1960) 1010; A study of the infra-red spectra of wool fibres using the KBr disk technique

G. A. Tirpak, J. P. Sibilia, *J. Appl. Polym. Sci. 17* (1973) 643...8; A new fiber-sampling technique for infrared spectroscopy as applied to nylon 6 and poly(ethylene terephthalate)

Kh. U. Usmanov, A. A. Yul'chibaev, A. Vallev, P. P. Larin, *Khim. Volokna 4* (1977) 28f. (Russ.); *IR* spectroscopic investigation of graft copolymers of capron fibers with tetrafluoroethene

F. Wood, G. King, *J. Text. Inst. 54* (1963) T111...T122; An infra-red spectroscopic investigation of the NHCO group in keratin, silk and nylon

3.3.5 Miscellaneous fibers

N. H. Faizi, A. I. Kurilenko, *Vysokomol. Soedin. B13* (1971) 216...20 (Russ.); *IR* spectroscopic investigation with polarized light of the structure of poly(vinylidene chloride), grafted onto orientated synthetic fibers

A. Ishitani, *ACS Polym. Prepr. 24/1* (1983) 221f.; Characterization of the surface and the interface of the carbon fiber

O. Kirret, E. Kullik, L. Lahe, *Eesti NSV Tead. Akad. Toim. Keem. Geol. 23* (1974) 187...92; Identifizierung von Zweikomponentenfasern durch *IR*-spektroskopische und pyrolyse-gaschromatographische Methoden

H. W. Siesler, D. O. Hummel, *Melliand Textilber. 54* (1973) 1093...7; *IR*-spektroskopische Untersuchungen an hochtemperaturbeständigen Fasern und Geweben mit der *ATR*-Technik. I.

K. Sujak, A. Wlochowicz, M. Wysocki, *Acta Polymer. 35* (1984) 581...4; *IR*-spectroscopic analysis of changes in the molecular structure of pitch carbon fibre precursor during oxidation

3.3.6 Fiber mixtures

T. A. Belousova, G. D. Litovchenko, N. V. Mikhailov, *Khim. Volokna 1971* 43f. (Russ.); The application of *IR* difference spectroscopy for the determination of polyacrylonitrile in mixed-structure fibers

M. J. Clark, T. S. Hickie, *J. Text. Inst. 66* (1975) 243...8; Quantitative analysis of some binary mixture of fibres by methods of infra-red spectroscopy

F. F. Elsworth, *J. Text. Inst., Proc., 50* (1959) 695; Analysis of ternary mixtures containing wool, nylon 6,6 and viscose rayon

P. B. Iyer, K. R. K. Iyer, N. B. Patil, *J. Appl. Polym. Sci. 20* (1976) 591...5; An infrared technique for the quick analysis of cotton-polyester blends

M. L. Sobolewski, T. S. Hickle, *J. Text. Inst. 68* (1977) 302...5; The infra-red analysis of cotton-Cordelan mixtures

3.4 Elastomers: Rubbers

M. Anderson, *Elastomerics 110* (1978) 40; Determining traces of EPDM or IIR in rubber blends

B. Antczak, B. Krajewska, *Polimery (Warsaw) 28* (1983) 132...4 (Pol.); Identification of vulcanized rubber mixtures by infrared absorption spectrophotometry

S. Badilescu, S. Beregic, V. Constantinescu, D. Casadjicov, *Mater. Plast. (Bucharest) 20* (1983) 104f. (Rum.); Infrared spectroscopic determination of the 5-ethylidene-2-norbornene content in ethylene-propylene-diene terpolymers

B. M. Banerjee, V. B. Tandon, *Labdev A9* (1971) 186...9; Spectroscopic studies on cyclized rubber

T. F. Banigan, A. J. Verbiscar, T. A. Oda, *Rubber Chem. Technol. 55* (1982) 407...15; An infrared spectrophotometric analysis for natural rubber in guayule shrubs

W. Brachaczek, W. R. Pierson, *Rubber Chem. Technol. 47* (1974) 150...60; Analytical method for measuring SBR tire debris in the environment

D. T. Burns, E. W. Johnson, R. F. Mills, *J. Chromatogr. 105* (1975) 43...8; Rapid identification of solid polyurethane elastomers

D. S. Cain, S. S. Stimler, *NRL Report 6503*; US Naval Research Laboratory, Washington, DC 1967; Infrared spectra of plastics and resins. Part 3. Related polymeric materials (elastomers)

B. Dawson, P. R. Sewell, *Rubber Ind. (London) 9* (1975) 180...2; The differentiation of natural and synthetic *cis*-polyisoprenes in vulcanizates

A. Fiorenza, G. Bonomi, *Rubber Chem. Technol. 36* (1963) 1129...47; Identification of elastomers by infrared spectrophotometry

J. Gallus-Olender, B. Franc, L. Firlus, *Spectrosc. Lett. 16* (1983) 413...18; Structural changes during the silica rubber filler precipitation investigated by *IR* and *NIR* spectroscopy

D. Gross, *Kautsch. Gummi Kunstst. 27* (1974) 225...34; Aufschluß von Vulkanisaten und Identifizierung durch *IR*-Spektrometrie

R. R. Hampton, *Rubber Chem. Technol. 45* (1972) 546...626; Applied infrared spectroscopy in the rubber industry

D. O. Hummel, *Kautsch. Gummi Kunstst. 11* (1958) 185; Die *IR*-spektroskopische Identifizierung von Kautschuk, Weich- und Hartgummi

D. O. Hummel, *Rubber Chem. Technol. 32* (1959) 854...69; The infrared-spectroscopic identification of rubber before and after cure to the soft and hard rubber states

N. V. Ionina et al., *Vysokomol. Soedin. 20* (1978) 1124...9 (Russ.); *IR* spectroscopic investigation of the structure of low-molecular diene rubber with high content of filler

H. Ishihara, I. Kimura, K. Saito, H. Ono, *J. Macromol. Sci. Phys. B10* (1974) 591...618; Infrared studies on segmented polyurethane-urea elastomers

V. A. Khranovskii, O. M. Fedorenko, S. F. Kercha, V. K. Grishchenko, *Kompoz. Polim. Mater. 20* (1984) 35...40 (Russ.); Comparative *IR* spectroscopic investigation of segmented elastomers based on poly(oxytetramethylene) and a poly(diene) diol

L. I. Kopusov, V. V. Zharkov, *Plast. Massy 1972* (9) 66...9 (Russ.); Spectral analysis of elastic polyurethanes

T. V. Kozlova, V. V. Zarkov, *Vysokomol. Soedin. B20* (1978) 285...7 (Russ.); Spectroscopic investigation of the thermodynamics of segment microaggregation in linear segmented polyetherurethanes

M. Kronstein, *Polym. Mater. Sci. Eng. 54* (1986) 681...5; The basic characteristics of natural rubber

E. K. Krupenikova, B. N. Dinzburg, *Vysokomol. Soedin. B21* (1979) 635...8 (Russ.); *IR* spectroscopic investigation of the mechanism of cross-linking of urethane rubbers with alkylphenol-formaldehyde resins

G. Lawson, J. A. Sidwell, *Plast. Rubber Intern. 8* (1983) (6) 15...20, 22; Techniques for analysing rubber and plastics, an overview

L. M. Luk'yanova, Yu. G. Chikishev, L. V. Vanchugova, *Kauch. Rezina 1984* (2) 31f. (Russ.); Some characteristics of the *IR* spectroscopic investigation of vulcanized rubber

F. E. Lussier, *Rubber World 188* (1983) 18...22; A practical method of the analysis of elastomer blends

F. Mersch, *Kautsch. Gummi Kunstst. 28* (1975) 317...24; Anwendung moderner analytischer Methoden für die Bestimmung der Ausgangsstoffe in Gummi-Artikeln

R. Merten, G. Braun, D. Lauerer, *Kunststoffe 55* (1965) 249...54; Über den Aufbau von Polyurethan-Schaumstoffen

R. Merten, D. Lauerer, G. Braun, M. Dahm, *Makromol. Chem. 101* (1967) 337...66; Über den Aufbau von Polyurethan-Kunststoffen. II.[1] Die Struktur von Polyurethan-Schaumstoffen in Abhängigkeit von der Temperatur, der Zeit und der Rezeptur; *IR*-spektroskopische Nachweisgrenzen für Urethan- und Harnstoffgruppen in Polymeren

W. Mills, M. J. Jordan, *J. Inst. Rubber Ind. 4* (1970) 60...6; Determination of tread vulcanisate polymers by pyrolysis-infrared spectrophotometry

K. Nakayama, T. Ino, I. Matsubara, *J. Macromol. Sci. Chem. A3* (1969) 1005...20; Infrared spectra and structure of polyurethane elastomers from poly(tetrahydrofuran), diphenylmethane-4,4'-diisocyanate, and ethylenediamine

R. C. J. Osland, W. J. Price, A. H. Devenish, *Am. Lab. 10* (1979) 111f., 114, 116...18, 120; Infrared techniques in the analysis of rubber

D. J. Patterson, J. L. Koenig, *Org. Coat. Appl. Polym. Sci. Proc. 48* (1983) 455...8; Characterization of chemically crosslinked natural rubber and *cis*-polybutadiene

E. O. Schmalz, G. Geiseler, *Z. analyt. Chem. 190* (1962) 293...304; Beitrag zur Isomerenanalyse des Kautschuks. I. Polybutadiene

R. Schmolke, W. Kimmer, *Plaste Kautsch. 21* (1974) 651...3; Infrarotspektroskopische Untersuchung von Nitrilkautschuk

R. W. Seymour, S. L. Cooper, *J. Polym. Sci. Symp. 46* (1974) 69...81; Viscoelastic properties of polyurethane block polymers

H. Tagawa, K. Kurita, E. Wada, *Makromol. Chem. 185* (1984) 2233...40; Investigations on linear segmented polyurethane elastomers. 1. Temperature dependence of microphase segregated structure

3.5 Resins, paints, coatings; paint oils

3.5.1 Fundamentals, reviews

R. J. Audette, R. F. E. Percy, *J. Forens. Sci. 24* (1979) 790...807; *ibid. 27* (1982) 622...70; A rapid, systematic and comprehensive classification system for the identification and comparison of motor vehicle paint samples (I and II)

I. L. Davies, *J. Oil Colour Chem. Assoc. 68* (1985) 109...15; Instrumental analysis in the coatings industry

J. D. Frazee, *J. Oil. Col. Chem. Assoc. 57* (1974) 300...9; Internal reflection spectroscopy: application to organic coatings and plastic sheeting

T. Helmen, *Farbe Lack 80* (1974) 715...31; Einsatzmöglichkeiten von *IR*-Spektroskopie und Gaschromatographie in der Lackindustrie, beleuchtet durch einige ausgewählte Beispiele

H. Herfeld, K. Schmidt, *Leder 23* (1972) 61...79; *IR*-spektroskopische Untersuchungen an Überzügen und Pigmenten

H. Jablonski, *Polimery (Warsaw) 23* (1978) 188...91 (Pol.); The application of modern methods to the analysis of polymers and lacquers

R. W. May, J. Porter, *J. Forensic Sci. Soc. 15* (2) (1975) 137...46; Evaluation of common methods of paint analysis. Pyrolysis-*GC*, pyrolysis-*IR*

R. F. E. Percy, R. J. Audette, *J. Forens. Sci. 25* (1980) 189...239; Automotive repaints: Just a new look?

J. Zieba, *Forensic Sci. Int. 17* (1981) 101...8; A statistical criterion for the value of evidence: application to the evaluation of the results of paint spectral analysis

3.5.2 Natural resins and modified natural resins

C. W. Beck, E. Wilbur, S. Meret, *Nature 201* (1964) 256f.; Infra-red spectra and the origin of amber

C. Beck, E. Wilbur, S. Meret, D. Kossove, K. Kermani, *Archaeometry 8* (1965) 96...109; The infrared spectra of amber and the identification of Baltic amber

C. W. Beck, *Proc. Univ. Bristol Spelaeological Soc. 10* (1965) 272...6; The origin of the amber found at Gough's Cave, Cheddar, Somerset

C. W. Beck, *Naturwiss. 59* (1972) 294...8; Aus der Bernstein-Forschung

C. W. Beck, T. Liu, *Gallia Prehistoire 19* (1976) 201...7; La grotte du Hasard a Tharaux (Gard) II. Origine de l'ambre des grottes du Hasard et du Prevel

D. O. Hummel, U. Pohl, *Farbe Lack 72* (1966) 517...25; Zur *IR*-spektroskopischen Identifizierung von Naturharzen und ihren Derivaten

J. H. Langenheim, C. W. Beck, *Science 149* (1965) 52...5; Infrared spectra as a means of determining botanical sources of amber

S. S. Savkevich, I. A. Shaks, *Ž. prikl. Chim. 37* (1964) 930f. (Russ.); *J. Appl. Chem. USSR 37* (1964) 940...2; Infrared absorption spectra of baltic amber (succinite)

J. M. Todd, M. H. Eichel, C. W. Beck, A. Macchiarulo, *J. Field Archaeology 3* (1976) 313...27; Bronze and iron age amber artifacts in Croatia and Bosnia-Hercegovina

3.5.3 Hydrocarbon resins

P. Vo, H. H. Le, Q. Nguyen, T. M. Vu, *Plaste Kautsch. 32* (1985) 86...8; Untersuchung der Struktur von cyclisiertem Naturkautschuk durch *IR*-Spektroskopie

3.5.4 Phenolic and epoxy resins

H. Alaminov, R. Markova, *Eur. Polym. J. 12* (1976) 481...4; A study of modified polymers by means of *IR* spectroscopy and thermal analysis

N. S. Allen, J. P. Binkley, B. J. Parsons, N. H. Tennent, G. O. Phillips, *Polym. Photochem. 2* (1982) 97...107; Spectroscopic properties and photosensitivity of epoxy resins

F. J. Boerio, S. L. Chen, *Appl. Spectrosc. 33* (1979) 121...6; Reflection-absorption infrared spectroscopy and ellipsometry of epoxy films on metals

J. Cazes; *Double Liaison 88* (1962) 17...22; Examen de diverses résines formophénoliques par spectrophotomètrie infrarouge

L. W. Chen, J. Kumanotani, *J. Appl. Polym. Sci. 9* (1965) 2785...97; Chemical and physical behavior of phenolic resins in air-dried films of phenolic varnishes

S. Chow, *Holzforschung 31* (1977) 200...5; Untersuchung des Härtens von Phenol-Formaldehydharzen durch die Anwendung Infrarotspektrometrie und Thermoanalyse

S. Chow, P. R. Steiner, *Holzforschung 32* (1978) 120...2; Bestimmung des Gehalts an Resorcinol in Phenol-Resorcinol-Formaldehyd-Harzen durch Infrarotspektrometrie

M. Cizmedioglu, S. D. Hong, J. Moacanin, A. Gupta, *ACS Polym. Prepr. 22/2* (1981) 224...5; Spectroscopic characterization of Narmco 5208 epoxy neat-resin formulations

V. A. Erä, H. Salo, T. Kaps, J. J. Lindberg, *Angew. Makromol. Chem. 48* (1975) 185...7; Determination of phenol/formaldehyde molar ratio of resol resins by infrared spectroscopy

J. P. Giboz, J. Lahaye, *Bull. Soc. Chim. Fr. 1971*, 1956f. (Fr.); Infrared spectrophotometric study of the chemical changes in an epoxy resin in the course of its electrodeposition on an iron electrode

J. L. Illinger, J. F. Sprouse, *Org. Coat. Plast. Chem. 38* (1978) 487...502; Effect of cure on structure and moisture interactions of 1009 epoxy resin

J. J. Lindberg, U. Brotherus, V. A. Erä, *Angew. Makromol. Chem. 45* (1975) 77...83; Untersuchung von Schaumstoffen auf Basis von Phenol-Formaldehyd-Harzen durch *IR*-Spektroskopie

I. Majer et al., *Chem. Prum. 27* (1977) 408...10 (Czech.); A contribution to the *IR* spectroscopy of uncured novolak resins

N. I. Makarevich, N. I. Sushko, A. I. Ivanov, T. I. Glazova, *Zh. Prikl. Spektrosk. 18* (1973) 671...5 (Russ.); Infrared spectra and structural characteristics of some types of industrial phenol-formaldehyde resins

K. Peltonen, P. Pfaffli, A. Itkonen, *Analyst (London) 110* (1985) 1173...6; Determination of aromatic epoxy resins and their thermal degradation products in air by infrared spectrometry

L. N. Piroznaya, *Vysokomol. Soedin. A12* (1970) 2466...51 (Russ.); Investigation of the reaction of phenyl glycidyl ether or epoxy resins with tertiary amine by *IR* spectroscopy

P. J. Secrest, *Official Digest 37* (1965) 187...204; Infrared studies of phenolic resins

D. P. Shvets, G. F. Yakovleva, *Fiz.-Khim. Metody Anal. 1* (1970) 96...9 (Russ.); Infrared spectroscopic determination of the *p*- and *o*-substituted phenol rings in phenol-formaldehyde novolak resins

P. V. Sidyakin, *Vysokomol. Soedin. A14* (1972) 979...88 (Russ.); Infrared spectroscopic investigation of the curing of epoxide polymers with amines

V. P. Solomko, S. E. Artemenko, L. G. Glukhova, N. B. Luchitskaya, *Khim. Tekhnol. (Kiev) 1977* (3), 14...17 (Russ.); Investigation of the reaction of aniline-formaldehyde and epoxy resins with capron and rayon fibers with *IR* spectroscopy

G. C. Stevens, *J. Appl. Polym. Sci. 26* (1981) 4259...78; Cure kinetics of a low epoxide/hydroxyl group-ratio bisphenol-A epoxy resin-anhydride system by infrared absorption spectroscopy

E. Veisova, *Plast. Hmoty Kauc. 7* (1970) 205...7; Infrarotspektren von Epoxidharzen und ihre Anwendungen

V. V. Zaitseva, L. V. Makarova, V. P. Sorokin, *Plast. Massy 1974* (9), 57...9 (Russ.); Analysis of epoxide compounds with an *IR* spectroscopic method

3.5.5 Ester-type resins

E. Fedeli, G. Favini, A. Brillo, D. Baroni, *Riv. Ital. Sostanze Grasse 58* (1981) 74...83 (Ital.); Detection of industrial products by infrared spectrometry. I. Alkyd resins

R. L. Harris, G. R. Svoboda, *Anal. Chem. 34* (1962) 1655; Determination of alkyd and monomer-modified alkyd resins by attenuated total reflectance infrared spectrometry

P. Weber, *Plaste Kautsch. 21* (1974) 537...40; Infrarotspektroskopische Untersuchung des Trockenvorganges von lufttrocknenden Alkydharzen unter verschiedenen Bedingungen

3.5.6 Nitrogen-containing resins

W. Dankelman, J. M. H. Daemen, A. J. J. de Breet, J. L. Mulder, W. G. B. Huysmans, J. de Wit, *Angew. Makromol. Chem. 54* (1976) 187...201; Modern methods for the analysis of urea formaldehyde resins

V. Farsirotu, I. Alexandru, E. Parligras, *Mater. Plast. 3* (1975) 169...72; Structural changes of several variants of poly(ester imide) varnish under the destructive effect of temperature and humidity as determined by infrared spectroscopy

C. G. Hill, A. M. Hedren, G. E. Myers, J. A. Koutsky, *J. Appl. Polym. Sci. 29* (1984) 2749...62; Raman spectroscopy of urea-formaldehyde resins and model compounds

J. B. Lear, *J. Coat. Technol. 52* (1980) 73...5; Determination of water-miscible melamine resins in water-based and solvent-based coatings

L. A. O'Neill, G. Christensen, *J. Oil Col. Chem. Assoc. 58* (1975) 178...81; Analysis of polyurethane resins: a cooperative *IUPAC* study

L. A. O'Neill et al., *J. Oil Col. Chem. Assoc. 59* (1976) 285...90; Analysis of polyamide resins: a cooperative *IUPAC* investigation

V. P. Pshenitsyna et al., *Vysokomol. Soedin. A 24* (1982) 1730...4 (Russ.); *IR* spectroscopic investigation of the structure of urea-formaldehyde oligomers, produced in the presence of amines

K.-H. Raehe et al., *Plaste Kautsch. 25* (1978) 48...51; Prüfverfahren für Melaminharze

D. K. Singh, K. K. Patidar, *Paintindia 28* (1978) 24...7; Identification of poly(ester imide) resins by *IR* spectroscopy

V. R. Zlobina, G. V. Rudnaya, E. S. Pyrakhina, A. V. Uvarov, *Lakokras. Mater. Ikh. Primen. 1974* (5) 45...6 (Russ.); Determination of styrene, melamine-formaldehyde resins and dicyandiamide in coatings by infrared spectroscopy

3.5.7 Paint oils and their components

N. B. Colthup, *Appl. Spectrosc. 25* (1971) 368...71; The interpretation of the infrared spectra of conjugated polyenes in the 1000...900 cm^{-1} region

K. Heinonen, A. Visapää, *Teknillisen Kem. Aikakauslehti [Z. techn. Chem.] 21* (1964) 18...47, 737; Infrared identification of fats and fatlike substances of technical importance

A. Huang, D. Firestone, *J. Ass. Offic. Anal. Chem. 54* (1971) 47...51; Determination of low level isolated *trans* isomers in vegetable oils and derived methyl esters by differential infrared spectrophotometry

L. Kahn, B. F. Dudenbostel, D. N. Speis, G. Karras, *Am. Lab. 9* (1977) 61...6; Determination of petroleum-derived oils and vegetable/animal oils in the presence of each other (from municipal wastewaters)

H. P. Kaufmann, F. Volbert, G. Mankel, *Fette, Seifen, Anstrichm. 61* (1959) 643...50; Anwendung der Infrarot-Spektrographie auf dem Fettgebiet. II. Quantitative Bestimmung *trans*-ungesättigter Fettsäuren in Gemischen mit *cis*-isomeren und gesättigten Verbindungen

H. P. Kaufmann, H. H. Thomas, *Fette, Seifen, Anstrichm. 62* (1960) 315...8; Anwendung der Infrarot-Spektrographie auf dem Fettgebiet. III. Untersuchung der Autoxydation synthetischer Triglyceride

H. P. Kaufmann, F. Volbert, G. Mankel, *Fette, Seifen, Anstrichm. 63* (1961) 8...13; Die Anwendung der Infrarotspektrographie auf dem Fettgebiet. IV. Untersuchung der Fettsäureester mehrwertiger Alkohole

M. J. D. Low, H. Mark, *Appl. Polym. Symp. 10* (1969) 145...58; Examination of organic coatings by infrared interference spectroscopy

J. A. Vance, N. B. Brakke, P. R. Quinney, *Anal. Chem. 51* (1979) 499...501; Determination of oil content in oil modified *o*-phthalic polyester resins by infrared spectrometry

Y. Yoshimura, *J. Appl. Polym. Sci. 29* (1984) 2735...47; Polymerization of tung oil by reaction of phenols with tung oil

3.5.8 Miscellaneous resins

A. Garton, A. Stolow, D. M. Wiles, *J. Mater. Sci. 16* (1981) 3211...14; Infrared spectroscopic characterization of surface coating on glass fibers

P. Gramain, V. J. D. Rascio, *Peint. Pigm. Vernis 43* (1967) 808...18 (Fr.); Study of marine paints. Infrared spectrophotometry for the analysis of binders

G. V. Lantuch, O. D. Kurilenko, *Ukr. Khim. Zh. 46* (1980) 366...70 (Russ.); Infrared spectroscopic determination of the complete dehydration of polystyrene sulfonates

G. Leukroth, *Seifen, Öle, Fette, Wachse 98* (1972) 829...34; Physicochemical analysis of glue and coating lacquers

3.6 Miscellaneous technical macromolecular systems

P. Diem, K. Krehl, *Betonwerk + Fertigteil-Technik 1975*, 299; Identifizierung und Klassifizierung von Betonzusatzmitteln mit der Infrarot-Analyse und anderen Untersuchungsmethoden

M. Hearing, *Chem. Rundsch. 29* (1976) 11...7; Identifizierung von Verpackungsfolien mittels Infrarotspektroskopie

R. Moser, A. Zeman, *Fette, Seifen, Anstrichmittel 75* (1973) 636...44; Identifizierung von Polymeren in kosmetischen Produkten. II. Spektrometrische Analytik von Kunststoffen

G. Rieche, W. Hensel, *Betonwerk + Fertigteil-Technik 1976*, 69...73; Die Infrarotspektroskopie als Analysenmethode auf dem Beschichtungssektor im Bauwesen

P. Svoboda, *Plaste Kautsch. 17* (1970) 560...4; Abtrennung der Zusätze aus polymeren Werkstoffen in Öfen mit Temperaturgefälle für die Erfordernisse der *IR*-Spektroskopie

3.7 Low molecular weight starting materials, additives

D. R. Battiste, J. P. Butler, J. B. Cross, M. P. McDaniel, *Anal. Chem. 53* (1981) 2232...4; Infrared spectrometric determination of catalysts used in the production of high-density polyethylene

V. Ya. Birshein, V. M. Tul'chinskii, *Khim. Prir. Soedin. 1977*, 271...5 (Russ.); Determination of beeswax and some of its impurities by an *IR* spectroscopic method

A. Caraculacu, C. Vasile, G. Caraculacu, *Acta Polymer. 35* (1984) 130...4; Poly(ethylene) waxes, structure and thermal characteristics

R. G. Davidson, G. I. Mathys, *J. Appl. Polym. Sci.* 28 (1983) 1975...68; Identification of some boron-based curing agents in cured epoxy systems by computer-assisted infrared spectroscopy

O. N. Gluskova, *Geol. Geof.* 1983 (7) 66...74 (Russ.); Bitumens of the Angara-Lena oil- and gas-bearing province

G. S. Khramaya, G. P. Sadakova, V. I. Kodolov, I. A. Nikulina, L. F. Knyazeva, *Plast. Massy* 1984 (4) 58f. (Russ.); *IR* spectroscopic investigation of additives containing phosphorus and vanadium

H. Kuhn, *Studies in Conservation* 5 (1960) 71; Detection and identification of waxes by infrared spectroscopy

R. Kumar, F. W. Billmeyer jr., M. Saltzman, *J. Coat. Techn.* 57 (1985) 720, 49...54; Identification of organic pigments in paints

F. J. Ludwig, *Anal. Chem.* 37 (1965) 1737...41; Analysis of microcrystalline and paraffin waxes by means of infrared spectra in the molten state

G. A. Luoma, L. K. Yee, R. Rowland, *Anal. Chem.* 54 (1982) 2140...2; Determination of microgram amounts of asbestos in mixtures by infrared spectrometry

H. Marsen, *Fette, Seifen, Anstrichm.* 63 (1961) 42...8; Infrarotspektroskopische Untersuchungen zur Temperaturabhängigkeit der Kristallinität von Kohlenwasserstoff-Wachsen

M. Nazir, *Anal. Chem.* 57 (1985) 1110...2; Analysis of paraffin wax oxidates by differential infrared spectrometry

H. Schweppe, *Microchim. Acta (Wien)* 1977, 583...96; Nachweis natürlicher organischer Künstlerpigmente

H. E. Schweyer, *Anal. Chem.* 30 (1958) 205...9; Spectral absorptions of asphaltic materials

N. H. Sung, S. Ni, C. S. Paik Sung, *Org. Coat. Plast. Chem.* 42 (1980) 743...8; *IR* studies of organic silanes and titanates adsorbed on single crystalline aluminum oxide and glass fibers

K. Volka, Z. Vymazal, Infrared spectroscopic study of the stabilization of PVC with metal stearates, in W. E. Steger (ed.), *Progress in Polymer Spectroscopy*; Teubner, Leipzig 1986

G. Zerbi, G. Minoni, A. P. Tulloch, *J. Chem. Phys.* 78 (1983) 5853...62; Conformational mapping of fatty acids in ordered and disordered phases: a spectroscopic study

4 Special *IR* spectroscopic problems (without *CIRS*, see 6)

4.1 Vibrational spectra and state of order in polymers, mechano-optical investigations, association of polymers

4.1.1 Fundamentals

R. S. Bretzlaff, R. P. Wool, *J. Appl. Phys.* 52 (1981) 5964...9; Temperature effect in quasiharmonic infrared bands of stressed polymers

V. L. Folt, J. J. Shipman, S. Krimm, *J. Polym. Sci.* 61 (1962) 17; Characterization of tacticity in high polymers

K. Holland-Moritz, Determination of the state of order in polymers by vibrational spectroscopy, in D. O. Hummel (ed.), *Proceedings of the 5th European Symposium on Polymer Spectroscopy*, Verlag Chemie, Weinheim 1979

D. W. van Krevelen, *Chimia* 32 (1978) 279...94; Crystallinity of polymers and the means to influence the crystallization process

I. V. Kumpanenko, K. S. Kazanskii, *J. Polym. Sci. Polym. Symp.* 42 (1973) 973...80; Analysis of *IR*-band shapes in studies on the monomer sequence distribution in macromolecules

I. V. Kumpanenko, N. V. Cukanov, *Uspekhi Khimii* 50 (1981) 1627...52 (Russ.); Regularity bands in *IR* spectra of polymers with disturbed periodicity

P. M. Pachomov, M. V. Sablygin, A. S. Cegolja, *Vysokomol. Soedin.* A27 (1985) 2327...32 (Russ.); *IR* spectroscopic investigation of tempered and high-pressure crystallized polymers

T. Shimanouchi, *Pure Appl. Chem.* 36 (1973) 93...107; Local and overall vibrations of polymer chains

C. Tosi, G. Zerbi, *Chimica e l'Ind.* 55 (1973) 334...9; Spectroscopy of amorphous and crystalline polymers

R. P. Wool, *Polym. Eng. Sci.* 20 (1980) 805...15; Infrared studies of deformation in semicrystalline polymers

R. P. Wool, *J. Polym. Sci. Polym. Phys. Ed.* 19 (1981) 449...57; Measurements of infrared frequency shifts in stressed polymers

G. Zerbi, *Pure Appl. Chem.* 26 (1971) 499...512; Defect-induced infrared absorption of polymers

G. Zerbi, *Pure Appl. Chem.* 36 (1973) 35...51; Vibrational spectra of conformationally impure polymers

G. Zerbi, *Org. Coat. Appl. Polym. Sci. Proc.* 44 (1981) 623f.; Probing the real structure of polymeric materials by vibrational spectroscopy. Recent results

4.1.2 Defined polymers

4.1.2.1 Polyethylene

M. A. Bagirov, A. A. Aliev, V. P. Marlin, Ju. N. Gazarjan, *Vysokomol. Soedin.* B23 (1981) 491...4 (Russ.); Changes to the *IR* spectra of polyethylene after γ irradiation in air during electrical aging

M. I. Bank, S. Krimm, *J. Polym. Sci.* B8 (1970) 143...8; Mixed-crystal infrared study of chain segregation in polyethylene

J. E. Bertie, E. Whalley, *J. Chem. Phys.* 41 (1964) 575; Infrared-active interchain vibration in polyethylene

D. J. Burchell, S. L. Hsu, *Polymer* 22 (1981) 907...11; Structure of polyethylene solid solutions. 2. Aspects of spectral deconvolution

G. Capaccio, M. A. Wilding, I. M. Ward, *J. Polym. Sci. Polym. Phys. Ed.* 19 (1981) 1489...1504; Morphology of oriented linear polyethylene: A study by Raman spectroscopy

C. Chang, S. Krimm, *J. Polym. Sci. Polym. Phys. Ed.* 22 (1984) 1871...84; Longitudinal acoustic mode in polymers. VII. Surface structure from swelling studies of freeze-dried polyethylene single crystals

T. C. Cheam, S. Krimm, *J. Polym. Sci. Polym. Phys. Ed.* 19 (1981) 423...47; Mixed-crystal infrared studies of chain folding in polyethylene single crystals: Low temperature and molecular weight studies

J. H. C. Ching, S. Krimm, *Macromolecules* 8 (1975) 894...7; Mixed-crystal infrared studies of annealed poly(ethylene) single crystals

A. Dahme, J. Dechant, *Acta Polymer.* 31 (1980) 610...2; Zur Temperaturabhängigkeit der *IR*-Absorptionsbanden des Polyethylens

A. Dahme, J. Dechant, *Acta Polymer.* 33 (1982) 490...4; Zur Temperaturabhängigkeit des *IR*-Spektrums von Polymeren. 1. Deutung der Temperaturabhängigkeit der *IR*-Banden von Polyethylen

A. Dahme, J. Dechant, *Acta Polymer.* 33 (1982) 546...9; Zur Temperaturabhängigkeit des *IR*-Spektrums von Polymeren. 2. Einfluß des Ordnungszustandes von Polyethylen auf die Temperaturabhängigkeit einiger *IR*-Banden

N. A. Peppas, *Makromol. Chem. 178* (1977) 595...601; Infrarotspektroskopie von semikristallinen Polyvinylalkoholnetzwerken

V. P. Roschtschunkin, N. S. Andreev, T. K. Gontscharov, *Vysokomol. Soedin. A 14* (1972) 477...84 (Russ.); *IR* spectroscopic investigation of the tertiary structure of poly(oxymethylene) as a function of synthesis and crystallization conditions

M. Shimomura, M. Iguchi, *Polymer 23* (1982) 509...13; Infra-red study on the conformational regularity in needle-like and other polyoxymethylene crystals

H. W. Siesler, H. Krässig, F. Grass, K. Kratzl, J. Derkosch, *Angew. Makromol. Chem. 42* (1975) 139...65; Strukturuntersuchungen an Cellulosefasern verschiedenen Verstreckungsgrades mittels *IR*-Reflexionsspektroskopie und Deuteriumaustausch

L. Terlemezyan, M. Mihailov, P. Schmidt, B. Schneider, *Makromol. Chem. 179* (1978) 2315...22; Temperature changes of poly(oxymethylene) structures studied by infrared spectroscopy

L. Terlemezyan, M. Mihailov, *Makromol. Chem. 179* (1978) 2807...10; Isothermal changes of conformationally sensitive bands in infrared spectra of poly(oxymethylene) at elevated temperatures

4.1.2.5.2 Polymeric esters

S. A. Baranova et al., *Vysokomol. Soedin. A 22* (1980) 536...42 (Russ.); Identification of the morphology of packed and folded poly(ethylene terephthalate) crystallites with *IR* spectroscopy

S. A. Baranova et al., *Vysokomol. Soedin. A 25* (1983) 290...5 (Russ.); The molecular orientation of poly(ethylene terephthalate)

F. Bosscher, G. ten Brinke, A. Eshuis, G. Challa, *Macromolecules 15* (1982) 1364...8; Crystal structure of isotactic poly(methyl methacrylate)

W. H. Cobbs, R. L. Burton, *J. Polym. Sci. 10* (1952) 275...90; Crystallization of polyethylene terephthalate

A. Cunningham, I. M. Ward, H. A. Willis, V. Zichy, *Polymer 15* (1974) 749...56; An infra-red spectroscopic study of molecular orientation and conformational changes in poly(ethylene terephthalate)

W. H. T. Davison, P. J. Corish, *J. Chem. Soc. [London] 1955*, 2428; Infrared spectra and crystallinity. Part I. Polyester

G. Farrow, I. M. Ward, *Polymer 1* (1960) 330...9; Crystallinity in poly(ethylene terephthalate): A comparison of *X*-ray, infra-red and density measurements

G. Farrow, J. McIntosh, I. M. Ward, *Makromol. Chem. 38* (1960) 147...58; The interpretation of transition phenomena in polymethylene terephthalate polymers

P. C. Gillette, S. D. Dirlikov, J. L. Koenig, J. B. Lando, *Polymer 23* (1982) 1759...64; An infra-red study of model compounds of poly(tetramethylene terephthalate)

P. C. Gillette, J. B. Lando, J. L. Koenig, *Polymer 26* (1985) 235; Infrared spectroscopic characterization of the $\alpha \rightarrow \beta$ phase transition in poly(tetramethylene terephthalate)

K. Holland-Moritz, D. O. Hummel, *Quad. Ricerca Sci. 84* (1973) 158...67; Spectroscopic studies on aliphatic polyesters

I. J. Hutchinson, I. M. Ward, H. A. Willis, V. Zichy, *Polymer 21* (1980) 55...65; Infra-red measurements on one-way drawn poly(ethylene terephthalate) films subjected to constant strain

A. H. Khan, G. M. Venkatesh, *J. Polym. Sci. Polym. Phys. Ed. 19* (1981) 589...98; Infrared spectroscopic study of solvent-induced structural changes in poly(ethylene terephthalate) film

S. Krimm, *J. Polym. Sci. 61* (1962) 40; The crystal structure of poly(bisphenol-A carbonate)

S.-B. Lin, J. L. Koenig, *J. Polym. Sci. Polym. Phys. Ed. 21* (1983) 2067...83; The effect of temperature on the infrared spectra of poly(ethylene terephthalate)

R. G. J. Miller, H. A. Willis, *Trans. Faraday Soc. 49* (1953) 433...41; Determination of the structure of oriented terylene film using polarized infra-red radiation

A. Miyake, *J. Polym. Sci. 38* (1959) 479; The infrared spectrum of polyethylene terephthalate. I. The effect of crystallization

I. Ouchi, M. Hosoi, S. Shimotsuma, *J. Appl. Polym. Sci. 21* (1977) 3445...56; Infrared spectra of poly(ethylene 2,6-naphthalate) and some related polyesters

B. Schneider, J. Štokr, J. Spěváček, J. Baldrian, *Makromol. Chem. 188* (1987) 2705...11; Infrared spectra and crystallinity of isotactic poly(methyl methacrylate) and of its deuterated analogues

P. Sedláček, J. Štokr, B. Schneider, *Coll. Czech. Chem. Commun. 46* (1981) 1646...57; Structure and vibrational spectra of methyl benzoate and dimethyl terephthalate

P. Simak, *Makromol. Chem. Macromol. Symp. 5* (1986) 61...8; Über die spektroskopische Bestimmung der spezifischen Volumina von amorphem (v_a) und kristallinem (v_c) Polyethylenterephthalat

B. D. Stambaugh, J. L. Koenig, J. B. Lando, *J. Polym. Sci. Polym. Lett. Ed. 15* (1977) 299...303; Infrared studies of the α crystal phase of poly(tetramethylene terephthalate)

J. Štokr, P. Sedláček, D. Doskočilova, B. Schneider, J. Loevy, *Coll. Czech. Chem. Commun. 46* (1981) 1658...74; Structure and molecular spectra of ethyl benzoate and diethyl terephthalate

J. Štokr, B. Schneider, D. Doskočilová, J. Loevy, P. Sedláček, *Polymer 23* (1982) 714...21; Conformational structure of poly(ethylene terephthalate). Infrared, Raman, and *NMR* spectra

H. Tadokoro, K. Tatsuka, S. Murahashi, *J. Polym. Sci. 59* (1962) 413...23; Infrared absorption spectra and structure of poly(ethylene terephthalate)

A. S. Ueda, Y. Chatani, H. Tadokoro, *Polymer J. 2* (1971) 387...97; Structural studies of polyesters. IV. Molecular and crystal structures of poly(ethylene succinate) and poly(ethylene oxalate)

G. W. Urbanczyk, *Faserforsch. Textiltech. 27* (1976) 183...7; Infrarotspektrometrische Untersuchung der durch Rekkung hervorgerufenen Orientierungsvorgänge in Polyäthylenterephthalatfäden

4.1.2.6 CHNO polymers

Y. Abe, S. Krimm, *Biopolymers 11* (1972) 1817...39; 1841...53; Normal vibrations of crystalline polyglycines, I−II

B. D'Alò, G. Coppola, B. Pallesi, *Polymer 15* (1974) 130...2; Studies of crystalline forms of nylon-6 by *X*-ray and *IR* spectrophotometry

P. D. Frayer, J. L. Koenig, J. B. Lando, *J. Macromol. Sci. Phys. B6* (1972) 129...49; Infrared studies of chain folding in polymers. X. Polycaprolactam

K. H. Illers, H. Haberkorn, P. Simak, *Makromol. Chem. 158* (1972) 285...311; Untersuchungen über die γ-Struktur in unverstrecktem und verstrecktem 6-Polyamid

P. K. Kim, S. L. Hsu, H. Ishida, *Macromolecules 18* (1985) 1905 ... 14; Normal vibrational analysis of benzanilide. A model for poly(*p*-phenylene terephthalamide)

P. K. Kim, S. L. Hsu, C. Chang, *Polymer 27* (1986) 34...46; Normal vibrational analysis of a rigid rod polymer. Poly(*p*-phenylene terephthalamide)

J. L. Koenig, M. Itoga, *J. Macromol. Sci. Phys. B6* (1972) 309...26; Infrared studies of chain folding in uniaxially oriented poly(hexamethylene adipamide)

S. V. Laptii, Yu. S. Lipatov, Yu. Yu. Kercha, L. A. Kosenko, V. N. Vatulev, R. L. Gaiduk, *Dokl. Akad. Nauk SSSR 261* (1981) 682...5 (Russ.); Inversion of the *IR* dichroism in linear crystallizable polyurethanes

R. L. Levy, *Org. Coat. Plast. Chem. 45* (1981) 727...31; Fatique-induced vibrational shifts in polyimide films

J. F. Rabolt, W. H. Moore, S. Krimm, *Macromolecules 10* (1977) 1065...74; Vibrational analysis of peptides, polypeptides, and proteins. 3. α-Poly(L-alanine)

D. Y. Shen, S. E. Molis, S. L. Hsu, *Polym. Eng. Sci. 23* (1983) 543...7; Vibrational spectroscopic characterization polymers. IV. Crystalline modifications of poly(*p*-phenylene terephthalamide)

J. P. Sibilia, *J. Polym. Sci. A-2 9* (1971) 27...42; Orientation in Nylon 6 films as determined by the three-dimensional polarized infrared technique

P. Simak, *Makromol. Chem. 178* (1977) 2927...37; Polymorphie, Kristallinität und Schmelzwärme von Poly(ε-caprolactam). 1. *IR*-spektroskopische Untersuchungen

A. L. Smolyanski, V. P. Shibaev, *Vysokomol. Soedin. A 21* (1979) 2221...8 (Russ.); The influence of hydrogen bonding on the intramolecular structure of comb-like polymers with functional groups in the side chains

G. W. Urbańczyk, *J. Polym. Sci. Polym. Symp. 58* (1977) 311...21; Orientation changes caused by stretching of PTE and PA-6 fibers evaluated on the basis of *IR* spectroscopy

4.1.2.7 Miscellaneous polymers

C. Chang, S. L. Hsu, *Makromol. Chem. 186* (1985) 2557...67; An infrared spectroscopic investigation of the phase behaviour of a polydiacetylene. The case of polydiacetylene with side groups containing a urethane function

S. Dobos, B. Zelei, *J. Polym. Sci. Polym. Chem. Ed. 17* (1979) 2651...62; Vibrational spectra and *IR* dichroism of poly(tetramethyl-*p*-silphenylene-siloxane) and its chain structure

B. L. Papke, M. A. Ratner, D. F. Shriver, *J. Phys. Chem. Solids 42* (1981) 493...500; Vibrational spectroscopy and structure of polymer electrolytes, poly(ethylene oxide) complexes of alkali metal salts

4.1.2.8 Liquid-crystalline polymers, polymer association

E. D. Andreeva, *Macromolecules 9* (1976) 238...43; Infrared investigation of the ionic aggregation of ionomers on the basis of ethylene and butadiene

B. J. Bulkin, *Adv. Liquid Cryst. 2* (1976) 199...231; Vibrational spectroscopy of liquid crystals

B. J. Bulkin, Infrared and Raman spectroscopy of liquid crystals, in F. D. Saeva (ed.) *Liquid Crystals: Fourth State Matter*; Dekker, New York 1979

V. L. Chodzaeva, M. V. Siskina, V. S. Grebneva, I. I. Konstantinov, *Vysokomol. Soedin. A 25* (1983) 612...6 (Russ.); Investigation of orientation properties of a thermotropic liquid-crystalline polymer with mesogenic sidegroups

F. Galleschi, G. Galli, E. Chiellini, R. W. Lenz, E. Benedetti, *Chim. Ind. Milano 68* (1986) 71 f. (Ital.); Vibrational spectroscopic investigation of thermotropic liquid-crystalline polymers

E. Iisuka, *Polym. J. 7* (1975) 650...4; Orientation of the atomic groups of poly(γ-benzyl glutamate)s in liquid-crystalline states

M. Kardan, B. B. Reinhold, S. L. Hsu, R. Thakur, C. P. Lillya, *Macromolecules 19* (1986) 616...21; Spectroscopic characterization of the microstructures in disklike liquid crystalline molecules: model compound for polymers

F. D. Saeva, *Makromol. Chem. Suppl. 5* (1981) 58...59; Photochemical and spectroscopic behavior some liquid-crystal polymer systems

M. V. Shablygin, T. A. Belousova, V. G. Kulichkhin, V. A. Platonov, V. D. Kalmykova, S. P. Papkov, *Vysokomol. Soedin. A 18* (1976) 942...4 (Russ.); Spectroscopic method for determining the liquid crystal phase fraction in anisotropic solutions of polymers

4.1.2.9 Conformational analysis

M. H. Baron, C. Deloze, G. D. Fasman, *Biopolymers 18* (1979) 411...24; Infrared and Raman study in the solid state of fully protected, monodispersed homooligopeptides of L-valine, L-isoleucine, and L-phenylalanine

E. Benedetti, A. D'Ulivo, *Chim. Ind. Milano 63* (1981) 520...3; Infrared investigation on 3-methylalkanes, model compounds of isotactic poly(α-olefins)

F. Ciampelli, C. Tosi, *Quad. Ricerca Sci. 84* (1973) 168...74; An infrared study of the regularity bands of 1,4-*trans*-polybutadiene

J. C. Day, I. D. Robb, *Polymer 21* (1980) 408...12; Conformation of adsorbed poly(vinyl pyrrolidone) studied by infra-red spectrometry

R. S. Hallos, *J. Appl. Polym. Sci. 29* (1984) 3907...14; A "chain fold band" in the infrared spectra of nylon 6

B. Jasse, A. Lety, L. Monnerie, *J. Molec. Struct. 18* (1973) 413...20; Influence de la structure conformationelle sur les spectres de vibration de molécules modèles du polystyrène

B. Jasse, L. Monnerie, *J. Molec. Struct. 39* (1977) 165...73; Influence of conformational structure on the vibrational spectra of the different isomers of 2,4,6,8-tetraphenyl nonane, a polystyrene model molecule

M. Kobayashi, K. Akita, H. Tadokoro, *Makromol. Chem. 118* (1968) 324...42; Infrared spectra and regular sequence lengths in isotactic polymer chains

M. Kobayashi, H. Tadokoro, *Rep. Progr. Polym. Phys. Japan 11* (1968) 461...4; Infrared spectra and regularities of isotactic polymer chains

M. Kobayashi, K. Tsumura, H. Tadokoro, *J. Polym. Sci. A-2 6* (1968) 1493...508; Infrared spectra of polymer solutions. I. Conformational stability of isotactic polymer chains in solution

V. Kumpanenko, N. V. Chukanov, Regularity bands behaviour in *IR* spectra of polymers with a partly disturbed regular structure, in W. E. Steger (ed.), *Progress in Polymer Spectroscopy*; Teubner, Leipzig 1986

W. F. Maddams, P. B. Tooke, *J. Macromol. Sci. Chem. A 17* (1982) 951...68; Quantitative conformational studies on poly(vinyl chloride)

H. Matsuura, K. Fukuhara, *J. Polym. Sci. Polym. Phys. Ed. 24* (1986) 1383...1400; Vibrational spectroscopic studies of conformation of poly(oxyethylene). II. Conformation spectrum correlations

F. R. Maxfield, J. Bandekar, S. Krimm, D. J. Evans, S. J. Leach, G. Nemethy, H. A. Scheraga, *Macromolecules 14* (1981) 997...1003; Conformation of cyclo(L-alanylglycyl-ε-aminocaproyl), a cyclized dipeptide model for a β bend. 3. Infrared and Raman spectroscopic studies

R. Mendelsohn, *Tech. Life Sci. Biochem. B 109* (1978) 1...28; Application of infrared and Raman spectroscopy to studies of protein conformation

M. Narita, Y. Tomotake, S. Isokawa, T. Matsuzawa, T. Miyauchi, *Macromolecules 17* (1984) 1903...6; Syntheses and properties of resin-bound oligopeptides. 2. Infrared spectroscopic conformational analysis of cross-linked polystyrene resin bound oligoleucines in the swollen state

J. M. O'Reilly, R. A. Mosher, *J. Polym. Sci. Polym. Phys. Ed. 19* (1981) 1187...98; Pressure-induced freezing of conformational states of poly(vinyl chloride)

M. Puterman, J. L. Koenig, J. B. Lando, *J. Macromol. Sci. Phys. B 16* (1979) 89...116; Conformational transitions of poly-2-vinylpyridine in aqueous solutions as a function of neutralization. I. Raman and infrared studies

B. Schneider, J. Štokr, S. Dirlikov, M. Mihailov, *Macromolecules 4* (1971) 715...8; Conformational structure and vibrational spectra of poly(methyl methacrylate) and of its models

V. V. Suvcik, R. G. Zhbankov, M. V. Astrejko, *Acta Polymer. 30* (1979) 689...93 (Russ.); Theoretical investigations of the vibrational spectrum of dextran

L. Terlemezyan, M. Mihailov, P. Schmidt, B. Schneider, *Makromol. Chem. 179* (1978) 807...13; Conformational changes of poly(oxymethylene) induced by pressure and mechanical treatment

L. Terlemezyan, M. Mihailov, P. Schmidt, B. Schneider, *Makromol. Chem. 179* (1978) 2807...10; Isothermal changes of conformationally sensitive bands in infrared spectra of poly(oxymethylene) at elevated temperatures

C. Toniolo, G. M. Bonora, V. N. Pillai, M. Mutter, *Macromolecules 13* (1980) 772...4; Infrared conformational study of poly(ethylene glycol)-bound homooligoglycines in the solid state and in solution

A. Ueno, Y. Morikawa, J.-I. Anzai, T. Osa, *Makromol. Chem. Rapid. Commun. 5* (1984) 639...42; Conformational versatility of polyaspartates with (*p*-phenylazo)phenethyl side chains in solid films

4.2 Copolymers and polymer mixtures

4.2.1 Fundamentals

M. M. Coleman, D. F. Varnell, *Macromolecules 15* (1982) 937; Comment on the paper of Fahrenholtz and Kwei concerning the compatibility of polymer mixtures containing Novolac resins

S. R. Fahrenholtz, T. W. Kwei, *Macromolecules 14* (1981) 1076...9; Compatibility of polymer mixtures containing novolac resins

S. R. Fahrenholtz, *Macromolecules 15* (1982) 937...8; Reply to comment on the paper of Fahrenholtz and Kwei

B. D. Gesner, *Appl. Polym. Symp. 7* (1968) 53...65; Analytical methods for the characterization of polyblends

H. J. Harwood, T. L. Ang, R. G. Bauer, N. W. Johnston, K. Shimizu, *ACS Polym. Prepr. 7/2* (1966) 980; The selection of infrared bands for use in copolymer composition and sequence distribution determinations

D. Heinze, *Makromol. Chem. 101* (1967) 166...87; Physikalische Charakterisierung von Copolymeren und Polymergemischen

J. F. Henderson, K. H. Grundy, E. Fischer, *J. Polym. Sci. C 16* (1968) 3121...31; Stress-birefringence properties of styrene-isoprene block copolymers

I. V. Kumpanenko, K. S. Kazanskii, *J. Polym. Sci. Polym. Symp. 42* (1973) 973...80; Analysis of *IR*-band shapes in studies on the monomer segment distribution in macromolecules

A. Ya. Menzheres, E. G. Moisya, *Kompoz. Polim. Mater. 17* (1983) 14...7 (Russ.); Investigation of the packing density of macromolecules in transition layers of polymer mixtures according to the method of the molecular sonde

I. D. Mihajlov, V. Z. Kompaniec, B. F. Olejnik, *Vysokomol. Soedin. A 21* (1979) 1774...80 (Russ.); Vibrational spectra of simple chains as models for linear block copolymers

E. J. Moskala, S. E. Howe, P. C. Painter, M. M. Coleman, *Macromolecules 17* (1984) 1671...8; On the role of intermolecular hydrogen bonding in miscible polymer blends

D. H. Richards, N. F. Scilly, S. M. Hutchison, *Polymer 10* (1979) 611...20; Synthesis of properties of regular copolymers. II. Spectroscopic analysis of regular copolymers of vinyl compounds with aliphatic dihalides

R. Sastre, J. L. Acosta, *Rev. Plast. Mod. 26* (1976) 203...11; Determinación de la composición de copolímeros. IV. Espectroscopia de infrarojo

G. Schnell, *Ber. Bunsenges. physik. Chem. 70* (1966) 297...320; Ultrarotspektroskopische Untersuchungen an Copolymerisaten

E. Schröder, W. Fieber, *Faserforsch. Textiltech. 26* (1975) 447...55; Die Veränderlichkeit der Bandenparameter bei infrarotspektroskopischen Analysen von Copolymeren am Beispiel Styrol/Acrylnitril

M. V. Sefton, W. E. Merrill, *J. Appl. Polym. Sci. 20* (1976) 157...68; Infrared spectroscopic analysis of complex polymer systems

J. C. West, S. L. Cooper, *J. Polym. Sci. Polym. Symp. 60* (1977) 127...50; Infrared studies of block polymers

4.2.2 CH copolymers and polymer mixtures

A. G. Altenau, *Anal. Chem. 42* (1970) 1280...2; Termonomer analysis in ethylene-propylene terpolymers

E. Benedetti, A. D'Alessio, M. Aglietto, G. Ruggeri, P. G. Vergamini, F. Ciardelli, *Polym. Eng. Sci. 26* (1986) 9...14; Vibrational analysis of functionalized polyolefins/PVC blends

T. N. Bowner, *J. Polym. Sci. Polym. Phys. Ed. 24* (1986) 1631...50; Infrared spectroscopy of ethylene-vinyl chloride copolymers

G. Bucci, T. Simonazzi, *J. Polym. Sci. C 7* (1964) 203; Contribution to the study of ethylene-propylene copolymers by infrared spectroscopy. Distribution of the monomeric units

F. Ciampelli, A. Valvassori, *J. Polym. Sci. C 16* (1967) 377; Infrared study on the distribution of propylene units in ethylen-propylene copolymers

W. Cooper, D. E. Eaves, M. E. Tunnicliffe, G. Vaughan, *Eur. Polym. J. 1* (1965) 121; The structure of ethylene-propylene-dicyclopentadiene terpolymers

H. V. Drushel, F. A. Iddings, *Anal. Chem. 35* (1963) 28; Infrared spectrophotometric analysis of ethylene-propylene copolymers

J. R. Ebdon, S. H. Kandil, K. J. Morgan, *J. Polym. Sci. Polym. Chem. Ed. 17* (1979) 2783...90; The effects of overall composition and monomer sequence distribution on the infrared carbonyl stretching frequencies of ethylene-vinylacetate and styrene-vinylacetate copolymers

B. Erussalimsky, N. Tumarkin, F. Duntoff, S. Lyubetzky, A. Goldenberg, *Makromol. Chem. 104* (1967) 288...96; Der Einfluß des Druckes auf die radikalische Polymerisation und Copolymerisation von Äthylen

W. Fieber, W. Kimmer, R. Schmolke, *Z. Chem. 12* (1972) 233f.; Frequenzverschiebungen in Ultrarotspektren von Styrol-Acrylnitril-Copolymeren

W. Fieber et al., *Faserforsch. Textiltech. 27* (1976) 311...2; Infrarotspektroskopische Bandenparameteränderungen bei Styrol-α-Methylstyrol-Copolymeren

J. E. Forrette, A. L. Rozek, *J. Appl. Polym. Sci. 18* (1974) 2973...81; Compositional analysis of the styrene-isobutylene copolymer

G. V. Fraser, P. J. Hendra, J. H. Walker, M. E. A. Cudby, H. A. Willis, *Makromol. Chem. 173* (1973) 205...11; The vibrational spectra of some ethylene-propylene copolymers

T. Gössl, *Makromol. Chem. 42* (1960) 1...11; *IR*-Spektrometrische Untersuchungen von Copolymerisation aus Äthylen und Propylen

H. Hendus, K. H. Illers, E. Ropte, *Kolloid-Z. Z. Polym. 216* (1967) 110...9; Strukturuntersuchungen an Styrol-Butadien-Styrol-Blockcopolymeren

H. Hoffmann, *IR*-spektroskopische Studien zur Reaktion von basischen Austauschern mit Hypochloritlösung, in *Kunstharz-Ionenaustauscher*; Akademie-Verlag, Berlin, DDR 1970, abstract: *Z. Chem. 9* (1969) 273

H. Hoffmann, K. Häupke, *Z. Chem. 10* (1970) 304f.; Infrarotspektroskopische Untersuchungen an Styrol-Divinylbenzol-Acrylsäure-Terpolymeren und daraus hergestellten Ionenaustauscherharzen

H. Hoffmann, G. Schwachula, *Plaste Kautsch. 18* (1971) 98f.; Styrol-Divinylbenzol-Kopolymere. VI. Infrarotspektroskopische Untersuchungen an Styrol-Divinylbenzol-Akrylnitril-Terpolymeren und an daraus hergestellten starksauren Kationenaustauschern

S. Hosoda, *Makromol. Chem. 185* (1984) 787...95; Investigation of molecular orientation and conformational change upon drawing for various ethylene/1-butene copolymers by *IR*-spectroscopy

N. T. Kakhramanov, Kh. T. Kakhramanova, K. A. Abbasov, A. A. Buniyat-Zade, *Azerb. Khim. Zh. 4* (1984) 87...91 (Russ.); *IR* spectral analysis of polymeric multicomponent systems of polyethylene, ethylene-propylene rubber and polyacrylonitrile

J. Kalal, M. Houska, O. Seycek, P. Adamek, *Makromol. Chem. 164* (1973) 249...63; Infrared spectra and sequence length distribution in free radical styrene/methacrolein copolymers

W. Kimmer, R. Schmolke, *Plaste Kautsch. 19* (1972) 260...2; Zur ultrarotspektroskopischen Analyse von Styrol-Acrylnitril-Copolymeren und ABS

R. J. de Kock, A. Veermans, *Makromol. Chem. 95* (1966) 179; Structure and content of dicyclopentadiene in ethylene-propylene-dicyclopentadiene terpolymers

W. H. Littke et al., *Faserforsch. Textiltech. 26* (1975) 503...8; Infrarotspektroskopische Untersuchungen am Bandenkomplex 760 cm^{-1} von Styrolcopolymeren mit Kleinsteuerrechner KSR 4100

J. N. Lomonte, G. A. Tirpak, *J. Polym. Sci. A 2* (1964) 705; Detection of ethylene homopolymer in ethylene-propylene block copolymers

F. J. Lu, E. Benedetti, S. L. Hsu, *Macromolecules 16* (1983) 1525...9; Spectroscopic study of polystyrene and poly(vinyl methyl ether) blends

K. Matsumura, O. Fukumoto, *J. Polym. Sci. A-1* (1971) 471...83; Copolymerization of propylene with acrylate by a Ziegler-Natta type catalyst

G. Natta, G. Mazzanti, A. Valvassori, G. Sartori, D. Morero, *Chim. e Ind. 42/2* (1960) 125 (Ital.); Copolymerization of ethene with aliphatic α-olefins. VII. Distribution of monomer units in ethene-propene copolymers

G. Natta, A. Valvassori, F. Ciampelli, G. Mazzanti, *J. Polym. Sci. A 3* (1965) 1...10; Some remarks on amorphous and atactic α-olefin polymers and random ethylene-propylene copolymers

N. Oi, K. Moriguchi, *Bunseki Kagaku 23* (1974) 794...801 (Jap.); Infrared analysis of polymers. III. Infrared determination of the sequence distribution of styrene units in acrylonitrile-styrene copolymers

G. N. Patel, A. Keller, E. Martuscelli, *J. Polym. Sci. Polym. Phys. Ed. 13* (1975) 2281...8; An investigation on the chain-folding structure of an ethylene-propylene copolymer by selective degradation

R. Schmolke, W. Kimmer, *Wiss. Z. TH Leuna-Merseburg 11* (1969) 9...15; Ultrarotspektroskopische Untersuchungen an statistischen Copolymeren

R. Schmolke, W. Kimmer, P. Kuzay, W. Hufenreuter, *Plaste Kautsch. 18* (1971) 95...8; Die Sequenzanalyse von Butadien-Methakrylnitril-Kopolymeren

J. van Schooten, E. W. Duck, R. Berkenbosch, *Polymer 2* (1961) 357; The constitution of ethylene-propylene copolymers

E. Schröder, W. Fieber, *Faserforsch. Textiltech. 26* (1975) 447...55; Änderung der Bandenparameter bei der *IR*-spektroskopischen Analyse von Copolymeren am Beispiel von Styrol-Acrylnitril-Copolymeren

P. Simak, E. Ropte, *Makromol. Chem. Suppl. 1* (1975) 507...20; *IR*-Untersuchung der Blockstruktur von 2-substituierten Propen-Copolymeren

A. D. Slukin et al., *Izv. Vyssh. Uchebn. Zaved. Khim. Khim. Tekhnol. 21* (1978) 882...5 (Russ.); Investigation of the relaxation phenomena of butadiene and styrene block copolymers with *IR* spectroscopy

R. M. B. Small, *Anal. Chem. 33* (1961) 1798; Determination of ethylene-propylene copolymer composition by infrared analysis

W. E. Smith, R. L. Stoffer, R. B. Hannan, *J. Polym. Sci. 61* (1962) 39...44; Analysis and properties of ethylene-propylene copolymers

L. V. Sokolova et al., *Vysokomol. Soedin. A 26* (1984) 1544...52 (Russ.); Investigation of the structure of butadiene-styrene copolymers with *IR* spectroscopy

C. Tosi, A. Valvassori, F. Ciampelli, *Eur. Polym. J. 5* (1969) 575...85; A study of inversions in ethylene-propylene copolymers

C. Tosi, F. Ciampelli, N. Cameli, *J. Appl. Polym. Sci. 16* (1972) 801...10; Spectroscopic examination of ethylene-propylene-norbornenic diene terpolymers

C. Tosi, F. Ciampelli, *Fortschr. Hochpolym. Forsch. 12* (1973) 87...130; Applications of infrared spectroscopy to ethylene-propylene copolymers

Th. A. Veerkamp, A. Veermans, *Makromol. Chem. 50* (1961) 147; On the structure of copolymers of ethylene and propylene

S. T. Wellinghoff, J. L. Koenig, E. Baer, *J. Polym. Sci. Polym. Phys. 15* (1977) 1913...25; Spectroscopic examination of chain conformation and bonding in poly(phenylene oxide)-polystyrene blends

4.2.3 CHal and CHHal copolymers and polymer mixtures

D. Brück, D. O. Hummel, *Makromol. Chem. 163* (1973) 245...57; Copolymere aus Vinylhalogeniden und Olefinen. I. Qualitative *IR*-spektroskopische Untersuchungen an Vinylchlorid-Isobuten-Copolymeren

D. Brück, D. O. Hummel, *Makromol. Chem. 163* (1973) 259...69; Copolymere aus Vinylhalogeniden und Olefinen. II. Quantitative *IR*-spektroskopische Untersuchungen an Vinylchlorid-Isobuten-Copolymeren

D. Brück, D. O. Hummel, *Makromol. Chem. 163* (1973) 271...9; Copolymere aus Vinylhalogeniden und Olefinen. III. *IR*-spektroskopische Sequenzanalyse an Vinylchlorid-Isobuten-Copolymeren und Bestimmung der Copolymerisationsparameter aus den gemessenen Diadenkonzentrationen

M. M. Coleman, R. J. Petcavich, P. Painter, *Polymer 19* (1978) 1253...7; Application of infra-red digital subtraction techniques to the microstructure of polychloroprenes. 3. Effect of structural irregularities on the crystalline infra-red bands of chloroprene copolymers

R. J. Grisenthwaite, *Plastics 27* (1962) 117; Analysis of vinyl chloride copolymers by infrared spectroscopy

S. Enomoto, *J. Polym. Sci. 55* (1961) 95; A study of vinylidene chloride-vinyl chloride copolymers

M. Iwasaki, M. Aoki, K. Okuhara, *J. Polym. Sci. 26* (1957) 116...20; The infrared spectra of tetrafluoroethylene-trifluorochloroethylene copolymers

H. U. Pohl, J. Denaxas, D. O. Hummel, *Makromol. Chem. 115* (1968) 125...40; Copolymere von Vinylhalogeniden mit Olefinen. 1. Qualitative *IR*-spektroskopische Untersuchungen an Vinylchlorid-Propen-Copolymeren

H. U. Pohl, D. O. Hummel, *Makromol. Chem. 115* (1968) 141...55; Copolymere von Vinylhalogeniden mit Olefinen. 2. Quantitative *IR*-spektroskopische Untersuchungen an Vinylchlorid-Propen-Copolymeren

E. G. Pomerantseva et al., *Plast. Massy 1983* (9) 39 f. (Russ.); The *IR* spectroscopic investigation of copolymers of vinyl chloride, vinyl acetate and vinyl alcohol

J. P. Sibilia, A. R. Paterson, *J. Polym. Sci. C8* (1965) 41...57; Application of infrared spectrometry to the study of some polymer problems

Y. Tabata, H. Shibano, H. Sobue, *J. Polym. Sci. A2* (1964) 1977...86; Copolymerization of tetrafluoroethylene with ethylene induced by ionizing radiation

C. B. Wang, S. L. Cooper, *J. Polym. Sci. Polym. Phys. Ed. 21* (1983) 11...27; Morphology and properties of poly(vinyl chloride)-poly(butadiene-*co*-acrylonitrile) blends

4.2.4 CHN and CHO copolymers and polymer mixtures

R. Boltze, J. Brunn, K. Doerffel, W. Höbold, G. Opitz, *J. prakt. Chem. 312* (1970) 596...602; Charakteristik von Trioxan-Dioxolan-Copolymeren

U. H. Gibson, Q. Quick, *J. Appl. Polym. Sci. 15* (1971) 2667...76; The determination of adjacent oxypropylene-oxyethylene units in propylene oxide-ethylene oxide adducts by infrared spectroscopy

V. Gröbe, R. Schmolke, W. Makschin, H. Herma, *Faserforsch. Textiltechn. 17* (1966) 525; Ultrarotspektroskopische Analyse von Acrylnitril-Allylsulfonat-Copolymeren

J. T. Guthrie, Zia Haq, *Polymer 15* (1974) 133...6; Synthesis of cellulosic graft copolymers and their analysis by ultraviolet and infra-red spectroscopy

S. H. Kandil, M. A. El-Gamal, *J. Polym. Sci. Polym. Chem. Ed. 24* (1986) 2765...71; Infrared spectroscopic analysis of poly(methyl acrylate-*co*-styrene)

K. Könnecke, *Makromol. Chem. 186* (1985) 2061...70; Nachweis von Teilverträglichkeit in den Phasengrenzflächen von Polymergemischen mittels *IR*-Spektroskopie

I. V. Kumpanenko, K. S. Kazanskii, *J. Polym. Sci. Polym. Symp. 42* (1973) 973...80; Analysis of *IR*-band shapes in studies on the monomer sequence distribution in macromolecules

D. Lefebvre et al., *Polymer 25* (1984) 318...22; Orientation and relaxation in uniaxially stretched poly(2,6-dimethyl-1,4-phenylene oxide) (PPO)/atactic polystyrene blends

S. Maudgal, *J. Macromol. Sci. Chem. A21* (1984) 631...8; Copolymerization of vinyl cinnamate with vinyl acetate. Infrared spectral studies

E. J. Moskala, M. M. Coleman, *Polym. Commun. 24* (1983) 206...8; Fourier-transform *IR* studies of poly(vinyl ether) blends with the poly(hydroxy ether of bisphenol A)

G. Opitz, *Faserforsch. Textiltechn. 29* (1978) 496...501; Zur Bestimmung der Mikrostruktur von Trioxan-1,3-Dioxolan-Copolymeren

C. Ruscher, R. Schmolke, *Faserforsch. Textiltechn. 14* (1963) 459...68; Ultrarotdichroitische und röntgenographische Untersuchungen an Copolymeren des Acrylnitrils

4.3 End group determination

G. Boccato, A. Rigo, G. Talamini, F. Zilio-Grandi, *Makromol. Chem. 108* (1967) 218...33; Determination of branching of polyvinylchloride

M. I. Bro, C. A. Sperati, *J. Polym. Sci. 38* (1959) 289; Endgroups in tetrafluoroethylene polymers

M. Carrega, C. Bonnebat, G. Zednik, *Anal. Chem. 42* (1970) 1807...9; Determination of the nature of the end groups of poly(vinyl chloride)

V. S. C. Chang, J. P. Kennedy, *Polym. Bull. 9* (1983) 518...24; End group determination in hydroxyl-telechelic polyisobutylenes by infrared spectroscopy

C. J. van den Heuvel, A. J. M. Weber, *Makromol. Chem. 184* (1983) 2261...73; End groups in poly(vinyl chloride) and their influence on the thermal stability

P. Hildenbrand, W. Ahrens, F. Brandstetter, P. Simak, *J. Macromol. Sci. Chem. A17* (1982) 1093...1106; The formation of terminal double bonds in vinyl chloride polymerization

K. Iimura, R. Endo, M. Takeda, *Bull. Chem. Soc. Japan 37* (1964) 874; Studies of polybutene. I. Determination of end-groups and the molecular weight by the infrared method

H. Kämmerer, F. Rocaboy, K.-G. Steinfort, W. Kern, *Makromol. Chem. 53* (1962) 80...90; Versuch einer quantitativen Endgruppenbestimmung mittels *IR*-Spektren in mit einem Diacylperoxyd hergestellten Polystyrol

W. Kern, M. A. Achon, R. C. Schulz, *Makromol. Chem. 15* (1955) 161...9; Nachweis und chemische Umsetzungen von Endgruppen in Polystyrolen

T. Kitagawa, A. Tanaka, M. Nishii, *J. Polym. Sci. Polym. Lett. Ed. 9* (1971) 579...82; End-group orientation in crystalline polyoxymethylene

P. J. Madec, E. Marechal, *J. Polym. Sci. Polym. Phys. Ed. 18* (1980) 2417...20; Molecular weight determination of silane-terminated poly(dimethyl-siloxane) by infrared spectroscopy

D. P. Mironov, Ju. N. Bozkov, G. N. Smirnova, V. G. Suvorova, *Zavodsk. Lab. 46* (1980) 1111 f. (Russ.); Spectroscopic determination of the composition of mixtures of polyoxypropylene glycols and their monomethyl ethers

I. Rosenthal, G. J. Frisone, J. K. Coberg, *Anal. Chem. 32* (1960) 1713; Spectrophotometric determination of sulfide end groups and number average molecular weight in high polymers

Y. Sato, M. Hoshino, F. Ebisawa, *J. Appl. Polym. Sci. 26* (1981) 2053...60; A study on hydroxyl groups in polyethylene

S. A. Taleb-Bendiab, J. M. Vergnaud, *Analysis 8* (1980) 435...41; Comparison of physical chemistry methods for an average molecular mass determination in weight and in number of polyethylene glycols (M < 1500)

R. Yamadera, *J. Polym. Sci. 50* (1961) S4...S7; Detection of the endgroups of polyacrylonitriles by infrared spectroscopy

4.4 Starting materials, defined degradation products

J. R. Durig, B. J. Streusand, *Appl. Spectrosc. 32* (1978) 457...62; Spectra and structure of silicon-containing compounds. X. Infrared and Raman spectra of methoxytrimethylsilane and methoxy-d$_3$-trimethylsilane

J. F. Shay, S. Skilling, R. W. Stafford, *Anal. Chem. 26* (1954) 652; Identification of polyhydric alcohols in polymeric esters

G. A. Kraseninnikova, A. A. Popov, M. M. Kaganskij, L. G. Privalova, G. E. Zaikov, *Vysokomol. Soedin. A 27* (1985) 2391...6 (Russ.); Oxidative degradation of polyamides under conditions of stress

R. W. Stafford, J. F. Shay, *Ind. Eng. Chem. 46* (1954) 1625; Acidic and alcoholic components of polyesters

R. W. Stafford, J. F. Shay, R. J. Francel, *Anal. Chem. 26* (1954) 656; Identification of dicarboxylic acids in polymeric esters

4.5 Pyrolysates

S. Badilescu, S. Beregic, Gh. Dogaru, *Mater. Plast. (Bucharest) 18* (1981) 223...5 (Rum.); Methods for the determination of propylene in ethylene-propylene-diene rubbers by pyrolysis *IR* spectroscopy

F. F. Bentley, G. Rappaport, *Anal. Chem. 26* (1954) 1980...5; Semiquantitative analysis of Buna N phenolic blends by the infrared spectra of their pyrolyzates

M. P. Brash, T. S. Light, *Appl. Spectrosc. 19* (1965) 114...7; Study of thermal decomposition products of silica-filled polytetrafluoroethylene with an infrared pyrolysis cell

J. E. Brown, M. Tryon, J. Mandel, *Anal. Chem. 35* (1963) 2172...6; Determination of propylene in ethylene-propylene copolymers by infrared spectrometry

J. W. Cassels, *Appl. Spectrosc. 22* (1968) 477...88; Infrared-pyrolysis studies of synthetic fibers

E. Cerceo, *Ind. Eng. Chem. Prod. Res. Develop. 9* (1970) 96...100; Effect of time on infrared spectra of epoxy pyrolyzates

B. Cleverley, R. Herrmann, *J. Appl. Chem. 10* (1960) 192...5; Rapid identification of elastomers and their additives

R. C. Crippen, C. F. Bonilla, *Anal. Chem. 21* (1949) 927...30; Determination of styrene in hydrocarbon copolymers

R. G. Davidson, *J. Appl. Polym. Sci. 34* (1987) 1631...44; Pyrolysis-evolved gas infrared spectroscopic characterization of poly(methyl methacrylate) copolymer glazing materials

H. Feuerberg, D. Gross, H. Zimmer, *Kautsch. Gummi Kunstst. Asbest 16* (1963) 199...201; Beitrag zur Analyse von Elastomeren in Vulkanisaten. III. Quantitative infrarotspektrometrische Bestimmung von Butadien-Styrol-Kautschuk in Vulkanisaten aus Naturkautschuk und Butadien-Styrol-Kautschuk

A. Fiorenza, G. Bonomi, *Rubber Chem. Technol. 36* (1963) 1129...47; Identification of elastomers by infrared spectrophotometry

D. Gross, *Z. analyt. Chem. 248* (1969) 40...1; Quantitative infrarotspektroskopische Analyse von Styrol-Acrylnitril-Copolymeren nach pyrolytischer Zersetzung

D. Gross, *Kautsch. Gummi Kunstst. 27* (1974) 225...32; Aufschluß von Vulkanisation und Identifizierung durch *IR*-Spektrometrie

R. R. Hampton, *Rubber Chem. Technol. 45* (1972) 546...626; Applied infrared spectroscopy in the rubber industry

D. L. Harms, *Anal. Chem. 25* (1953) 1140...55; Identification of complex organic materials

J. H. Hartshorn, *Org. Coat. Plast. Chem. 40* (1979) 500...5; Time-lapse infrared spectroscopic investigation of alkyd and linseed oil cure

J. van der Heyden, *Plastica, Rotterdam 34* (1981) 70...7; Apparaat voor het gecontroleerd pyrolysere van polymeren

D. O. Hummel, *Kautsch. Gummi Kunstst. 11* (1958) WT 185; *Rubber Chem. Technol. 32* (1959) 854; Die *IR*-spektroskopische Identifizierung von Kautschuk, Weich- und Hartgummi

B. T. Jasper, *J. Inst. Rubber Ind. 3* (1969) 72...6; The identification and determination of selected polymers using infrared spectroscopy

J. Kaczai, *Appl. Spectrosc. 21* (1967) 180...1; Simple, rapid infrared method for the positive identification of polyurethanes

P. F. Kruse, W. B. Wallace, *Anal. Chem. 25* (1953) 1140...55; Identification of polymeric materials

M. Lerner, R. C. Gilbert, *Anal. Chem. 36* (1964) 1382; Rapid determination of relative proportions of natural and SBR rubber in manufactured articles

G. Leukroth, *Gummi Asbest Kunstst. 27* (1974) 794, 796, 798, 800, 802, 814; Pyrolyse-*IR*-Spektroskopie an hochgefüllten Vulkanisaten und Kunststoffen

F. Luigart, *Kunststoffe 70* (1980) 66...7; Pyrolyse-*IR*-Spektroskopie von Polymeren — Analyse im Mikromaßstab

D. A. MacKillop, *Anal. Chem. 40* (1968) 607...9; Pyrolysis-infrared spectrophotometric analysis of rubber vulcanizates

A. I. Malyshev, I. K. Shmyrev, I. P. Kotova, *Zh. Prikl. Spektrosk. 24* (1976) 95...9 (Russ.); Analysis of rubbers from relative optical densities of characteristic frequencies in *IR* spectra of pyrolyzates

V. Markovic, S. Marinkovic, *Carbon 18* (1980) 329...35; A study of pyrolysis of phenolic resin reinforced with carbon fibers and oxidized PAN fibers

G. Melber, H. Szymanski, *Progress in IR Spectroscopy 3* (1967) 25...38; Pyrolysis in infrared spectroscopy

W. Millis, M. J. Jordan, *J. Inst. Rubber Ind. 4* (1970) 60...6; Determination of tread vulcanisate polymers by pyrolysis-infrared spectrophotometry

C. Morterra, M. J. D. Low, *Carbon 23* (1985) 525...30; *IR* studies of carbons. VII. The pyrolysis of a phenol-formaldehyde resin

Z. Mzourek, O. Mikl, *Plaste Kautsch. 8* (1961) 3...6; Thermische Zersetzung von Gummiabfällen. IV. Analyse von Produkten der Pyrolyse von Gummiabfällen

G. Oehme, H. Baudisch, H. Mix, *Makromol. Chem. 177* (1976) 2657...67; Analyse von Polystyrolharzen mit funktionellen Gruppen mittels *IR*-Spektroskopie und Pyrolyse-Gaschromatographie-Massenspektroskopie

J. Pfeiffer, D. Steger, *Plaste Kautsch. 25* (1978) 459...62; Zur infrarotspektroskopischen Identifizierung thermischer Zersetzungsprodukte von PVC und PUR-Hartschaum

A. J. Scism, *Chemist Analyst 56* (3) (1967) 71; Technique for obtaining pyrolyzate infrared spectra from a minute amount of material

K. W. Smalldon, *Forensic Sci. Soc. J. 9* (1969) 135...40; Identification of paint resins and other polymeric materials from the infrared spectra of their pyrolysis products

R. R. Stromberg, S. Straus, B. C. Achhammer, *J. Res. Nat. Bur. Std. 60* (1960) 147...52; Infrared spectra of thermally degraded poly(vinyl chloride)

W. L. Truett, *Appl. Spectrosc. 21* (1967) 400...1; The characterization of polymeric substances by pyrolysis-infrared spectroscopy

W. L. Truett, *ACS Polym. Prep. 18/2* (1977) 107...9; Characterization of organic polymers by pyrolysis-infrared

W. L. Truett, *Am. Lab. 9* (1977) 33f., 36...8; Pyrolysis-infrared analysis of polymeric materials

M. Tryon, E. Horowitz, J. Mandel, *J. Res. Natl. Bur. Stand. 55* (1955) 219...22; Determination of natural rubber in GRS-natural rubber vulcanizates by infrared spectroscopy

4.6 Time-dependent physical or chemical processes

J. C. Andries, H. E. Diem, *J. Polym. Sci. Polym. Lett. Ed. 12* (1974) 281...6; A study of ozone attack on elastomer surfaces by attenuated total reflectance spectroscopy

N. S. Baer, N. Indictor, *J. Coat. Technol. 48* (1976) Nr. 623, 58...62; Linseed oil-metal acetylacetonate systems. III. Infrared spectroscopic observations on the drying film

D. R. Bauer, L. M. Briggs, *Org. Coat. Appl. Polym. Sci. Proc. 48* (1983) 737...41; *IR* spectroscopic studies of degradation in crosslinked networks. Photoenhanced hydrolysis of acrylic/melamine coatings

J. V. Benham, T. J. Pullukat, *J. Appl. Polym. Sci. 20* (1976) 3295...303; Analysis of the types and amounts of carbonyl species present in oxidized polyethylene

W. Brockmann, E. Roeder, *Gummi Asbest Kunstst. 35* (1982) 570...4; Über Alterungsvorgänge in Kunststoffen. 2. Mitt.

M. Buback, *Z. Naturforsch. 39a* (1984) 399...411; Spectroscopic investigation of the high pressure ethylene polymerization

B. J. Bulkin, C. S. Chen, E. M. Pearce, *Org. Coat. Appl. Polym. Sci. Proc. 44* (1981) 638; Infrared spectroscopic studies of environmental effect on polymers

T.-C. Chung, Y. Schlesinger, S. Etemad, A. G. Macdiarmid, A. J. Heeger, *J. Polym. Sci. Polym. Phys. Ed. 22* (1984) 1239...46; Optical studies of pyrolyzed polyacrylonitrile

R. T. Conley, J. F. Bieron, *J. Appl. Polym. Sci. 7* (1963) 103...17; A study of the oxidative degradation of phenol-formaldehyde polycondensates using infrared spectroscopy

R. T. Conley, J. F. Bieron, *J. Appl. Polym. Sci. 7* (1963) 171...80; A kinetic study of the oxidative degradation of phenol-formaldehyde polycondensates using infrared spectroscopy

C. U. Davanzo, N. Sheppard, F. Al-Mashta, *Spectrochim. Acta 41A* (1985) 263...9; An infrared spectroscopic study of the polymerization of styrene on titania catalysts

R. G. Davidson, G. I. Mathys, *J. Appl. Polym. Sci. 28* (1983) 1957...68; Identification of some boron-based curing agents in cured epoxy systems by computer-assisted infrared spectroscopy

R. G. Davidson, G. I. Mathys, *Anal. Chem. 58* (1986) 837...41; Polymer characterization by envolved gas-infrared spectrometry using a dispersive spectrometer

P. K. Dutta, K. R. Grap, *J. Appl. Polym. Sci. 29* (1984) 2247...50; Migration of plasticizer in vinyl resins: An infrared spectroscopic study

M. Eguiluz, H. Ishida, A. Hiltner, *J. Polym. Sci. Polym. Phys. Ed. 18* (1980) 2295...8; Compatibility of blends of polyesters with the polyhydroxyether of Bisphenol-A

P. Eyerer, *J. Appl. Polym. Sci. 18* (1974) 975...92; Reaction course during the hardening of an epoxy resin with dimethylaminopropylamine

M. A. Golub, *ACS Polym. Prepr. 21/2* (1980) 152f.; Thermal rearrangements of polybutadienes with different vinyl contents

H. Hoffmann, R. Hauptmann, *IR*-spektroskopische Untersuchungen zur Chlormethylierungsreaktion an Styrol-Divinylbenzol-Copolymerisaten, in *Kunstharz-Ionenaustauscher*; Akademie-Verlag, Berlin 1970, abstract: *Z. Chem. 9* (1969) 232f.

D. O. Hummel, K. U. Heinen, H. Stenzenberger, H. Siesler, *J. Appl. Polym. Sci. 18* (1974) 2015...24; Infrared spectroscopic determination of the kinetic data of the polymerization of aliphatic bismaleimides

H. Jablonski, M. Lewezuk, *Plaste Kautsch. 21* (1974) 775...82; Untersuchung der Härtung lösungsmittelfreier Epoxidharzlacke

W. Jank, *J. Polym. Sci. Polym. Lett. Ed. 15* (1977) 679...82; Far-infrared spectrum of irradiated polyethylene

X. Jing, Y. Wu, X. Gong, H. Yu, W. Zhang, F. Wang, *Makromol. Chem. Rapid Commun. 5* (1984) 311...8; *IR* study of thermal isomerization of polyacetylene

M. Kato, H. Kamogawa, *J. Polym. Sci. A-1 6* (1968) 2993...3006; Polymerization of allyl(vinyl phenyl) ethers and reactions of the resulting polymers

E. W. Kinkelaar, J. T. Rozsa, L. J. Vavruska, *J. Paint Technol. 46* (1974) 63...8; Cure determination of coil coatings by the use of attenuated total reflectance *(ATR)* infrared techniques

J. Klaban, J. Smrčka, J. Mleziva, *Makromol. Chem. 111* (1968) 1...13; Die Härtung von Epoxyharzen durch Dicarbonsäureanhydride

M. Kolínský, D. Doskočilová, B. Schneider, J. Štokr, E. Drahorádová, V. Kuška, *J. Polym. Sci. A-1 9* (1971) 791...800; Structure of chlorinated poly(vinyl chloride). I. Determination of the mechanism of chlorination from infrared and *NMR* spectra

V. V. Korshak, V. G. Danilov, L. G. Komarova, N. I. Bekasova, L. A. Leumes, *Vysokomol. Soedin. A13* (1971) 1517...21 (Russ.); Investigation of the thermal stability of polyamido-*m*-carboranes

B. E. Krisyuk, A. A. Popov, G. E. Zaikov, *Vysokomol. Soedin. A22* (1980) 329...34 (Russ.); Effect of surface stresses of polymer films on chemical reaction kinetics. Effect of ozone on polypropylene

P. Laurenson, E. Fanton, G. Roche, J. Lemaire, *Eur. Polym. J. 17* (1981) 989...97; Etude en phase polymère de la réticulation chimique du polyéthylène basse densité

J. Lucki, B. Rånby, *Polym. Degrad. Stabil. 1* (1979) 251...76; Photo-oxidation of polystyrene. Part 3. Photo-oxidation of 2-phenyl butane as model compound for polystyrene

J. Lucki, B. Rånby, J. F. Rabek, *Eur. Polym. J. 15* (1979) 1101...10; Comparative studies of reactions of commercial polymers with molecular oxygen, singlet oxygen, atomic oxygen and ozone. II. Reactions with 1,2-polybutadiene

M. A. McRae, W. F. Maddams, *Makromol. Chem. 177* (1976) 461...71; Infrared spectroscopic studies on polyethylene. 3. The bromination of unsaturated groups

K. K. R. Mocherla, W. O. Statton, *J. Appl. Polym. Sci., Appl. Polym. Symp. 31* (1977) 183...91; Stress-strain behavior of oriented poly(ethylene terephthalate) by dynamic infrared studies. 1. Loadbearing of the average molecular backbone bonds

K. Müller, *Angew. Makromol. Chem. 114* (1983) 69...82; Untersuchung der „Werkstoffwirksamkeit" unterschiedlicher Strahlungssysteme und Bewitterungsverfahren

G. E. Myers, *J. Appl. Polym. Sci. 26* (1981) 747...64; Investigation of urea-formaldehyde polymer cure by infrared

K. V. Nel'son et al., *Sint. Fiz. Khim. Polim. 22* (1978) 66...9 (Russ.); *IR* spectroscopic investigation of Si containing urethane prepolymers

J. Ostrowska, A. Narebska, *Colloid Polym. Sci. 261* (1983) 93...8; Infrared study of hydration and association of functional groups in a perfluorinated Nafion membrane. Part 1

D. E. Peerman, W. Tolberg, D. E. Floyd, *Ind. Engng. Chem. 49* (1957) 1091...4; Reaction of polyamide resins and epoxy resins

N. V. Platonov, V. I. Gracev, I. V. Klimenko, B. E. Glocin, L. V. Snuzov, *Vysokomol. Soedin. B20* (1978) 915...7 (Russ.); Spectroscopic investigation of the thermo-oxidative degradation of poly(methacrylonitrile)

H. U. Pohl, H.-J. Traenckner, H. J. Rosenkranz, *Angew. Makromol. Chem. 98* (1981) 1...34; Analytische Untersuchungen an photochemisch vernetzbaren allylethermodifizierten Fumarsäureestern

H. U. Pohl, H.-J. Traenckner, *Angew. Makromol. Chem. 136* (1985) 11...28; Untersuchung der Reaktionen von Alkydharzen mit Melaminvernetzern

H. U. Pohl, H.-J. Traenckner, *Angew. Makromol. Chem. 136* (1985) 29...43; Solvolyse- und Umesterungsreaktionen bei der Vernetzung von Alkyd- und Acrylatharzen mit Melaminvernetzern

A. A. Popov, B. E. Krisyuk, N. N. Blinov, G. E. Zaikov, *Eur. Polym. J. 17* (1981) 169..73; On the effect of stress on oxidative destruction of polymers. The action of ozone on polyolefins

J. F. Rabek, J. Lucki, B. Rånby, *Eur. Polym. J. 15* (1979) 1089...100; Comparative studies of reactions of commercial polymers with molecular oxygen, singlet oxygen, atomic oxygen and ozone. I. Reactions with *cis*-1,4-polybutadiene

J. Roda, *Makromol. Chem. 178* (1977) 203...10; Infrarotspektren der Koordinationsverbindungen von Polyvinylpyridinen mit den Chloriden von Rh, Ru und Pd

D. R. Rueda, E. Cagio, F. J. Baltá-Calleja, *Makromol. Chem. 182* (1981) 2705...13; Degradation of bulk polyethylene by nitric acid. 1. *IR* study of oxidized groups

R. Sastre, G. Martinez, F. Castillo, J. L. Millan, *Makromol. Chem. Rapid Commun. 5* (1984) 541...6; The *UV*-visible second derivative spectroscopy as a useful tool for studying the PVC degradation mechanism

G. Serboli, *Schweiz. Arch. angew. Wiss. Techn.*, Feb. 1966, 29; Infrarotspektroskopische Untersuchung des Härtungsmechanismus von Epoxidharzen

D. Y. Shen, S. L. Hsu, *Polymer 23* (1982) 969...73; Vibrational spectroscopic characterization of rigid rod polymers. 3. Microstructural changes in stressed polymers

B. A. Shipilevskii, *Tr. Fergan. Politekh. Inst. 2* (1969) 71...7; Curing of epoxy coatings at a normal temperature studied by an infrared spectroscopic method

G. C. Stevens, *J. Appl. Polym. Sci. 26* (1981) 4259...78; Cure kinetics of a low epoxide/hydroxyl group-ratio bisphenol A epoxy resin-anhydride system by infrared absorption spectroscopy

S. S. Stivala, L. Reich, P. G. Kelleher, *Makromol. Chem. 59* (1963) 28; Kinetics of the thermal oxidation of isotactic polypropylene by infrared spectroscopy

S. S. Stivala, E. B. Kaplan, *J. Appl. Polym. Sci. 9* (1965) 3357; Kinetics of uncatalyzed thermal oxidation of atactic polybutene-1 by infrared spectroscopy

L. Terlemezyan, M. Mihailov, *Makromol. Chem. 179* (1978) 2807...10; Isothermal changes of conformationally sensitive bands in infrared spectra of poly(oxymethylene) at elevated temperatures

L. Terlemezyan, M. Mihailov, B. Ivanova, *Makromol. Chem. Rapid Commun. 6* (1985) 619...23; Study of the oxidation of polyacetylene in aqueous medium by *IR* spectroscopy

J. J. P. Tovborg, J. Kops, *J. Polym. Sci. Polym. Chem. Ed. 18* (1980) 2737...46; Photochemical degradation of blends of polystyrene and poly(2,6-dimethyl-1,4-phenylene oxide)

H.-J. Traenckner, *Defazet 31* (1977) 370...1; Untersuchungen zum Trocknungsmechanismus lufttrocknender, ungesättigter Polyesterharze

A. M. Usmani, *J. Coat. Techn. 56* (1984) 99...103; Application of infrared spectroscopy in curing kinetics of polyurethane coatings

M. Yamao, S. Nukui, T. Yamada, S. Tanaka, *Kogyo Kagaku Zasshi 74* (1971) 2571...6; Study on curing reactions of resol type phenolic resins by infrared spectroscopy

J. R. Wright, P. G. Campbell, *J. Appl. Chem. 12* (1962) 256...66; Determination of oxidation rates of air-blown asphalts by infra-red spectroscopy

4.7 Hydrogen bonds

T. Akahane, Y. Kazusa, H. Nakayasu, *Kobunshi Ronbunshu 37* (1980) 383...7 (Jap.); An investigation of hydrogen bonds in CP-ethylene-vinyl alcohol on the basis of spectra in the near infrared range

M. K. Antoon, J. L. Koenig, T. Serafini, *J. Polym. Sci. Polym. Phys. Ed. 19* (1981) 1567...75; Fourier-transform infrared study of the reversible interaction of water and a crosslinked epoxy matrix

R. Barbes, R. Audebert, C. Quivoron, *J. Chim. Phys. Physicochim. Biol. 76* (1979) 486...8; Etude, par spectroscopie infrarouge des properties complexantes, de quelques polyacrylamides N,N-disubstitutés vis-à-vis des phenols

B. W. Brodman, M. P. Devine, *J. Appl. Polym. Sci. 25* (1980) 1245...7; Hydrogen bonding in nitrocellulose

B. A. Brozoski, P. C. Painter, M. M. Coleman, *Macromolecules 17* (1984) 1591...4; Concerning the origin of broad bands observed in the *FT-IR* spectra of ionomers. Cluster formation or water absorption?

C. M. Brunette, S. L. Hsu, W. J. MacKnight, *Macromolecules 15* (1982) 71...7; Hydrogen-bonding properties of hard-segment model compounds in polyurethane block copolymers

F. Cangelosi, M. T. Shaw, *SPE Ann. Techn. Conf. Techn. Pap. 28* (1982) 137...9; Hydrogen bonding in polymer-polymer systems. II. Infrared studies of poly(styrene-*co*-allyl alcohol) mixtures

M. M. Coleman, D. J. Skrovanek, S. E. Howe, P. C. Painter, *Macromolecules 18* (1985) 299f.; On the validity of a commonly employed infrared procedure used to determine thermodynamic parameters associated with hydrogen bonding in polymers

M. M. Coleman, K. H. Lee, D. J. Skrovanek, P. C. Painter, *Macromolecules 19* (1986) 2149...57; Hydrogen bonding in polymers. 4. Infrared temperature studies of a simple polyurethane

M. M. Coleman, D. J. Skrovanek, P. C. Painter, *Makromol. Chem. Macromol. Symp. 5* (1986) 21...33; Hydrogen bonding in polymers. III. Further infrared temperature studies of polyamides

S. L. Cooper, R. W. Seymour, Infrared studies of polyurethane block copolymers, in J. J. Burke (ed.): *Block, Graft Copolymers*; Proc. Sagamore Army Mater. Res. Conf.; Syracuse Univ. Press, Syracuse, N.Y. 1973

D. Hadži, S. Bratos, Vibrational spectroscopy of the hydrogen bond, in P. Schuster, G. Zundel, C. Sandorfy (eds.): *The Hydrogen Bond*; North-Holland Publ. Comp., Amsterdam etc. 1976

V. I. Kovalenko, *Zh. Prikl. Spektrosk. 21* (1974) 506...10 (Russ.); Spectroscopic investigation of hydrogen bonds in thermoplastic urethane elastomers with respect to their domain structure

C. Leonard, J. L. Halary, L. Monnerie, *Polymer 26* (1985) 1507...13; Hydrogen bonding in PMMA-fluorinated polymer blends. *FTIR* investigations using ester model molecules

R. Lindemann, G. Zundel, *Biopolymers 16* (1977) 2407...18; Proton transfer and polarizability of hydrogen bonds in proteins coupled with conformational changes. I. Infrared investigation of poly(glutamic acid) with various N bases

R. Lindemann, G. Zundel, *Biopolymers 17* (1978) 1285...304; Proton transfer in and polarizability of hydrogen bonds coupled with conformational changes in proteins. II. *IR* investigation of polyhistidine with various carboxylic acids

S. Nishi, T. Kotaka, *Macromolecules 18* (1985) 1519...25; Complex-forming poly(oxyethylene)-poly(acrylic acid) interpenetrating polymer networks. 1. Preparation, structure, and viscoelastic properties

P. C. Painter, B. Thomson, *ACS Polym. Prepr. 27/1* (1986) 297 f.; Infrared spectroscopic studies of hydrogen bonding in polydiacetylenes

J. F. Rabolt, *J. Polym. Sci. Polym. Phys. Ed. 17* (1979) 1457...64; Hydrogen bonding effects on the skeletal optical and the longitudinal acoustical modes in long chain molecules and polymers

P. Schuster, G. Zundel, C. Sandorfy, *The Hydrogen Bond — Recent Developments in Theory and Experiments*; North Holland, Amsterdam 1976

R. W. Seymour, G. M. Estes, S. L. Cooper, *Macromolecules 3* (1970) 579...83; Infrared studies of segmented polyurethane elastomers. I. Hydrogen bonding

M. V. Shablygin et al., *Vysokomol. Soedin. B21* (1979) 612...6 (Russ.); Spectroscopic investigation of hydrogen bonds in aromatic polyamides

D. J. Skrovanek, S. E. Howe, P. C. Painter, M. M. Coleman, *Macromolecules 18* (1985) 1676...83; Hydrogen bonding in polymers. Infrared temperature studies of an amorphous polyamide

D. J. Skrovanek, P. C. Painter, M. M. Coleman, *Macromolecules 19* (1986) 699...705; Hydrogen bonding in polymers. 2. Infrared temperature studies of nylon 11

R. Stadler, L. F. De Lucca, *Polym. Bull. 15* (1986) 173...9; Thermoplastic elastomers by hydrogen bonding. 2. *IR*-spectroscopic characterization of the hydrogen bonding

H. H. Teo, A. Marshall, C. Booth, *Makromol. Chem. 183* (1982) 2265...72; Hydrogen bonding in monodisperse and polydisperse oligo(ethylene glycol)s

T. Yokoyama, *Adv. Urethane Sci. Technol. 6* (1978) 1...29; The hydrogen bond in urethanes

G. Zundel, Proton polarizability of hydrogen bonds: Infrared methods, relevance to electrochemical and biological systems, in L. Packer (ed.): *Biomembranes, Proton and Water: Structure and Translocation*; Academic Press, New York 1986

G. Zundel, J. Fritsch, Interactions in and structures of ionic solutions and polyelectrolytes, in *Chemical Physics of Solvation*, Vol. II; Elsevier, Amsterdam 1986

5 Quantitative *IR* spectroscopy (without *CIRS*, s. 6)

5.1 Fundamentals, functional groups

V. P. Boiko, V. K. Grishchenko, *Acta Polymer. 36* (1985) 459...72; Determination of hydroxyl groups in polymers. Review

W. J. Driscoll, Absolute intensities of vibrational absorption bands, in H. A. Szymanski (ed.): *Progress in Infrared Spectroscopy,* Vol. 1, 125...42; Plenum Press, New York 1962

M. St. C. Flett, *Spectrochim. Acta 18* (1962) 1537...56; Intensities of some group characteristic infrared bands

D. M. Haaland, R. G. Easterling, *Appl. Spectrosc. 36* (1982) 665...73; Application of new least-squares methods for the quantitative infrared analysis of multicomponent samples

Z. Łukasiewicz-Ziarkowska, *Chem. Anal. (Warsaw) 24* (1979) 1075...87 (Pol.); Present state of research in transmittance (absorbance) standards for infrared spectrophotometry

J. A. Miller, R. J. Obremski, *ACS Polym. Prepr. 25/2* (1984) 179; Applying vector software concepts to the quantitation of polymer systems

M. Peraldo, *Quad. Ricerca Sci. 84* (1973) 147...57; Density by plane and internal standard bands in absorption spectra of polymers

E. M. Pereplechikova, E. G. Pomerantseva, L. A. Tsareva, G. V. Andreeva, E. O. Krats, *Plast. Massy 1972* (8) 71 f. (Russ.); Quantitative analysis of copolymers with *IR* spectroscopy

D. Z. Robinson, *Anal. Chem. 24* (1952) 619...22; Quantitative analysis with infrared spectrophotometers

R. Sastre, J. L. Acosta, *Rev. Plast. Mod. 26* (1976) 203...11; Determinación de la composición de copolímeros. IV. Espectroscopia de infrarrojo

K. S. Seshadkri, R. N. Jones, *Spectrochim. Acta 19* (1963) 1013...85; The shapes and intensities of infrared absorption bands. A review

M. M. Sharabash, R. L. Guile, *J. Macromol. Sci. Chem. A 10* (1976) 1021...38; Determination of copolymer compositions by quantitative infrared analysis

Y. Tanaka, Y. Takeuchi, M. Kobayashi, H. Tadokoro, *J. Polymer Sci. A-2 9* (1971) 43...57; Characterization of diene polymers. I. Infrared and *NMR* studies: Nonadditive behaviour of characteristic infrared bands

5.2 CH polymers

B. Antczak, *Polimery (Warsaw) 24* (1979) 121...3 (Pol.); Determination of the styrene content of cross-linked butadiene-styrene rubber

F. Assioma, J. Cornibert, J. Marchal, *C. R. Acad. Sci. (Paris) C 265* (1967) 1023...6 (Fr.); *IR* spectrometric analysis of the microstructure of polyisoprenes. Determination of the molar absorption coefficient of the γ_{CH} vibration of the isopropenyl group (3,4-addition) at 888 cm^{-1}

F. Assioma, J. Marchal, *C. R. Acad. Sci. (Paris) C 266* (1968) 1563...6 (Fr.); *IR* spectrometric analysis of the microstructure of polyisoprenes: Determination of the molar absorption coefficient of the γ_{CH} vibration of the vinyl group (1,2-addition) at 906 cm^{-1}

S. Bădilescu, S. Beregic, G. Dogaru, *Mater. Plast. 18* (1981) 223...5 (Rum.); Method for the determination of propylene in ethylene-propylene-diene terpolymers by pyrolysis-infrared spectroscopy

S. Bădilescu, S. Beregic, V. Constantinescu, D. Casadjicov, *Mater. Plast. 20* (1983) 104f. (Rum.); Determination of 5-ethylidene-2-norbornene in ethylene-propylene-diene terpolymers by pyrolysis-infrared spectroscopy

C. Baker, W. F. Maddams, *Makromol. Chem. 177* (1976) 437...48; Infrared spectroscopic studies on polyethylene. 1. The measurement of low levels of chain branching

G. Bald, H. Markert, *Z. analyt. Chem. 268* (1974) 360; Beitrag zur infrarotspektroskopischen Bestimmung des Methylgruppen- und Doppelbindungsgehaltes von Polyäthylen niederer Dichte

T. Bogdanzaliew, G. Nenkow, B. Jordanow, *Plaste Kautsch. 27* (1980) 555...6; Quantitative Bestimmung der Zusammensetzung der Styren-Vinylketten-Copolymere mittels *IR*-Spektroskopie

E. G. Brame, J. E. Barry, F. J. Toy jr., *Anal. Chem. 44* (1972) 2022...26; Automated infrared analyses of ethylene/propylene copolymers

J. E. Brown, M. Tryon, J. Mandel, *Anal. Chem. 35* (1963) 2172; Determination of propylene in ethylene-propylene copolymers by infrared spectrometry

J. E. Brown, *J. Res. Nat. Bur. Stand. Sect. A 76* (1972) 141f.; Characterization of linear polyethylene SRM 1475. II. Determination of total methyl content by infrared spectrophotometry

D. W. Carlson, H. C. Ransaw, A. G. Altenau, *Anal. Chem. 42* (1970) 1278f.; Determination of polymer composition of rubber vulcanizates

J. K. Clark, H. Yu Chen, *J. Polym. Sci. Polym. Chem. Ed. 12* (1974) 925...8; Proposed method for determining the sequence distributions of the configurations in high 1,4-polybutadienes by infrared spectroscopy

G. L. Collier, A. C. M. Panting, *Spectrochim. Acta 14* (1959) 104...18; The use of derivative spectroscopy for determining methyl groups in polythene

P. J. Corish, *Anal. Chem. 33* (1961) 1798; Determination of ethylene-propylene copolymer composition by infrared analysis

P. J. Corish, M. E. Tunnicliffe, *J. Polym. Sci. C7* (1963) 187; A critical evaluation of infrared methods for the determination of the E/P ratio of ethylene-propylene rubbers

M. E. A. Cudby, *J. Polym. Sci. B3* (1965) 73...6; *Cis* vinylene unsaturation in polyethylene

A. Dankovics, L. Füzes, *J. Appl. Polym. Sci. 28* (1983) 3707...14; Determination of total short-chain branching in polyethylenes by computerized data processing of infrared spectra

O. Ďurčová, A. Diačikova, V. Hurt, *Acta Polymer. 34* (1983) 410...2; Contribution to the quantitative *IR* analysis of modified polypropylene fibers

T. Z. Efendieva, H. D. Ibragimov, F. O. Gusejnov, A. E. Portjanskij, *Vysokomol. Soedin. A21* (1979) 2392...5 (Russ.); Quantitative determination of the composition of CP-ethylene-propylene-hexene by means of infrared spectroscopy

H. Feuerberg, D. Gross, H. Zimmer, *Kautsch. Gummi Kunstst. Asbest 16* (1963) 199...201; Beitrag zur Analyse von Elastomeren in Vulkanisaten. III. Quantitative infrarotspektrometrische Bestimmung von Butadien-Styrol-Kautschuk in Vulkanisaten aus Naturkautschuk und Butadien-Styrol-Kautschuk

Z. Fodor, M. Iring, F. Tüdős, T. Kelen, *J. Polym. Sci. Polym. Chem. Ed. 22* (1984) 2539...50; Determination of carbonyl-containing groups in oxidized polyethylene

J. E. Forrette, A. L. Rozek, *J. Appl. Polym. Sci. 18* (1974) 2973...81; Compositional analysis of the styrene-isobutylene copolymer

P. Frêche, M. F. Grenier-Loustalot, A. Cascoin, *Makromol. Chem. 183* (1982) 883...91; Etude par spectroscopie infrarouge d'alcanes ramifiés et de polymères modeles. Application à la determination du taux de ramifications dans les polyéthylènes basse densité

I. J. Gardner, *Rubber Chem. Technol. 44* (1971) 1015...24; Infrared determination of the composition of ethylene-propylene copolymers

D. Gross, *Z. analyt. Chem. 248* (1969) 40...1; Quantitative infrarotspektroskopische Analyse von Styrol-Acrylnitril-Copolymeren nach pyrolytischer Zersetzung

D. Hummel, E. Lünebach, *Spectrochim. Acta 18* (1962) 823; Quantitative *IR*-Messungen an *p*-substituierten Polystyrolen

V. K. Kaushik, Y. N. Sharma, *Polym. Bull. 13* (1985) 373...7; Quantitative analysis of natural rubber, polybutadiene rubber and styrene/butadiene rubber blends by infra-red spectroscopy

W. Kimmer, E. O. Schmalz, *Z. analyt. Chem. 170* (1959) 132...47; Beitrag zur *IR*-spektroskopischen Kautschukanalyse

W. Kimmer, E. O. Schmalz, *Kautsch. Gummi 16* (1963) 606...14; Die quantitative infrarotspektroskopische Bestimmung der Isomeren in Polybutadien und Butadien-Styrol-Copolymerisaten

W. Kimmer, R. Schmolke, *Plaste Kautsch. 15* (1968) 807...11; Die ultrarotspektroskopische Analyse von Äthylen-Propylen-Kopolymeren

W. Kimmer, R. Schmolke, *Plaste Kautsch. 19* (1972) 260...2; Zur ultrarotspektroskopischen Analyse von Styrol-Acrylnitrilcopolymeren und ABS

W. Kimmer, R. Schmolke, *Plaste Kautsch. 20* (1973) 274...7; Zur ultrarot- und kernresonanzspektroskopischen Kettenstrukturanalyse von Copolymeren

R. J. de Kock, P. A. H. M. Hol, *J. Polym. Sci. B2* (1964) 339...41; Infrared determination of unsaturation in polyethylene

R. J. de Kock, P. A. H. M. Hol, H. Bos, *Z. analyt. Chem. 205* (1964) 371...81; Infrared determination of unsaturated bonds in polyethylene

R. J. de Kock, A. Veermans, *Makromol. Chem. 95* (1966) 179...186; Structure and content of dicyclopentadiene in ethylene-propylene-dicyclopentadiene terpolymers

J. L. Koenig, A. van Roggen, *J. Appl. Polym. Sci. 9* (1965) 359...67; Integrated infrared band intensity measurement of stereoregularity in polypropylene

V. L. Kofman, M. P. Teterina, G. N. Bondarenko, *Vysokomol. Soedin. A21* (1979) 1526...30 (Russ.); Investigation of the composition and structure of copolymers of isoprene and butadiene by *IR* spectroscopy

A. P. Korobko, *Vysokomol. Soedin. A17* (1975) 195...8 (Russ.); Spectroscopic determination of the *cis* and *trans* content of polypentenamers

A. P. Korobko, S. N. Svešnikova, L. N. Kurkovskaja, V. M. Čередničенко, *Vysokomol. Soedin. A20* (1978) 2810...2 (Russ.); Infrared spectroscopic determination of the content of *trans* and *cis* units in polyoctenylene

G. Kostov, P. Komitov, Z. Nikolova, *Eur. Polym. J. 21* (1985) 561...4; Application of *IR*-compensation technique for study of the oxidation degree of high impact polystyrene

A. Kotschkina, M. Grell, *J. Polym. Sci. C16* (1968) 3731...6; Determination of the isotacticity of polypropylene by infrared spectroscopy

N. V. Kozlova, F. F. Suchov, V. P. Bazov, *Zavod. Labor. (Moscow)* 31 (1965) 968...70 (Russ.); Spectroscopic determination of the relative content of 1,4-*cis*, 1,4-*trans* and 1,2 configurations in polybutadiene

I. Kral, *Plaste Kautsch.* 14 (1967) 88; Analyse von Polypropylen-Butylkautschuk-Mischungen mit Hilfe der *IR*-Spektroskopie

E. Küpper, *Colloid Polym. Sci.* 257 (1979) 365...66; Die *IR*-Bande bei 1378 cm⁻¹ als innerer Standard bei anisotropem, verzweigtem Polyethylen

A. A. Levin, G. P. Muromceva, L. B. Icikson, A. P. Ogorodnikov, V. I. Ivanov, *Plast. Massy 1982* (7) 44f. (Russ.); Determination of the methyl group content in low molecular weight polyethylene by means of infrared spectroscopy in the melt

J. N. Lomonte, *Anal. Chem.* 34 (1962) 129...31; Infrared determination of vinylidene unsaturation in polyethylene

J. N. Lomonte, *J. Polym. Sci. B1* (1963) 645...47; The infrared spectrum of ethylene-propylene copolymers and the determination of propylene content

J. N. Lomonte, *Anal. Chem.* 36 (1964) 192...4; Integrated absorption standardization for infrared determination of ester content in oxidized polyethylene

D. A. MacKillop, *Anal. Chem.* 40 (1968) 607...9; Pyrolysis-infrared spectrophotometric analysis of rubber vulcanizates

W. Mills, M. J. Jordan, *J. Inst. Rubber Ind.* 4 (1970) 60...6; Determination of tread vulcanisate polymers by pyrolysis-infrared spectrophotometry

F. Mirabella, E. M. Barrall, *J. Appl. Polym. Sci.* 20 (1976) 959...65; Determination of copolymer composition as a function of molecular weight by preparative gel permeation chromatography and comparison to the rapid stop-and-go *GPC/IR* method

M. Morimoto, Y. Okamoto, *J. Appl. Polym. Sci.* 17 (1973) 2801...10; Analysis of organic solvent-insoluble portions included in ethylene-propylene-diene terpolymer

G. Müller, E. Schröder, E. Kludas, *Acta Polymer.* 31 (1980) 239...42; Studien zur Verzweigung von Kettenmolekülen. XIV. Betrachtungen zur Ermittlung von Verzweigungszahlen im Hochdruckpolyethylen aus dem CH₃-Deformationsschwingungsspektrum

G. Müller, E. Schröder, J. Osterode, *Acta Polymer.* 32 (1981) 270...6; Studien zur Verzweigung von Kettenmolekülen. XVIII. Zur Separierung der Methylbande durch Zerlegung des Absorptionskomplexes bei 1330 bis 1400 cm⁻¹ im *IR*-Spektrum des Polyethylens

D. Munteann et al., *Mater. Plast.* 13 (1976) 97...9; Determination of the composition of graft copolymers of polyethylene with vinyl acetate by infrared spectroscopy

A. G. Nerheim, *Anal. Chem.* 47 (1975) 1128...30; Circular polymethylene wedge for determining the methyl-group content and density of polyethylene by infrared spectrometry

P. C. Ng, P. L. Yeh, M. Gilbert, A. W. Birley, *Polym. Commun.* 25/8 (1984) 250...1; The determination of ethylene units in ethylene-propylene systems

P. M. Pacmomov, V. E. Korsukov, *Vysokomol. Soedin. B23* (1981) 668...70 (Russ.); Absorption coefficients of the "amorphous" *IR* bands in polyethylene

D. R. Rueda, F. J. Baltá-Calleja, A. Hidalgo, *Spectrochim. Acta 30A* (1974) 1545...9; Infrared differential method for the quantitative study of unsaturations in polyethylene

D. R. Rueda, F. J. Baltá-Calleja, A. Hidalgo, *Spectrochim. Acta 35A* (1979) 847...9; Determination of the degree of branching in polyethylene by an *IR* method of decomposition of bands

E. O. Schmalz, W. Kimmer, *Z. analyt. Chem.* 181 (1961) 229...43; Beitrag zur infrarotspektroskopischen Simultananalyse. II. Report

E. O. Schmalz, G. Geiseler, *Z. analyt. Chem.* 183 (1961) 333...50; Beitrag zur infrarotspektroskopischen Simultananalyse. III. Report

E. O. Schmalz, G. Geiseler, *Z. analyt. Chem.* 190 (1962) 293...305; Beitrag zur Isomerenanalyse des Kautschuks. I. Polybutadiene; *ibid.* 191 (1962) 1...16; II. Polyisoprene

R. Schmolke, W. Kimmer, *Plaste Kautsch.* 21 (1974) 651...3; Ultrarotspektroskopische Untersuchungen an Nitrilkautschuk

J. Schnetger et al., *Kautsch. Gummi Kunstst.* 33 (1980) 185...9; Einsatz von Extraktionsverfahren und Infrarotspektroskopie zur quantitativen Bestimmung von unvernetzten EPDM-Anteilen in vulkanisierten Verschnittmischungen

J. Štokr, B. Schneider, A. Frydrychová, J. Coupek, *J. Appl. Polym. Sci.* 23 (1979) 3553...61; Composition analysis of cross-linked styrene-ethylene dimethacrylate and styrene-divinylbenzene copolymers by Raman spectroscopy

T. Takeuchi, S. Tsuge, Y. Sugimura, *Anal. Chem.* 41 (1969) 184...6; Near-infrared spectrophotometric analysis of ethylene-propylene copolymers

A. S. Tompa, *Anal. Chem.* 44 (1972) 628...30; Infrared determination of carboxyl and hydroxyl contents of functionally terminated polybutadienes

C. Tosi, A. Valvassori, F. Ciampelli, *Eur. Polym. J.* 4 (1968) 107...14; A new spectroscopic method for the determination of the product of reactivity ratios corresponding to ethylene-propylene copolymers

C. Tosi, *Makromol. Chem.* 170 (1973) 231...4; The shape of calibration curves in the *IR* analysis of copolymer composition

C. Tosi, F. Ciampelli, *Fortschr. Hochpolym. Forsch.* 12 (1973) 87...130; Applications of infrared spectroscopy to ethylene-propylene copolymers

C. Tosi, T. Simonazzi, *Angew. Makromol. Chem.* 32 (1973) 153...61; Evaluation of the propylene content in ethylene-rich copolymers by infrared spectroscopy

J. Vodehnal, I. Kössler, *Coll. Czechoslov. Chem. Commun.* 36 (1971) 4040...6; Quantitative analysis of polybutadienes using difference infrared spectra

P. E. Wei, *Anal. Chem.* 33 (1961) 215...7; Determination of ethylene-propylene copolymer composition by infrared analysis

A. S. Wexler, *Anal. Chem.* 36 (1964) 1829...31; Analysis of bound styrene-butadiene content of copolymers by infrared absorbance ratio method

G. A. Yur'eva, F. O. Guseinov, A. E. Portyanskii, N. M. Seldov, V. M. Mamedova, A. I. Abasov, M. G. Malova, *Vysokomol. Soedin. A19* (1977) 2401...5 (Russ.); The quantitative *IR* analysis of ethylene/propylene/butylene terpolymers

V. A. Zyabina, L. M. Korobova, I. A. Lifshits, N. N. Novikova, K. V. Nel'son, *Zh. Prikl. Spektrosk.* 17 (1972) 1048...51 (Russ.); Determination of ethylidene-norbornene in ethylene-propylene-ethylidene-norbornene copolymers

5.3 CHal and CHHal polymers

C. Baker, W. F. Maddams, G. S. Park, B. Robertson, *Makromol. Chem.* 165 (1973) 321...3; A note on the quantitative estimation of chain branching in poly(vinyl chloride)

D. Brück, D. O. Hummel, *Makromol. Chem.* 163 (1973) 259...69; Copolymere aus Vinylhalogeniden und Olefinen. II. Quantitative *IR*-spektroskopische Untersuchungen an Vinylchlorid/Isobuten-Copolymeren

M. M. Coleman, R. J. Petcavich, P. C. Painter, *Polymer 19* (1978) 1243...8; Application of infra-red digital substraction techniques to the microstructure of polychloroprenes. 1. Accentuation and assignment of bands due to structural irregularities

J. Helmuth, *Polim. Vehomarim Plast. 3* (1973) 7f.; Analysis of PVC compounds

D. O. Hummel, E. Lünebach, *Spectrochim. Acta 18* (1962) 823; Quantitative *IR*-Messungen an *p*-substituierten Polystyrolen

P. Kohn, C. Marechal, J. Verdu, *Anal. Chem. 51* (1979) 1000...2; Determination of conjugated polyenes in solid poly(vinyl chloride) by selective photooxidation

V. N. Mironova, V. V. Zharkov, *Plast. Massy 1984* (3) 59 (Russ.); The determination of double bonds in poly(vinyl chloride) compositions containing triethyleneglycol dimethacrylate

H. U. Pohl, D. O. Hummel, *Makromol. Chem. 113* (1968) 190...202; Quantitative *IR*-spektroskopische Untersuchungen zur Temperaturabhängigkeit der CCl-Streckschwingungen von Polyvinylchlorid

H. U. Pohl, D. O. Hummel, *Makromol. Chem. 113* (1968) 208...14; Quantitative *IR*-spektroskopische Untersuchungen der Mikrostruktur von Polyvinylchlorid

H. U. Pohl, D. O. Hummel, *Makromol. Chem. 115* (1968) 141...55; Copolymere von Vinylhalogeniden mit Olefinen. 2. Quantitative *IR*-spektroskopische Untersuchungen an Vinylchlorid-Propen-Copolymeren

P. Simak, *J. Macromol. Sci. Chem. A 17* (1982) 923...33; *IR* investigations of the structure of PVC

5.4 CHN polymers

D. Gross, *Z. analyt. Chem. 248* (1969) 40...1; Quantitative infrarotspektroskopische Analyse von Styrol-Acrylnitril-Copolymeren nach pyrolytischer Zersetzung

E. I. Krasnova et al., *Zh. Prikl. Khim. (Leningrad) 49* (1976) 903...4 (Russ.); Determination of the composition of copolymers of acrylonitrile with vinylimidazole by *IR* spectroscopy

P. B. Kurapov, N. A. Klyuev, T. A. Mal'tseva, L. A. Palagushkina, *Izv. Vyssh. Uchebn. Zaved, Khim. Khim. Tekhnol. 20* (11) (1977) 1638...40 (Russ.); Quantitative determination of acrylonitrile in SAN vulcanizates by *IR* spectroscopic method

R. C. Schulz, E. Kaiser, W. Kern, *Makromol. Chem. 76* (1964) 99...108; Über Segmentlängenverteilung und Lichtabsorption bei Copolymeren aus Methacrylnitril und Acrolein oder Methacrolein. 31st Report. Polymeric acroleins

C. A. Sergides, A. R. Chughtai, D. M. Smith, P. Schissel, *J. Polym. Sci. Polym. Phys. Ed. 23* (1985) 1573...84; Relationship between the functional group concentrations and the infrared reflection-absorbance of polyacrylonitrile films

5.5 CHO polymers

R. L. Addleman, V. J. I. Zichy, *Polymer 13* (1972) 391...8; Accurate measurement of carboxyl and hydroxyl endgroups concentrations in poly(ethylene terephthalate) film by infrared spectroscopy

M. K. Antoon, K. M. Starkey, J. L. Koenig, Application of Fourier transform infrared spectroscopy to quality control of epoxy matrix, in *Composite Materials: Testing and Design*. Fifth ASTP Conf., Mar, 541...52; New Orleans 1978

V. P. Boiko, V. K. Grishchenko, *Acta Polymer. 36* (1985) 459...72; Determination of hydroxyl groups in polymers, a review

K. Edelmann, H. Wyden, *Kautsch. Gummi Kunstst. 25* (1972) 353...7; Absolute Bestimmung der Kristallinität von Poly(ethylenterephthalat)-Fasern durch Infrarotspektrophotometrie

V. A. Erä, H. Salo, T. Kaps, J. J. Lindberg, *Angew. Makromol. Chem. 48* (1975) 185...7; Determination of phenol/formaldehyde molar ratio of resol by infrared spectroscopy

U. H. Gibson, Q. Quick, *J. Appl. Polym. Sci. 15* (1971) 266; The determination of adjacent oxypropylene-oxyethylene units in propylene oxide-ethylene oxide adducts by infrared spectroscopy

G. W. Griffith, C. L. Long, R. E. Smith, *J. Appl. Polym. Sci. 29* (1984) 407...11; Determination of pendant allyl and monomer content in polydiallylphthalate

T. Hirai, *Angew. Makromol. Chem. 43* (1975) 93...103; Determination of composition in vinyl acetate-vinyl propionate copolymers

M. A. Ivanov, E. I. Pokrowski, *Dokl. Akad. Nauk SSSR 260* (1981) 1173...6 (Russ.); Quantitative investigation of the structure of cellulose by infrared spectroscopy

P. B. Iyer, K. R. K. Iyer, N. B. Patil, *J. Appl. Polym. Sci. 20* (1976) 591...5; An infrared technique for the quick analysis of cotton-polyester blends

K. Janicka, S. Iwanska, E. Wojtynska, *Chem. Anal. (Warsaw) 20* (1975) 893...7 (Pol.); Determination of the hydroxyl groups in epoxy resins with *IR* absorption spectroscopy

C. S. Kim, A. L. Dodge, S. Lau, A. Kawasaki, *Anal. Chem. 54* (1982) 232...8; Determination of hydroxyl concentrations in prepolymers from the infrared absorption band of tetrahydrofuran-associated hydroxyl groups

J. Klaban, J. Smrčka, F. Mleziva, *Makromol. Chem. 111* (1968) 1...13; Die Härtung von Epoxyharzen durch Dicarbonsäurenanhydride

R. J. Koopmans, R. van der Linden, E. F. Vansant, *Polym. Eng. Sci. 22* (1982) 878...82; Quantitative determination of the vinylacetate content in ethylene vinyl-acetate copolymers. A critical review

R. J. Koopmans, R. van der Linden, E. F. Vansant, *Spectrosc. Int. J. 1* (1982) 152...67; Qualitative and quantitative infrared spectrometry of ethylene-vinyl acetate copolymer, ethylene-vinyl alkohol copolymer, and ethylene-vinyl alkohol-vinyl acetate copolymer

R. J. Koopmans, R. A. Domisse, R. van der Linden, F. C. Alderweirelt, *J. Adhes. 15* (1983) 117...23; Quantitative measurements of vinyl acetate content in high pressure ethylene-vinyl acetat copolymers

V. V. Korshak, T. A. Sidorov, S. V. Vinogradova, L. I. Komarova, P. M. Valetskii, A. S. Lebedeva; *Izv. Akad. Nauk SSSR Khim. 2* (1965) 261...8 (Russ.); Concerning mixed polyesters. 52. Determination of the double bonds in unsaturated polyarylates by means of infrared spectroscopy

D. Kyriacou, *Anal. Chem. 33* (1961) 153f.; Spectrophotometric determination of hydroxyl groups in poly(propylene glycols)

I. V. Lejkin, V. V. Zakov, *Plast. Massy 1983* (3) 55 (Russ.); Determination of the degree of substitution of purified sodium carboxymethyl cellulose

T. T. Minakova et al., *Vysokomol. Soedin. A 18* (1976) 469...71 (Russ.); The quantitative determination of epoxy groups in polymers and copolymers of ethylene glycol-vinyl glycidyl ether (I)

D. P. Mitronov et al., *Ind. Lab. (USSR) 41* (1975) 857 (Russ.); Determination of hydroxyl groups in highly substituted cellulose ethers

D. Munteann, *Mater. Plast. 13* (1976) 97 (Rum.); Determination of the composition of grafted mixed polymers of polyethylene with vinyl acetate by infrared spectroscopy

K. Nitzl, M. C. Zech, *Adhäsion 11* (1975) 305...9; IR-spektroskopischer Nachweis von Vinylacetat in Äthylenvinylacetat-Copolymeren

N. I. Pakuro, N. V. Kozlova, D. K. Poljakov, *Vysokomol. Soedin. A 27* (1985) 2196...2200 (Russ.); Study of oligodiene diols by *IR* spectroscopy method

S. Paul, B. Rånby, *Anal. Chem. 47* (1975) 1428...9; Determination of epoxy side groups in polymers: Infrared analysis of methyl methacrylate-glycidyl methacrylate copolymers

E. G. Pomeranceva, E. M. Perepletchikova, E. O. Krac, *Plast. Massy 1979* (4) 39 f. (Russ.); Determination of the double bonds in insoluble polymers

E. G. Pomeranceva, A. G. Kronman, G. N. Cervjakova, L. F. Ivanova, *Plast. Massy 1983* (9) 39 f. (Russ.); Infrared spectroscopic investigation of copolymers of vinyl chloride, vinyl acetate and vinyl alcohol

G. Rudnaja, M. Owtschinnikowa, *Plaste Kautsch. 25* (1978) 102...3; Bestimmung des Restgehalts an ungesättigten Bindungen in ausgehärteten Polyesterspachteln mit Hilfe der Infrarotspektroskopie

M. V. Sablygin, N. P. Okromcelidze, A. V. Volochina, E. M. Sablygin, *Khim. Volokna 1981* (5) 52...3 (Russ.); Infrared spectroscopic determination of the composition of phthalic acids

N. S. Shaglaeva, E. I. Brodskaja, A. V. Rzhepka, V. A. Lopyrev, M. G. Voronkov, *Vysokomol. Soedin. A 21* (1979) 950...2 (Russ.); Determination of the composition of CP-acrylamide-acrylic acid or acrylic acid salts

M. M. Sharabash, R. L. Guile, *J. Macromol. Sci. A 10* (1976) 1021...38; Determination of copolymer composition by quantitative infrared analysis

P. A. Turley, A. Pietrantonio, *J. Cell. Plast. 20* (1984) 274...8; Rapid determination of OH number by reflection analysis in the near infrared

J. A. Vance, M. B. Brekke, P. R. Quinney, *Anal. Chem. 51* (1979) 499...501; Determination of oil content in oil modified ortho-phthalic polyester resins by infrared spectrometry

I. M. Ward, *Adv. Polym. Sci. 66* (1985) 81...115; Determination of molecular orientation by spectroscopic techniques

F. A. Zochova, V. V. Zarkov, *Plast. Massy 1981* (1) 35...6 (Russ.); Spectroscopic determination of methoxy and oxypropyl groups in methoxypropyl cellulose

5.6 CHNO polymers

D. T. Ages, B. C. Bowen, *J. Materials 6* (1971) 766...73; The quantitative analysis of nitrocellulose in alkyd lacquers by infrared spectroscopy

N. I. Bekasova, V. V. Korshak, M. A. Surikova, L. I. Komarova, I. Ju. Volosina, *Vysokomol. Soedin. A 23* (1981) 138...44 (Russ.); Quantitative determination of the constitutional inhomogeneities of carborane-containing polyoxyamides with *IR* spectroscopy

B. W. Brodman, M. P. Devine, *J. Appl. Polym. Sci. 25* (1980) 1245...7; Hydrogen bonding in nitrocellulose

J. G. Domszy, G. A. F. Roberts, *Makromol. Chem. 186* (1985) 1671...7; Evaluation of infrared spectroscopic techniques for analysing chitosan

P. B. Iyer, K. R. K. Iyer, N. B. Patil, *J. Appl. Polym. Sci. 22* (1978) 2677...83; Quantitative analysis of wool/cotton blends: an infrared method

T. V. Kozlova, V. V. Zarkov, *Vysokomol. Soedin. B 20* (1978) 285...7 (Russ.); Spectroscopic investigation of thermodynamics of segment microaggregation in linear segmented polyether urethanes

N. V. Kozlova et al., *Ind. Lab. 49* (1983) 611...3; Die quantitative Analyse des Monomerengehalts in Acrylamid-Polymeren

A. N. Krasovskij, N. P. Antonov, M. M. Koton, K. K. Kalinsh, V. V. Kudrjavcev, *Vysokomol. Soedin. A 21* (1979) 945...50 (Russ.); On the determination of the degree of imidization of polyamido acids

W.-M. Kulicke, H.-H. Hörl, *Colloid Polym. Sci. 263* (1985) 530...40; Preparation and characterization of a series of poly(acrylamide-*co*-acrylates), with a copolymer composition between 0 and 96.3 mol-% acrylate units with the same degree and distribution of polymerization

S. S. Lord, *Anal. Chem. 29* (1957) 497...9; Infrared analysis of toluene-2,4-diisocyanate and toluene-2,6-diisocyanate mixtures

S. Montsarrat, P. Colomer, G. M. Guzman, *Cellul. Chem. Technol. 13* (1979) 159...62; Polyelectrolytes derived from carboxymethylcellulose. IV. Analysis of nitrogenated derivatives through infrared spectroscopy

L. P. Razumovskij, V. S. Markin, G. E. Zaikov, *Vysokomol. Soedin. A 21* (1979) 1671...3 (Russ.); Determination of the degree of crystallinity of polycaproamide according to the method of isotopic H-D exchange

H. M. Rosenberger, C. J. Shoemaker, *Anal. Chem. 31* (1959) 1315...7; Infrared determination of nitrocellulose in mixtures of cellulose resins

P. Simak, *Makromol. Chem. 178* (1977) 2927...37; Polymorphie, Kristallinität und Schmelzwärme von Poly(ε-caprolactam)

5.7 Miscellaneous polymers

I. K. Ahmed, M. A. Rashid, J. K. Jawad, *J. Appl. Polym. Sci. 31* (1986) 2315...23; Quantitative and qualitative *IR* studies of some synthesized aromatic polysulfides

T. Biernacka, A. Wokroj, *Chem. anal. (Warsaw) 10* (1965) 1233...45 (Pol.); On the application of infrared absorption measurement to the determination of the content of methyl and phenyl groups in siloxane resins

M. J. Clark, T. S. Hickle, *J. Text. Inst. 68* (1975) 243...8; Quantitative analysis of some binary mixtures of fibers by methods of infrared spectroscopy

A. A. Efendiev, G. M. Mamedjarov, D. D. Orudzev, I. M. Mamedov, I. I. Sidorcuk, V. A. Kabanov, *Vysokomol. Soedin. A 23* (1981) 2374...6 (Russ.); Determination of the concentration of the cross-linking agent N,N'-methylenediacrylamide in cross-linked CP-diethyl vinylphosphonate-acrylic acid

J. Fuhrmann, K. Glaenzer, *Pharm. Ind. 47* (1985) 652...6; Quantitative determination of silicon oils and the degree of siliconization of surfaces by *IR* spectroscopy

G. D. Grant, A. L. Smith, *Anal. Chem. 30* (1958) 1016; Determination of phenyl to methyl ratio in phenyl and methyl containing polysiloxanes

G. Heidermanns, *Staub — Reinhalt. Luft 33* (1973) 66...70; Quantitative Bestimmung von Asbest durch optische, chemische, Röntgen- und Infrarotspektroskopische Analyse

J. D. Lady, G. M. Bower, R. E. Adams, F. P. Byrne, *Anal. Chem. 31* (1959) 1100; Determination of the ratio of methyl to phenyl groups in silicone polymers

G. A. Luoma, L. K. Yee, R. Rowland, *Anal. Chem. 54* (1982) 2140...2; Determination of microgram amounts of asbestos in mixtures by infrared spectrometry

P. J. Madec, E. Marechal, *J. Polym. Sci. Polym. Phys. Ed. 18* (1980) 2417...20; Molecular weight determination of silane-terminated poly(dimethylsiloxane) by infrared spectroscopy

L. V. Morozova, E. I. Brodskaja, D.-S. D. Tarjasinova, S. V. Amosova, B. A. Trofimov, *Vysokomol. Soedin. A 23* (1981) 1668...70 (Russ.); Quantitative determination of vinyl groups in divinyl sulfide copolymers by *UV* and *IR* spectroscopy

J. R. Parrish, *Anal. Chem. 47* (1975) 1999...2003; Quantitative analysis of cation-exchange resins by infrared spectrophotometry and pyrolysis-gas chromatography

J. C. Petersen, *Anal. Chem. 47* (1975) 112...7; Quantitative method using differential infrared spectrometry for the determination of compound types absorbing in the carbonyl region in asphalts

J. C. Petersen, H. Plancher, *Anal. Chem. 53* (1981) 786...9; Quantitative determination of carboxylic acids and their salts and anhydrides in asphalts by selective chemical reactions and differential infrared spectrometry

K. Petrack, I. Degen, P. Beynon, *J. Polym. Sci. Polym. Chem. Ed. 20* (1982) 783...93; Some 1-substituted quaternary imidazolium compounds and related polymers. Qualitative and quantitative infrared analysis

A. M. Podoba, N. I. Solnceva, E. A. Goldovskij, A. A. Doncov, *Kauchuk Rezina 1981* (7) 52...4 (Russ.); Method for the determination of silicon hydride groups in siloxane-based rubbers

M. A. Post, *Paint Varn. Prod. 61* (1971) 31...8; Copolymer determination in surface filler

M. A. Post, *Paint Varn. Prod. 63* (1973) 21...5; Liquid latex paint analysis

H. Rotzsche, H. Clauss, H. Hahnewald, *Plaste Kautsch. 26* (1979) 630...2; Nachweis und Bestimmung von Methylsilikonölspuren

A. Snowacka-Wokroj, T. Biernacka, *Chem. anal. (Warsaw) 9* (1964) 303...14 (Pol.); On the *IR* spectroscopic determination of methyl and phenyl groups in siloxane polymers

M. G. Voronkov, V. Z. Annenkova, N. P. Romankova, E. I. Brodskaja, V. M. Annenkova, *Vysokomol. Soedin. A 23* (1981) 1666...8 (Russ.); Spectroscopic determination of the composition of bisulfite derivatives of CP-acrolein-acrylic acid

E. Wojtynska, *Polymery 24* (1979) 238...41 (Pol.); Determination of silanol groups in phenyl silicone resins by infrared spectroscopy

6 Computer-assisted *IR* spectrometry (*CIRS*)

6.1 Fundamentals

6.1.1 Experimental methodology

J. E. Bertie, *NATO Adv. Study Inst. Ser. C 57* (1980) 25...50; *FT-IR* spectrometry. Apodization and phase correction

M. M. Coleman, P. C. Painter, Computer-assisted vibrational spectroscopy, in D. O. Hummel (ed.): *Proceedings of the 5th European Symposium on Polymer Spectroscopy*; Verlag Chemie, Weinheim 1979

M. J. Dignam, M. D. Baker, *Appl. Spectrosc. 35* (1981) 186...93; Analysis of a polarizing Michelson interferometer for dual beam Fourier transform infrared, circular dichroism infrared, and reflection ellipsometric infrared spectroscopies

A. M. Dwivedi, D. S. Jayasuriya, *Polym. Mat. Sci. Eng. 54* (1986) 392...6; *FTIR* studies of poly(ethylene oxide) in acqueous solution using cylindrical internal reflection cell

A. A. Garrison, R. A. Crocombe, G. Mamantov, J. A. de Haseth, *Appl. Spectrosc. 34* (1980) 399...405; Practical aspects of rapid scanning Fourier transform time-resolved infrared spectroscopy

R. Geick, *Chem. Labor Betr. 23* (1972) 193...203; Einführung in die Fourierspektroskopie

R. T. Graf, J. L. Koenig, H. Ishida, *ACS Polym. Prepr. 25/2* (1984) 188; Comparison of *FTIR* transmission, specular reflectance, and attenuated total reflectance spectra of polymers

R. T. Graf, J. L. Koenig, H. Ishida, *Anal. Chem. 58* (1986) 64...8; Fourier transform infrared ellipsometry of thin polymer films

P. R. Griffiths, *Appl. Spectrosc. 31* (1977) 497...505; Recent applications of Fourier transform infrared spectrometry in chemical and environmental analysis

P. R. Griffiths, *NATO Adv. Study Inst. Ser. C 57* (1980) 11...24; Basic theory and instrumentation for *FT-IR* spectrometry

P. R. Griffiths, *NATO Adv. Study Inst. Ser. C 57* (1980) 141...8; Accessories and sampling techniques for *FT-IR* spectrometry

G. Guelachvili, *Appl. Opt. 20* (1981) 2121...32; Differential Fourier spectroscopy with simultaneous interferograms: application to extensive accurate pressure-shift measurements

R. W. Hannah, S. C. Pattacini, J. G. Grasselli, S. E. Mocadlo, *Appl. Spectrosc. 1* (1978) 69; Trace analysis by infrared spectroscopy using preconcentration, separation, and computer techniques

W. Herres, *Chimia 39* (1985) 64...8; *FT-IR:* the renaissance of infrared spectrometry

T. Hirschfeld, K. Kizer, *Appl. Spectrosc. 4* (1975) 345; Direct recording of intermolecular interaction perturbation spectra by *FTIR* spectroscopy

R. J. Jakobsen, Application of *FT-IR* to surface studies, in J. R. Ferraro, L. J. Basile (eds.): *Fourier Transform Infrared Spectroscopy*, Vol. 1; Academic Press, New York 1978

G. J. Kemeny, P. R. Griffiths, *Appl. Spectrosc. 35* (1981) 128 f.; Feasibility of using dual-beam Fourier transform infrared spectrometry to study adhesives on metal surfaces

W. Kiefer, J. Laane, *NATO Adv. Study Inst. Ser. C 57* (1980) 537...77; Comparisons of *FTIR* and Raman spectroscopy

J. L. Koenig, *Appl. Spectrosc. 29* (1975) 293...308; Application of Fourier transform infrared spectroscopy to chemical systems

J. L. Koenig, *Acc. Chem. Res. 14* (1981) 171...8; Fourier transform infrared spectroscopy of chemical systems

J. L. Koenig, *Pure Appl. Chem. 47* (1985) 971...6; Recent advances in *FT-IR* spectroscopy of polymers

M. J. D. Low, A. J. Goodsel, *J. Paint Technol. 43* (1871) 49...57; Infrared Fourier transform spectroscopy in the coatings industry. III. Transmission/absorption spectra

A. S. Manocha, R. M. Montgomery, *Appl. Spectrosc. 4* (1978) 344...52; Absorbance compensation technique in the analytical laboratory

D. R. Mattson, *Appl. Spectrosc. 4* (1978) 335...8; Sensitivity of a *FTIR* spectrometer

K. Molt, *Kontrolle 2* (1984) 15...23; Rechnerunterstützte Infrarot-Spektroskopie

S. Naviroj, J. L. Koenig, H. Ishida, *J. Adhesion 18* (1985) 93...110; Diffuse reflectance Fourier transform infrared

spectroscopic study of chemical bonding and hydrothermal stability of an aminosilane on metal oxide surfaces
T. Nguyen, *Progr. Org. Coat. 13* (1985) 1...34; Applications of Fourier transform infrared spectroscopy in surface and interface studies

N. N., *Chem. Eng. News 63* (1985) 15f.; Low-cost *FTIR* microscopy units gain wider use in microanalysis

E. M. Salazar-Rojas, M. W. Urban, *ACS Polym. Prepr. 28/1* (1987) 1f.; Surface studies of dehydrofluorinated PVF$_2$ films using photoacoustic (*PA*) and attenuated total reflectance (*ATR*) *FT-IR* spectroscopy

B. W. Tattershall, *Anal. Chem. 49* (1977) 772...5; Identification of components of mixtures by retrospective computer subtraction of gas-phase infrared spectra

6.1.2 General investigations of polymers

M. K. Antoon, J. H. Koenig, J. L. Koenig, *Appl. Spectrosc. 31* (1977) 518...24; Least-squares curve-fitting of Fourier transform infrared spectra with applications to polymer systems

M. M. Coleman, P. C. Painter, *J. Macromol. Sci. Rev. Macromol. Chem. C16* (1977...8) 197...313; Fourier transform infrared studies of polymeric materials

S. R. Culler, H. Ishida, J. L. Koenig, *Ann. Rev. Mater. Sci. 13* (1983) 363...86; The use of infrared methods to study polymer interfaces

C. U. Davanzo, N. Sheppard, F. Al-Mashta, *Spectrochim. Acta 41 A* (1985) 263...9; An infrared spectroscopic study of the polymerization of styrene on titania catalysts

B. M. Fanconi, *J. Testing Evaluation 12* (1984) 33...9; Fourier transform infrared spectroscopy of polymers. Theory and application

A. Garton, D. J. Carlsson, D. M. Wiles, *Textile Research J. 51* (1981) 28...34; Infrared spectroscopy of polyethylene terephthalate fibers: Uses and limitations

R. T. Graf, J. L. Koenig, H. Ishida, *Appl. Spectrosc. 39* (1985) 405; Optical constant determination of thin polymer films in the infrared

R. T. Graf, J. L. Koenig, H. Ishida, *Anal. Chem. 58* (1986) 64...8; Fourier transform infrared ellipsometry of thin polymer films

S. Hotta, W. Shimotsuma, M. Taketani, *Synth. Metals 10* (1984/85) 85...94; Fourier transform infrared study of electrochemically prepared polythienylene films with varying doping levels

D. O. Hummel, C. Votteler, M. Winter, *Kunststoffe 73* (1983) 193...8; Die computerunterstützte Infrarot-Spektrometrie (*CIRS*) in der Kunststoff-Analytik. I. Voraussetzung für die Anwendung der *IR*-Differenzspektrometrie

A. Ishitani, *ACS Polym. Prepr. 25/2* (1984) 186f.; *FT-IR* as a tool for the characterization of industrial materials

B. Jasse, Fourier transform infrared spectroscopy of synthetic polymers, in J. V. Dawkins (ed.): *Developments in Polymer Characterization*, Vol. 4, 91...129; Applied Science, London 1983

J. L. Koenig, M. K. Antoon, *Appl. Opt. 17* (1978) 1374...85; Recent applications of *FT-IR* spectroscopy to polymer systems

J. L. Koenig, *NATO Adv. Study Inst. Ser. C57* (1980) 229...40; Applications of Fourier transform infrared to polymers

J. L. Koenig, *Pure Appl. Chem. 57* (1985) 971; Recent advances in *FT-IR* (Fourier transform infrared spectroscopy) of polymers

M. J. D. Low, H. Mark, *Appl. Polym. Symp. 10* (1969) 145...58; The examination of organic coatings by infrared interference spectroscopy

M. J. D. Low, H. Mark, *J. Paint Technol. 42* (1970) 265...75; Infrared Fourier transform spectroscopy in the coatings industry. I. Infrared spectra of clear coatings on metals

M. J. D. Low, H. Mark, *J. Paint Technol. 43* (1971) 31...41; Infrared Fourier transform spectroscopy in the coatings industry. II. Optical subtraction

M. J. D. Low, H. Mark, A. J. Goodsel, *J. Paint Technol. 43* (1971) 49...57; Infrared Fourier transform spectroscopy in the coatings industry. III. Transmission/absorption spectra

W. F. Maddams, *Makromol. Chem. Macromol. Symp. 5* (1986) 35...48; Spectral quality enhancement as an aid to polymer characterization

L. C. Sander, J. B. Callis, L. R. Field, *Anal. Chem. 55* (1983) 1068...75; Fourier transformed infrared spectrometric determination of alkyl chain conformation on chemically bonded reversed-phased liquid-chromatography packings

H. W. Siesler, *J. Molec. Struct. 59* (1980) 15...37; Fourier-transform infrared (*FTIR*) spectroscopy in polymer research

A. Solti, D. O. Hummel, P. Simak, *Makromol. Chem. Macromol. Symp. 5* (1986) 105...33; Computer-supported infrared spectrometry of polyethylene, ethene copolymers, and amorphous poly(alkyl ethylene)s

T. Usami, S. Takayama, *Polymer J. 16* (1984) 731...8; Identification of branches in low-density polyethylene by Fourier-transform infrared spectroscopy (*FTIR*)

H. Vanni, J. F. Rabolt, *J. Polym. Sci. Polym. Phys. Ed. 18* (1980) 587...96; Fourier transform infrared investigation of the effects of irradiation on the 19 and 30 Cel phase transitions in polytetrafluorethylene

6.2 States of order in polymers

D. L. Allara, R. G. Nuzzo, *ACS Polym. Prepr. 25/2* (1984) 185; Fourier transform infrared reflection spectroscopy studies of spontaneous organization of long chain *n*-alkanoic acids on aluminum oxide

S. Bloembergen, D. A. Holden, G. K. Hamer, T. L. Bluhm, R. H. Marchessault, *Macromolecules 19* (1986) 2865...71; Studies of composition and crystallinity of bacterial poly(β-hydroxybutyrate-*co*-β-hydroxyvalerate)

B. A. Brozoski, M. M. Coleman, P. C. Painter, *Macromolecules 17* (1984) 230...4; Local structures in ionomer multiplets. A vibrational spectroscopic analysis

B. A. Brozoski, P. C. Painter, M. M. Coleman, *Macromolecules 17* (1984) 1591...4; Concerning the origin of broad bands observed in the *FT-IR* spectra of ionomers. Cluster formation or water adsorption?

Z. Chen, M. Liu, M. Shi, Z. Shen, D. O. Hummel, *Makromol. Chem. 188* (1987) 2687...95; Fourier transform infrared spectroscopic study of polyacetylene. 1. Spectral assignment and characteristics of *Z/E* ("*cis*"/"*trans*") geometric isomers; 2. Thermal isomerization kinetics and mechanism, *ibid.* 2697...2703

M. M. Coleman, P. C. Painter, D. L. Tabb, J. L. Koenig, *J. Polym. Sci. Polym. Lett. Ed. 12* (1974) 577...81; A Fourier transform infrared spectroscopic study of *trans*-1,4-polychloroprene. A novel method for the determination of the crystalline vibrational bands

L. D'Esposito, J. L. Koenig, *J. Polym. Sci. Polym. Phys. Ed. 14* (1976) 1731...41; Application of Fourier transform infrared spectroscopy to the study of semicrystalline polymers: poly(ethylene terephthalate)

B. Fanconi, D. Sarazin, *ACS Polym. Prepr. 25/2* (1984) 173 f.; *FTIR* studies of molecular organization in polyethylene

L. J. Fina, J. L. Koenig, *Macromolecules 17* (1984) 2572...9; Studies of chain folding in solution-crystallized poly(ethylene terephthalate)

R. T. Graf, J. L. Koenig, H. Ishida, *Anal. Chem. 56* (1984) 773...8; Characterization of silane-treated glass fibers by diffuse reflectance Fourier transform spectrometry

K. Holland-Moritz, Determination of the state of order in polymers by vibrational spectroscopy, in D. O. Hummel (ed.): *Proceedings of the 5th European Symposium on Polymer Spectroscopy*; Verlag Chemie, Weinheim 1979, 93...135

K. Holland-Moritz, I. Holland-Moritz, K. van Werden, *Colloid Polym. Sci. 259* (1981) 156...62; Application of *FTIR*-spectroscopy on orientation processes in polyethylene films

H. Ishida, S. E. Rickert, A. J. Hopfinger, J. B. Lando, E. Baer, J. L. Koenig, *J. Appl. Phys. 51* (1980) 5188...93; Epitaxial polymerization of (SN)$_x$: chemical defects

B. Jasse, J. L. Koenig, *J. Polym. Sci. Polym. Phys. Ed. 16* (1978) 1869...75; Fourier transform infrared analysis of the stereoregularity of atactic polystyrene

K. Knutson, D. J. Lyman, *Polym. Sci. Technol. 14* (1981) (Biomed. Dent. Appl. Polym.) 173...88; Morphology of block copolyurethanes. II. *FTIR* and *ESCA* techniques for studying surface morphology

J. L. Koenig, D. Kormos, *Contemp. Top. Polym. Sci. 3* (1979) 127...41; Fourier transform infrared spectroscopy of the polymeric amorphous phase

R. L. Levy, *ACS Polym. Prepr. 21/2* (1980) 263 f.; Polarized *FT-IR* investigation of stress-induced molecular phenomena in polyimide

R. L. Levy, R. P. Wool, *ACS Polym. Prepr. 21/2* (1980) 239 f.; Difference infrared spectroscopy of stressed polymers

S. B. Lin, J. L. Koenig, *J. Polym. Sci. Polym. Symp. 71 C* (1984) 121; The transitions and melting behaviour of thermally crystallized poly(ethylene terephthalate) and their correlations with *FT-IR* and density measurements

B. Love, R. P. Wool, *Polym. Mat. Sci. Eng. 53* (1985) 317...20; Molecular deformation in semicrystalline polymers as characterized by *FTIR*

L. A. Nafie, E. D. Lipp, A. Farrell, G. Paterlini, *ACS Polym. Prepr. 25/2* (1984) 145...6; Fourier transform vibrational circular dichroism in the carbonyl region of peptides and polypeptides

H. X. Nguyen, H. Ishida, *ACS Polym. Prepr. 26/1* (1985) 273 f.; Molecular analysis of the melting and crystallization behavior of poly(arylether-ether-ketone)

J. M. O'Reilly, R. A. Mosher, *Macromolecules 14* (1981) 602...8; Conformational energies of stereoregular poly(methyl methacrylate) by Fourier transform infrared spectroscopy

P. C. Painter, J. Havens, W. W. Hart, J. L. Koenig, *J. Polym. Sci. Polym. Phys. Ed. 15* (1977) 1223...35; A Fourier transform infrared spectroscopic investigation of polyethylene single crystals. I. Methylene wagging mode

P. C. Painter, J. Havens, W. W. Hart, J. L. Koenig, *J. Polym. Sci. Polym. Phys. Ed. 15* (1977) 1237...49; A Fourier transform infrared spectroscopic investigation of polyethylene single crystals. II. Fine structure of the CH$_2$ rocking mode

P. C. Painter, J. L. Koenig, *J. Polym. Sci. Polym. Phys. Ed. 15* (1977) 1885...904; A normal vibrational analysis of isotactic polystyrene

P. C. Painter, J. Runt, M. M. Coleman, I. R. Harrison, *J. Polym. Sci. Polym. Phys. Ed. 15* (1977) 1647...54; A Fourier transform infrared spectroscopic investigation of polyethylene single crystals

P. C. Painter, M. Watzek, J. L. Koenig, *Polymer 18* (1977) 1169...72; Fourier transform infra-red study of polypropylene

P. C. Painter, J. Runt, M. M. Coleman, I. R. Harrison, *J. Polym. Sci. Polym. Phys. Ed. 16* (1978) 1253...60; Effect of polymorphism on the C-H stretching region of the infrared spectrum of polyethylene

P. C. Painter, R. E. Kessler, R. W. Snyder, *J. Polym. Sci. Polym. Phys. Ed. 18* (1980) 723...9; Fourier-transform infrared study of the gel form of isotactic polystyrene

B. C. Perry, J. L. Koenig, J. B. Lando, *Macromolecules 20* (1987) 422; Relaxation behavior of the β-phase of poly(butylene terephthalate)

R. J. Petcavich, P. C. Painter, M. M. Coleman, *Polymer 19* (1978) 1249...52; Application of infra-red digital subtraction techniques to the microstructure of polychloroprenes. 2. Mechanism of oxidative degradation at 60°C

V. Renugopalakrishnan, R. S. Bhatnagar, *J. Am. Chem. Soc. 106* (1984) 2217...9; Fourier transform infrared photoacoustic spectroscopy. A novel conformational probe. Demonstration of α-helical conformation of poly(γ-benzyl glutamate)

D. R. Rueda, A. Hidalgo, F. J. Baltá-Calleja, *Spectrochim. Acta 34 A* (1978) 475...80; An *IR* study of the "amorphous" phase in melt crystallized polyethylene

N. E. Schlotter, J. F. Rabolt, *Macromolecules 7* (1984) 1581...5; Studies of chain-extended morphology in polyethylene by vibrational spectroscopy

N. E. Schlotter, *ACS Polym. Prepr. 28/1* (1987) 27 f.; Structural characterization of polymers using Fourier transform infrared spectroscopy

H. W. Siesler, Characterization of chemical and physical changes of polymer structure by rapid-scanning Fourier-transform *IR* (*FTIR*) spectroscopy, in D. O. Hummel (ed.): *Proceedings of the 5th European Symposium on Polymer Spectroscopy*; Verlag Chemie, Weinheim 1979

H. W. Siesler, *Colloid Polym. Sci. 262* (1984) 223...9; Rheo-optical Fourier-transform infrared (*FTIR*) spectroscopy of polymers. 5. Strain-induced crystallization of cross-linked natural rubber

H. W. Siesler, *Infrared Phys. 24* (1984) 239...44; Rheo-optical Fourier-transform infrared spectroscopy (*FTIRS*) of polymers. 6. Changes of crystal-axes orientation and state of order during uniaxial elongation of high-density polyethylene

H. W. Siesler, *Makromol. Chem. Macromol. Symp. 5* (1986) 151...5; Rheo-optical Fourier-transform infrared spectroscopy of polymers. 12. Variable temperature studies of strain-induced crystallization in sulfur-crosslinked natural rubber

S. J. Spells, *Polym. Commun. 25* (1984) 162...6; Fourier self-deconvolution of mixed crystal polyethylene infra-red spectra

W. Stach, K. Holland-Moritz, *J. Molec. Struct. 60* (1980) 49...54; Vibrational spectroscopic studies on conformational changes in poly(tetramethylene terephthalate)

D. L. Tabb, J. L. Koenig, *J. Polym. Sci. Polym. Phys. Ed. 13* (1975) 1145...1158; Infrared spectroscopic evidence of structural defects in the crystalline regions of *trans*-1,4-polychloroprene

G. Walters, P. C. Painter, P. Ika, H. Frisch, *Macromolecules 19* (1986) 888...94; Fourier transform study of a poly(diacetylene)

P. P. Wu, S. L. Hsu, O. Thomas, A. Blumstein, *J. Polym. Sci. Polym. Phys. Ed. 24* (1986) 827...37; Fourier-transform infrared study of the nematic order in thermotropic main-chain polyesters

Gi Xue, *Makromol. Chem. Rapid Commun. 6* (1985) 811...4; Orientation studies of poly(ethylene terephthalate) film and fiber surfaces using *FT-IR* diffuse reflectance optics

C. K. Yeung, B. Jasse, *J. Appl. Polym. Sci. 27* (1982) 4587...97; Fourier-transform infrared study of uniaxially oriented polytetrafluoroethylene

Y. Zhao, B. Jasse, L. Monnerie, *Makromol. Chem. Macromol. Symp. 5* (1986) 87...97; Fourier transform infrared study of orientation and relaxation in poly(methyl methacrylate)

6.3 Multicomponent polymer systems

6.3.1 Polymer mixtures

D. L. Allara, *Appl. Spectrosc. 33* (1979) 358...61; Infrared spectra of polymer mixtures. Problems caused by dispersion effects in difference spectra

M. M. Coleman, J. Zarian, D. F. Varnell, P. C. Painter, *J. Polym. Sci. Polym. Lett. Ed. 15* (1977) 745...50; A Fourier transform infrared study of polymer blends. I. Poly(vinylidene fluoride)-poly(methyl methacrylate) system

M. M. Coleman, J. Zarian, *J. Polym. Sci. Polym. Phys. Ed. 17* (1979) 837...50; Fourier-transform infrared studies of polymer blends. II. Poly(ε-caprolactone)-poly(vinyl chloride) system

M. M. Coleman, D. F. Varnell, *J. Polym. Sci. Polym. Phys. Ed. 18* (1980) 1403...12; Fourier-transform infrared studies of polymer blends. III. Poly(β-propiolactone)-poly(vinyl chloride) system

M. M. Coleman, E. J. Moskala, *Polymer 24* (1983) 251...7; *FTIR* studies of polymer blends containing the poly(hydroxy ether of bisphenol A) and poly(ε-caprolactone)

M. M. Coleman, E. J. Moskala, P. C. Painter, D. J. Walsh, S. Rostami, *Polymer 24* (1983) 1410...4; A Fourier transform infra-red study of the phase behaviour of polymer blends. Ethylene-vinyl acetate copolymer blends with poly(vinyl chloride) and chlorinated polyethylene

M. M. Coleman, D. F. Varnell, J. P. Runt, A critical assessment on the application of *FT-IR* spectroscopy to the study of crystalline/compatible polymer blends, in D. Klempner, K. C. Frisch (eds.): *Polymer Alloys* III; Plenum Publ. Corp. New York – London 1983

M. M. Coleman, E. J. Moskala, S. E. Howe, P. C. Painter, *Polym. Mat. Sci. Eng. 51* (1984) 286...90; The role of intermolecular interactions in compatible polymer blends

M. M. Coleman, P. C. Painter, *Applied Spect. Rev. 20* (1984) 255...346; Fourier transform infrared spectroscopy: Probing the structure of multicomponent polymer blends

M. M. Coleman, D. J. Skrovanek, J. Hu, P. C. Painter, *ACS Polym. Prepr. 28/1* (1987) 19f.; *FTIR* studies of hydrogen bonding in polymer blends. 1. Experimental

P. Cousin, R. E. Prud'homme, *Polym. Mat. Sci. Eng. 51* (1984) 291...4; *FTIR* and *NMR* studies of blends of polyvinyl chloride and polyvinyl bromide with polyesters

D. Garcia, *J. Polym. Sci. Polym. Phys. Ed. 22* (1984) 107...15; Fourier-transform infrared study of polystyrene/poly(vinyl methyl ether) blends

J. A. Gardella, G. L. Grobe, W. L. Hopson, E. M. Eyring, *Anal. Chem. 56* (1984) 1169...77; Comparison of attenuated total reflectance and photoacoustic sampling for surface analysis of polymer mixtures by Fourier transform infrared spectroscopy

A. Garton, *Polym. Eng. Sci. (Greenwich) 23* (1983) 663...8; Competitive equilibria in miscible polymer blends and low molecular weight analogues. A Fourier transform infrared study

A. Garton, M. Aubin, R. E. Prud'homme, *J. Polym. Sci. Polym. Lett. Ed. 21* (1983) 45...7; FTIR of polycaprolactone/poly(vinylidene chloride-co-acrylonitrile) miscible blends

D. O. Hummel, C. Votteler, *Kemia-Kemi 9* (1982) 660...5; Computer-supported *IR* spectrometry (*CIRS*), especially difference spectrometry, of multi-component polymeric systems

D. O. Hummel, C. Votteler, M. Winter, *Kunststoffe 73* (1983) 193...8; Computerunterstützte Infrarot-Spektrometrie (*CIRS*) in der Kunststoff-Analytik. Voraussetzungen für die Anwendung der *IR*-Differenzspektrometrie

D. O. Hummel, C. Votteler, *Angew. Makromol. Chem. 117* (1983) 171...94; Analytische Differenz-*IR*-Spektrometrie von Mehrkomponentenkunststoffen und Copolymeren. 1. Identifizierung der Komponenten in Polymergemischen

M. Iskandar, C. Tran, L. M. Robeson, J. E. McGrath, *Polym. Eng. Sci. (Greenwich) 23* (1983) 682...8; Fourier transform infrared studies of poly(vinyl chloride) blends with ethylene co- and terpolymers

J. L. Koenig, M. J. M. Tovar Rodriguez, *Appl. Spectrosc. 35* (1981) 543...8; Factor analysis and Fourier transform infrared spectra of compatible blends of polyphenylene oxides and polystyrene

B. Lotz, J.-C. Wittmann, *Makromol. Chem. 185* (1984) 2043...52; Epitaxy of helical polyolefins: polymer blends and polymer-nucleating agent systems

F. J. Lu, E. Benedetti, S. L. Hsu, *Macromolecules 16* (1983) 1525...9; Spectroscopic study of polystyrene and poly(vinyl methyl ether) blends

Y. H. Mariam, P. W. Pemawansa, K. B. Bota, *ACS Polym. Prepr. 27/1* (1986) 271 f.; *FTIR* investigation of compatibility in comblike liquid crystalline polymers

M. A. Maris, C. W. Brown, D. S. Lavery, *Anal. Chem. 55* (1983) 1694...1703; Nonlinear multicomponent analysis by infrared spectrophotometry

E. J. Moskala, S. E. Howe, P. C. Painter, M. M. Coleman, *Macromolecules 17* (1984) 1671...8; On the role of intermolecular hydrogen bonding in miscible polymer blends

S. Nagarajan, Z. H. Stachurski, *J. Polym. Sci. Polym. Phys. Ed. 20* (1982) 989...1000; A study of the PE-PTFE system. I. *IR* and *NMR* measurements

P. C. Painter, Y. Park, M. M. Coleman, *ACS Polym. Prepr. 28/1* (1987) 21 f.; *FTIR* studies of hydrogen bonding in polymer blends. 2. Theory

R. H. Pater, D. A. Scola, *Natl. SAMPE Tech. Conf. 11* (1979) 151...65; Non-destructive analysis of composite surface contamination by Fourier transform infrared spectroscopy

E. M. Pearce, T. K. Kwei, B. Y. Min, *Polym. Mat. Sci. Eng. 50* (1984) 16...8; Polymer compatibility through hydrogen bonding

H. C. Price, *Org. Coat. Appl. Polym. Sci. Proc. 48* (1983) 795...8; *FTIR* multi-component analysis of copolymers and polymer blends. A comparison of the methods

G. R. Rao, C. Castiglioni, M. Gussoni, G. Zerbi, E. Martuscelli, *Polymer 26* (1985) 811...20; Probing the structure of polymer blends by vibrational spectroscopy: the case of poly(ethylene oxide) and poly(methyl methacrylate) blends

D. L. Tabb, J. L. Koenig, *Macromolecules 8* (1975) 929...34; Fourier transform infrared study of plasticized and unplasticized poly(vinyl chloride)

R. Tannenbaum, M. Rutkowska, A. Eisenberg, *ACS Polym. Prepr.* 27/1 (1986) 345f.; *FTIR* studies of ionic interactions in polyurethane-styrene blends

D. F. Varnell, J. P. Runt, M. M. Coleman, *Org. Coat. Plast. Chem.* 45 (1981) 170...3; *FT-IR* studies of poly(bisphenol A carbonate)-poly(ε-caprolactone) blends

D. F. Varnell, J. P. Runt, M. M. Coleman, *Macromolecules* 14 (1981) 1350...6; Fourier transform infrared studies of polymer blends. 4. Further observations on the poly(bisphenol A carbonate)-poly(ε-caprolactone) system

D. F. Varnell, M. M. Coleman, *Polymer* 22 (1981) 1324...8; *FTIR* studies of polymer blends. V. Further observations on polyester-poly(vinyl chloride) blends

D. F. Varnell, E. J. Moskala, P. C. Painter, M. M. Coleman, *Polym. Eng. Sci. (Greenwich)* 23 (1983) 658...62; On the application of Fourier transform infrared spectroscopy to the elucidation of specific interactions in miscible polyester-poly(vinyl chloride) blends

D. F. Varnell, J. P. Runt, M. M. Colemann, *Polymer* 24 (1983) 37...42; *FTIR* and thermal analysis studies of blends of poly(ε-caprolactone) with homo- and copolymers of poly(vinylidene chloride)

G. M. Venkatesh, R. D. Gilbert, R. E. Fornes, *Polymer* 26 (1985) 45...9; Fourier-transform infra-red spectroscopy of nylon-6 blends: binary blends with poly(methyl methacrylate) and ethylene vinyl ester/alcohol copolymer

C. Votteler, V. Hoffmann, G. Trafara, *Makromol. Chem.* 185 (1984) 1953...77; Untersuchungen zu Modifikationen von Polyamid-6 und Polyamid-4 mit eingelagerten Alkalihalogeniden

6.3.2 Copolymers

E. F. Devlin, *Rubber Chem. Technol.* 59 (1986) 666...70; The effect of cure variables on *cis/trans* isomerization in carbon-black-reinforced *cis*-1,4-polybutadiene

G. Fischer, I. Lüderwald, P. Ottenbreit, *Angew. Makromol. Chem.* 149 (1987) 179...87; Characterization of acrylonitrile-butadiene-styrene terpolymers by computer-aided *FT-IR* spectroscopy

W. H. Littke, W. Fieber, R. Schmolke, W. Kimmer, *Faserforsch. Textiltechn.* 26 (1975) 503...8; Infrarotspektroskopische Untersuchungen am Bandenkomplex 760 cm^{-1} von Styrolcopolymeren mit Kleinsteuerrechner KSR 4100

P. C. Painter, B. A Brozoski, M. M. Colemann, *J. Polym. Sci. Polym. Phys. Ed.* 20 (1982) 1069...80; *FTIR* studies of calcium and sodium ionomers derived from an ethylene-methacrylic acid copolymer

A. E. Tonelli, T. N. Bowmer, *ACS Polym. Prepr.* 28/1 (1987) 23...6; Fourier-transform infrared spectroscopy of ethylene-vinyl chloride copolymers

M. W. Urban, J. L. Koenig, L. B. Shih, J. R. Allaway, *Appl. Spectrosc.* 41 (1987) 539; Structure of styrene/acrylic acid copolymer in aqueous solution determined by Fourier transform infrared spectroscopy

6.3.3 Modified fibers, fiber-reinforced or filled materials

M. K. Antoon, B. E. Zehner, J. L. Koenig, *Polym. Composites* 2 (1981) 81...8; Spectroscopic determination of the in-situ composition of epoxy matrices in glass fiber-reinforced composites

E. G. Chatzi, H. Ishida, J. L. Koenig, *Appl. Spectrosc.* 40 (1986) 847; An *FT-IR* study of the water adsorbed in Kevlar-49 fibers

E. F. Devlin, *J. Polym. Sci. Polym. Lett. Ed.* 19 (1981) 189...192; The Fourier transform infrared spectrum of cured, black-reinforced SBR

A. Garton, *ACS Polym. Prepr.* 25/2 (1984) 163f.; *FT-IR* of the polymer-reinforcement interphase in composites

W. W. Hart, P. C. Painter, J. L. Koenig, M. M. Coleman, *Appl. Spectrosc.* 31 (1977) 220...4; A Fourier transform infrared method of studying elastomers filled with carbon black

H. Ishida, J. L. Koenig, *J. Colloid Interface Sci.* 64 (1978) 565...76; Fourier transform infrared spectroscopic study of the structure of silane coupling agent on E-glass fiber

H. Ishida, J. L. Koenig, *J. Polym. Sci. Polym. Phys. Ed.* 18 (1980) 1931...43; A Fourier-transform infrared spectroscopic study of the hydrolytic stability of silane coupling agents on E-glass fibers

Y. T. Liao, J. L. Koenig, *Dev. Reinf. Plast.* 4 (1984) 31...87; Applications of Fourier transform infrared spectroscopy to the study of fiber-resin composites

E. T. Mones, R. J. Morgan, *ACS Polym. Prepr.* 22/2 (1981) 249f.; *FTIR* studies of the chemical structure of high performance composite matrices

U. Schumacher-Hamedat, J. Föhles, H. Zahn, *Textilveredlung 21* (1986) 121...5; Oxidationszwischenstufen des Cystins nach Bleichprozessen

U. Schumacher-Hamedat, H. Höcker, *Textilveredlung 21* (1986) 294f.; Unterscheidung zwischen Hercosett- und XCP-filzfrei ausgerüsteter Wolle durch *FT*-Infrarot-Spektroskopie

G. Wiedemann, B. Wustmann, H. Maulhardt, D. Kunath, *Acta Polymer. 35* (1984) 584...7; Analytische Charakterisierung von Methacrylsilan auf Glasseidengewebe mittels *FTIR*-Remissionsspektroskopie

6.4 Time-dependent physical or chemical processes in macromolecular systems

6.4.1 Deformation and relaxation (rheo-optical investigations)

G. Bayer, W. Hoffmann, H. W. Siesler, *Polymer 21* (1980) 235...8; Characterization of deformation phenomena in polymers by rapid-scanning Fourier transform infrared spectroscopy and mechanical measurements

D. J. Burchell, J. E. Lasch, R. J. Farris, S. L. Hsu, *Polymer 23* (1982) 965...8; Deformation studies of polymers by time resolved Fourier transform infra-red spectroscopy. 1. Development of the technique

E. Dobrovolny-Marand, S. L. Hsu, C.-K. Shih, *Macromolecules 20* (1987) 1022...9; Spectroscopic characterization of the α ⇌ β crystalline phase transition in poly(butylene terephthalate) and its copolymers with poly(tetramethylene oxide)

W. G. Fately, J. L. Koenig, *J. Polym. Sci. Polym. Lett. Ed. 20* (1982) 445...52; Time-resolved spectroscopy of streched polypropylene films

V. B. Gupta, C. Ramesh, H. W. Siesler, *J. Polym. Sci. Polym. Phys. Ed. 23* (1985) 405...11; Rheo-optical Fourier-transform infrared spectroscopy of polymers. VII. Uniaxial deformation of heat-set poly(ethylene terephthalate) film

K. Holland-Moritz, W. Stach, I. Holland-Moritz, *Progr. Colloid Polym. Sci. 67* (1980) 161...4; Investigation of time-dependent phenomena in polymers by Fourier transform infrared spectroscopy

K. Holland-Moritz, W. Stach, I. Holland-Moritz, *J. Mol. Struct. 60* (1980) 1...6; Possibilities of *FTIR* instrumentation of fast processes: elongation and relaxation phenomena in polymers

K. Holland-Moritz, H. W. Siesler, *Polym. Bull. 4* (1981) 165...70; Characterization of deformation phenomena in polymers by rapid-scanning Fourier transform *IR (FTIR)* spectroscopy and mechanical measurements

K. Holland-Moritz, I. Holland-Moritz, K. van Werden, *Colloid Polym. Sci. 259* (1981) 156...62; Application of *FTIR* spectroscopy on orientation processes in polyethylene films

K. Holland-Moritz, K. van Werden, *Makromol. Chem. 182* (1981) 651...5; *FTIR*-spectroscopic studies on polyethylene during elongation

K. Holland-Moritz, *ACS Polym. Prepr. 25/2* (1984) 196...8; *FTIR* spectroscopic studies on polymers during elongation and relaxation

S. L. Hsu, D. J. Burchell, *ACS Org. Coat. Plast. Chem. 44* (1981) 635...7; Characterization of deformation phenomena in polymers by Fourier transform infrared spectroscopy

B. Jasse, J. L. Koenig, *J. Polym. Sci. Polym. Phys. Ed. 17* (1979) 799...810; Fourier transform infrared study of uniaxially oriented atactic polystyrene

B. Jasse, J. L. Koenig, *IUPAC 26. Int. Symp. Macromolecules, Mainz 3* (1979) 1198...200; Fourier transform infrared study of uniaxially oriented isotactic polystyrene

B. Jasse, J. L. Koenig, *Polymer 22* (1981) 1040...4; Fourier transform infra-red study of uniaxially-oriented isotactic polystyrene

J. E. Lasch, D. J. Burchell, T. Masoaka, S. L. Hsu, *Appl. Spectrosc. 38* (1984) 351...8; Deformation studies of polymers by time-resolved Fourier transform infrared spectroscopy. III. A new approach

J. E. Lasch, E. Dobrovolny, S. E. Molis, S. L. Hsu, *ACS Polym. Prepr. 25/2* (1984) 169...70; Deformation studies of polymers by time resolved and polarization modulation spectroscopy

A. Lee, R. P. Wool, *Macromolecules 19* (1986) 1063...8; *FT-IR* study of orientation relaxation in uniaxially oriented monodisperse atactic polystyrene

B. Love, R. P. Wool, *Polym. Mat. Sci. Eng. 53* (1985) 317...20; Molecular deformation in semicrystalline polymers as characterized by *FTIR*

K. K. R. Mocherla, W. O. Statton, *Appl. Polym. Symp. 31* (1977) 183...91; Investigation of the stress-strain behavior of oriented poly(ethylene terephthalate) by dynamic infra-red method. 1. Load of the average bond of the molecular backbone

R. S. Moore, J. K. O'Loane, J. C. Shearer, *Polym. Eng. Sci. 21* (1981) 903...6; Fourier transform infrared characterization of conformational changes in amorphous poly(ethylene terephthalate) during volume recovery

I. Noda, A. E. Dowrey, C. Marcott, *ACS Polym. Prepr. 24/1* (1983) 122f.; *J. Polym. Sci. Polym. Lett. Ed. 21* (1983) 99...103; Dynamic infrared linear dichroism of polymer films under oscillatory deformation

P. M. Pachomov, M. V. Sablygin, *Vysokomol. Soedin. A 28* (1986) 2564...9 (Russ.); Infrared spectroscopic investigation of the deformation of polymers

A. Rivaton, D. Sallet, J. Lemaire, *Polym. Degrad. Stab. 14* (1986) 1f.; The photo-chemistry of bisphenol-A polycarbonate reconsidered. Part 2. *FTIR*-analysis of the solid-state photo-chemistry in "dry" conditions

D. Y. Shen, S. L. Hsu, *Polymer 23* (1982) 969...73; Vibrational spectroscopical characterization of rigid rod polymers. 3. Microstructural changes in stressed polymers

H. W. Siesler, Characterization of chemical and physical changes of polymer structure by rapid-scanning Fourier-transform *(FTIR)* spectroscopy, in D. O. Hummel (ed.): *Proceedings of the 5th European Symposium on Polymer Spectroscopy*; Verlag Chemie, Weinheim 1979

H. W. Siesler, *J. Polym. Sci. Polym. Lett. Ed. 17* (1979) 453...8; Characterization of deformation phenomena in polymers by rapid-scanning Fourier-transform infrared *(FTIR)* spectroscopy and mechanical measurements. I. The stress-induced crystalline phase transition in poly(butyleneterephthalate)

H. W. Siesler, *Makromol. Chem. 180* (1979) 2261...3; Characterization of deformation phenomena in polymers by rapid-scanning Fourier transform *IR (FTIR)* spectroscopy and mechanical measurements. 2. The effect of stress relaxation on the reversible, stress-induced conformational transition in poly(butylene terephthalate)

H. W. Siesler, *ACS Polym. Prepr. 21/1* (1980) 163f.; Recent developments of dynamic Fourier transform *IR (FTIR)* spectroscopy in polymer research

H. W. Siesler, *Polym. Bull. 9* (1983) 382...9; Rheo-optical Fourier transform *IR* spectroscopy of polyurethane elastomers. 1. Principle of the method and measurements at ambient temperature

H. W. Siesler, *Polym. Bull. 9* (1983) 471...8; Rheo-optical Fourier-transform *IR (FTIR)* spectroscopy of polyurethane elastomers. 2. Measurements at elevated temperature

H. W. Siesler, *Polym. Bull. 9* (1983) 557...62; Rheo-optical Fourier transform *IR (FTIR)* spectroscopy. 3. Investigation of NH-deuterated specimens

H. W. Siesler, *Colloid Polym. Sci. 262* (1984) 223...9; Rheo-optical Fourier-transform infrared *(FTIR)* spectroscopy of polymers. 5. Strain-induced crystallization of crosslinked natural rubber

H. W. Siesler, *Infrared Phys. 24* (1984) 239...44; Rheo-optical Fourier transform infrared spectroscopy *(FTIRS)* of polymers. 6. Changes of crystal-axes orientation and state of order during uniaxial elongation of high-density polyethylene

H. W. Siesler, *Polym. Bull. 12* (1984) 481...6; Rheo-optical Fourier transform infrared spectroscopy of polymers. 8. Stress-relaxation of sulfur-cross-linked natural rubber

H. W. Siesler, *ACS Polym. Prepr. 25/2* (1984) 165f.; Recent advances in rheo-optical *FTIR* spectroscopy of polymers

H. W. Siesler, *Adv. Polym. Sci. 65* (1984) 1...77; Rheo-optical Fourier-transform infrared spectroscopy: vibrational spectra and mechanical properties of polymers

H. W. Siesler, *J. Polym. Sci. Polym. Phys. Ed. 23* (1985) 2413...22; Rheo-optical Fourier-transform infrared spectroscopy of polymers. 9. Stretching-induced $II(\alpha) - I(\beta)$ crystal phase transformation in poly(vinylidene fluoride)

H. W. Siesler, *Appl. Spectrosc. 39* (1985) 761...5; Rheo-optical Fourier transform infrared spectroscopy of polymers. 10. Strain-induced crystallization of sulfur-crosslinked natural rubber during cyclic deformation

H. W. Siesler, *Makromol. Chem. Rapid Commun. 6* (1985) 699...705; Rheo-optical Fourier-transform infrared spectroscopy of polymers. 11. Strain-induced crystallization of polychloroprene

S. S. Sikka, H. H. Kausch, *Colloid Polym. Sci. 257* (1979) 1060...7; Study of stress-induced changes in poly(ethylene terephthalate) through Fourier transform infrared spectroscopy

W. Stach, K. Holland-Moritz, *J. Mol. Struct. 60* (1980) 49...54; Vibrational spectroscopic studies on conformational changes in poly(tetramethylene terephthalate)

W. Stach, *Schwingungsspektroskopische Untersuchungen zu mechanisch und thermisch induzierten Konformationsänderungen im Poly(tetramethylenterephthalat)*. Thesis, University of Cologne, Math. Nat. Sci. Faculty, 1982

W. Stach, K. Holland-Moritz, *J. Mol. Struct. 79* (1982) 469...76; A dynamic study on the solid-state transition from the α- to the β-form of poly(tetramethylene terephthalate)

B. Stambaugh, J. B. Lando, J. L. Koenig, *J. Polym. Sci. Polym. Phys. Ed. 17* (1979) 1063...71; Infrared studies of the reversible stress-induced crystal-crystal phase transition of poly(tetramethylene terephthalate)

M. Theodorou, B. Jasse, *J. Polym. Sci. Polym. Phys. Ed. 21* (1983) 2263...74; Fourier-transform infrared study of conformational changes in plasticized poly(vinyl chloride)

V. N. Vatulev et al., *Sint. Fiz. Khim. Polim. 22* (1978) 59...62 (Russ.); Structure transformations in poly(amido urethane)s

R. P. Wool, R. S. Bretzlaff, B. Y. Li, C. H. Wang, R. H. Boyd, *J. Polym. Sci. Polym. Phys. Ed. 24* (1986) 1039...66; Infrared and Raman spectroscopy of stressed polyethylene

6.4.2 Physico-chemical and chemical processes

M. K. Antoon, K. M. Starkey, L. J. Koenig, *Composite Materials: Testing and Design. Fifth ASTM Conf., New Orleans* (1978) 541...52; Applications of Fourier transform infrared spectroscopy to quality control of the epoxy matrix

M. K. Antoon, J. L. Koenig, *J. Polym. Sci. Polym. Chem. Ed. 19* (1981) 549...70; Crosslinking mechanism of an anhydride-cured epoxy resin as studied by Fourier transform infrared spectroscopy

M. K. Antoon, J. L. Koenig, T. Serafini, *J. Polym. Sci. Polym. Phys. Ed. 19* (1981) 1567...75; Fourier-transform infrared study of the reversible interaction of water and a crosslinked epoxy matrix

B. J. Bulkin, *Org. Coat. Plast. Chem. 42* (1980) 642; The influences of metal surfaces on epoxide degradation. An *FT-IR* study

B. J. Bulkin, C. S. Chen, E. M. Pearce, *Org. Coat. Appl. Polym. Sci. Proc. 44* (1981) 638f.; Infrared spectroscopic studies of environmental effect on polymers

C. S. Chen, B. J. Bulkin, E. M. Pearce, *J. Appl. Polym. Sci. 28* (1983) 1077...91; New epoxy resins. III. Application of Fourier transform *IR* to degradation and interaction studies of epoxy resins and their copolymers

Z. Chen, Z. Shen, M. Liu, M. Shi, *Makromol. Chem. 188* (1987) 2697...703; Fourier transform infrared spectroscopic study of polyacetylene. 2. Thermal isomerization kinetics and mechanism

C. H. Chiang, J. L. Koenig, *Polym. Composites 1* (1980) 88...92; Chemical reactions occurring at the interface of epoxy matrix and aminosilane coupling agents in fiber-reinforced composites

M. M. Coleman, R. J. Petcavich, *J. Polym. Sci. Polym. Phys. Ed. 16* (1978) 821...32; Fourier transform infrared studies on the thermal degradation of polyacrylonitrile

M. M. Coleman, G. T. Sivy, *Org. Coat. Appl. Polym. Sci. Proc. 44* (1981) 630...4; Fourier transform infrared studies of the degradation of polyacrylonitrile copolymers

M. M. Coleman, G. T. Sivy, *Carbon 19* (1981) 123...6; Fourier transform *IR* studies of the degradation of polyacrylonitrile copolymers. I. Introduction and comparative rates of the degradation of three copolymers below 200°C and under reduced pressure

S. R. Culler, H. Ishida, J. L. Koenig, *J. Colloid Interface Sci. 109* (1986) 1...10; *FT-IR* characterization of the reaction at the silane/matrix resin interphase of composite materials

R. G. Davidson, *Polym. Mat. Sci. Eng. 50* (1984) 194...8; Computer assisted *IR* spectroscopy of the dicyandiamide-epoxide reaction

C. Decker, T. Bendaikha, *Eur. Polym. J. 20* (1984) 753...8; Photopolymerisation de macromères multifonctionel. I. Etude cinetique

C. Decker, K. Moussa, *Makromol. Chem. 189* (1988) in print; A new method for monitoring ultra-fast photopolymerizations by real-time infrared (*RTIR*) spectroscopy

L. D'Esposito, J. L. Koenig, *Org. Coat. Plast. Chem. 38* (1978) 306...9; A comparison of the thermal and mechanical degradation of glassy polystyrene by *FT-IR* spectroscopy

R. A. Fenner, J. O. Lephardt, *J. Agric. Food Chem. 29* (1981) 846...9; Examination of the thermal decomposition of Kraft pine lignin by Fourier transform infrared evolved gas analysis

C. di Giulio, M. Gautier, B. Jasse, *J. Appl. Polym. Sci. 29* (1984) 1771...9; Fourier transform infrared spectroscopic characterization of aromate bismaleimide resin cure states

P. R. Griffiths, *ACS Polym. Prepr. 25/2* (1984) 161f.; Kinetics of coal oxidation by combined Fourier selfdeconvolution and curve-fitting

H. Ishida, C. Scott, *J. Polym. Eng. 6* (1986) 201...17; Fast polymerization and crystallization kinetic studies of nylon 6 by combined use of computerized micro-*RIM* machine and *FT-IR*

J. J. Jutier, Y. Harrison, S. Premont, R. E. Prud'homme, *J. Appl. Polym. Sci. 33* (1987) 1359...75; A nonisothermal Fourier transform infrared degradation study of nitrocellulose derived from wood and cotton

J. L. Koenig, C. M. Shields, *J. Polym. Sci. Polym. Phys. Ed. 23* (1985) 845...59; Spectroscopic characterization of acetylene-terminated sulfone resin

J. O. Lephardt, G. Vilcins, *Appl. Spectrosc. 29* (1975) 221...5; Application of the rapid scan Fourier transform infrared spectrometer to kinetics

J. O. Lephardt, R. A. Fenner, *Appl. Spectrosc. 34* (1980) 174...85; Characterization of pyrolysis and combustion of complex systems using Fourier transform infrared spectroscopy

S. C. Lin, B. J. Bulkin, E. M. Pearce, *J. Polym. Sci. Polym. Chem. Ed. 17* (1979) 3121...48; Epoxy resins. III. Application of Fourier transform *IR* to degradation studies of epoxy systems

S. B. Lin, J. L. Koenig, *J. Polym. Sci. Polym. Phys. Ed. 21* (1983) 2067...83; The effect of temperature on the infrared spectra of poly(ethylene terephthalate)

S. B. Lin, J. L. Koenig, *J. Polym. Sci. Polym. Phys. Ed. 21* (1983) 2365...79; A kinetic analysis of the *gauche-trans* isomerization in semicrystalline poly(ethylene terephthalate)

E. T. Mones, C. M. Walkup, J. A. Happe, R. J. Morgan, *Natl. SAMPE Tech. Conf. 14* (1982) 89...100; The characterization of diaminodiphenyl sulphone (DDS)-cured tetraglycidyl-4,4'-diaminodiphenylmethane (TG-DDM) epoxies

T. Nguyen, W. E. Byrd, *Polym. Mater. Sci. Eng. 53* (1985) 568...73; Reflection/absorption Fourier transform infrared spectroscopy studies of the degradation of organic protective coatings on steel

P. C. Painter, R. W. Snyder, D. E. Pearson, J. Kwong, *Fuel 59* (1980) 282...6; Fourier transform infrared study of the variation in the oxidation of a coking coal

E. M. Pearce, B. J. Bulkin, S. C. Lin, *Org. Coat. Plast. Chem. 39* (1978) 91...8; Epoxy resins. III. Application of Fourier transform *IR* to degradation studies of epoxy systems

R. L. Pecsok, P. C. Painter, J. R. Shelton, J. L. Koenig, *Rubber Chem. Technol. 49* (1976) 1010...8; Fourier transform infrared studies of the mechanism of oxidation of *cis*-1,4-polybutadiene

R. L. Pecsok, J. R. Shelton, J. L. Koenig, *Polym. Degrad. Stab. 3* (1981) 161...76; Fourier transform infrared studies of inhibited autoxidation in *cis*-1,4-polybutadiene

R. J. Petcavich, P. C. Painter, M. M. Coleman, *Polymer 19* (1978) 1249...52; Application of infra-red digital subtraction techniques to the microstructure of polychloroprenes. 2. Mechanism of oxidative degradation at 60°C

R. J. Petcavich, P. C. Painter, M. M. Coleman, *J. Polym. Sci. Polym. Phys. Ed. 17* (1979) 165...8; Fourier-transform infrared studies on the thermal degradation of poly-α-deuteroacrylonitrile under reduced pressure

J. J. Rafalko, *J. Polym. Sci. Polym. Phys. Ed. 22* (1984) 1211...22; Fourier-transform infrared studies of the thermal degradation of isotopically labeled polyacrylonitriles

P. B. Roush, *Org. Coat. Plast. Chem. 43* (1980) 686...90; The curing reaction of an epoxy polymer with an anhydride as followed by *FT-IR* spectroscopy

B. S. H. Royce, Y. C. Teng, J. A. Ors, *Ultrasonics Symp. 2* (1981) 784...7; Reactions in polymers studied with *FTIR*-photoacoustic spectroscopy

S. Sack, H. Wagner, E. Steger, *Acta Polymer. 36* (1985) 305...10; Infrared spectroscopic investigation of thermal oxidation at copper/polyethylene interfaces by computer-assisted measurement of attenuated total reflection

D. O. Saperstein, *Anal. Chem. 52* (1980) 1565...70; Analysis of the gaseous components of reactions by Fourier transform infrared spectrometry

U. Schernau, G. Holtmann, *Farbe Lack 92* (1986) 1154...8; *IR*-Spektroskopie zur Untersuchung von Vernetzungsreaktionen

G. A. Senich, W. J. MacKnight, *Macromolecules 13* (1980) 106...10; Fourier transform infrared thermal analysis of a segmented polyurethane

G. A. Senich, *ACS Polym. Prepr. 25/2* (1984) 211f.; Kinetics of the hardening of polymer-laminate combinations

C. A. Sergides, A. R. Chughtai, D. M. Smith, P. Schissel, *Macromolecules 19* (1986) 1448...53; Spectroscopic study of the photodegradation pathways of silver-backed polyacrylonitrile films

R. E. Smith, *J. Appl. Polym. Sci. 29* (1984) 3713...26; Epoxy resin cure. II. *FTIR* analysis

S. A. Sojka, R. A. Wolfe, G. D. Guenther, *Macromolecules 14* (1981) 1539...43; Formation of phenolic resins: Mechanism and time dependance of the reaction of phenol and hexamethylene tetramine as studied by carbon-13 nuclear magnetic resonance and Fourier transform infrared spectroscopy

J. F. Sprouse, *Org. Coat. Plast. Chem. 40* (1979) 934; Analysis of curing processes in composites by *FTIR* spectroscopy

D. L. Tabb, J. J. Sevcik, J. L. Koenig, *J. Polym. Sci. Polym. Phys. Ed. 13* (1975) 815...824; Fourier transform infrared study of the effects of irradiation on polyethylene

C. M. Tung, *ACS Polym. Prepr. 28/1* (1987) 7f.; The effect of cure states on the mechanical properties of bismaleimides. 4. Fourier transform infrared spectroscopy

G. Xue, H. Ishida, J. L. Koenig, *Angew. Makromol. Chem. 140* (1986) 127...34; Chemical reactions in the bulk of the epoxy-functional silane hydrolyzate

G. Xue, H. Ishida, J. L. Koenig, *Angew. Makromol. Chem. 142* (1986) 17...27; Chemical reactions of poly(vinyl pyridine)s with epoxy compounds

6.5 Quantitative *CIRS* analysis

E. G. Bartick et al., *Org. Coat. Plast. Chem. 45* (1981) 700...5; Quantitative analysis of copolymers by computer supported *IR* spectrometry

R. G. Davidson, G. I. Mathys, *Anal. Chim. Acta 160* (1984) 197...204; The determination of thiol groups in polysulfide prepolymers by infrared spectrometry

W. D. Domke, H. Steinke, *J. Polym. Sci. Polym. Chem. Ed. 24* (1986) 2701...5; Oxidative structures in polyolefins. *FT-IR* method of quantitative determination

G. Gidály, R. Kellner, *Mikrochim. Acta 1* (1981) 131...8; Simultaneous qualitative and quantitative *FTIR-ATR* spectroscopic analysis of sub-micrometer organic films and of the surface layer of bulk polymer samples

W. Herres, *Kunststoffe 76* (1986) 591...4; Zerstörungsfreie Methoden zur Quantifizierung des Weichmachergehalts in PVC-Folie

T. Hirschfeld, Quantitative *FT-IR*: A detailed look at the problems involved, in J. R. Ferraro, L. J. Basile (eds.): *Fourier Transform Infrared Spectroscopy, Applications to Chemical Systems,* Vol. 1; Academic Press, New York 1978

R. Iwamoto, K. Ohta, *Appl. Spectrosc. 38* (1984) 359...65; Quantitative surface analysis by Fourier transform attenuated total reflection infrared spectroscopy

J. L. Koenig, C. M. Shields, *J. Polym. Sci. Polym. Phys. Ed. 23* (1985) 845...59; Spectroscopic characterization of acetylene-terminated sulfone resin

P. G. Kosky, R. S. McDonald, E. A. Guggenheim, *Polym. Eng. Sci. 25* (1985) 389...94; Determination of end-group concentrations and molecular weight of poly(butylene terephthalate) by solid-state Fourier transform infrared spectroscopy

G. J. Kostov, P. G. Komitov, Z. G. Nikolova, *Eur. Polym. J. 21* (1985) 561...4; Application of *IR*-compensation technique for study of the oxidation degree of high impact polystyrene

W. F. Maddams, P. B. Tooke, *J. Macromol. Sci. Chem. A 17* (1982) 951...68; Quantitative conformational studies on poly(vinyl chloride)

K. Molt, *Chemie-Technik 11* (1982) 321...33; Quantitative Analytik in Labor und Produktion mit Hilfe der rechnerunterstützten Infrarot-Spektroskopie

P. B. Roush, R. W. Hannah, A. Bunn, H. A. Willis, *ACS Polym. Prepr. 25/2* (1984) 175f.; Application of curve fit and deconvolution to polymer analysis

D. W. Vidrine, *ACS Polym. Prepr. 25/1* (1984) 147f.; Photoacoustic and reflection *FT-IR* spectroscopy. Photometric approximations for practical quantitative analysis

6.6 Miscellaneous *CIRS* investigations of macromolecular systems

C. R. Anderson, J. C. Wright, *SPE J. 148* (1978) 86...92; Computerized direct real time infrared detection as applied to five different temporally and spectrally varying experiments

M. K. Antoon, K. M. Starkey, J. L. Koenig, *ASTM Spec. Tech. Publ. STP 674* (1979) 541...52; Applications of Fourier transform infrared spectroscopy to quality control of the epoxy matrix

K. W. Bieg, D. K. Ottesen, *ACS Polym. Prepr. 19/2* (1978) 471...6; Fourier transform infrared analysis of plasma polymerized 2-vinylpyridine thin films

R. D. Blackledge, *J. Forensic Sci. 26* (1981) 554...6; Examination of automobile rubber bumper guards by attenuated total reflectance spectroscopy using a Fourier transform infrared spectrometer

R. S. Bretzlaff, R. P. Wool, *Macromolecules 16* (1983) 1907...17; Frequency shifting and asymmetry in infrared bands of stressed polymers

B. A. Brozoski, P. C. Painter, M. M. Coleman, *Macromolecules 17* (1984) 1591...4; Concerning the origin of broad bands observed in the *FT-IR* spectra of ionomers. Cluster formation or water adsorption?

M. M. Coleman, R. J. Petcavich, P. C. Painter, *Polymer 19* (1978) 1243...8; Application of infra-red digital subtraction techniques to the microstructure of polychloroprenes. 1. Accentuation and assignment of bands due to structural irregularities

M. M. Coleman, R. J. Petcavich, P. Painter, *Polymer 19* (1978) 1253...7; Application of infra-red digital subtraction techniques to the microstructure of polychloroprenes. 3. Effect of structural irregularities on the crystalline infra-red bands of chloroprene copolymers

E. F. Devlin, *J. Polym. Sci. Polym. Lett. Ed. 19* (1981) 189...92; The Fourier transform infrared spectrum of cured, black-reinforced SBR

J. B. Ems, R. F. Boyer, H. Ishida, J. L. Koenig, *Org. Coat. Plast. Chem. 38* (1978) 373...8; Fourier transform infrared spectroscopic study of transitions above T_g in atactic polystyrene

A. Garton, A. Stolow, D. M. Wiles, *J. Mater. Sci. 16* (1981) 3211...5; Infra-red spectroscopic characterization of surface coatings on glass fibres

M. J. D. Low, H. Mark, *Appl. Polym. Symp. 10* (1969) 145...58; The examination of organic coatings by infrared interference spectroscopy

M. J. D. Low, H. Mark, *J. Paint Technol. 42* (1970) 265...75; Infrared Fourier transform spectroscopy in the coatings industry. I. *IR* spectra of clear coatings on metals

M. J. D. Low, H. Mark, *J. Paint Technol. 43* (1971) 31...41; Infrared Fourier transform spectroscopy in the coatings industry. II. Optical subtraction

M. J. D. Low, A. J. Goodsel, *J. Paint Technol. 43* (1971) 49...57; Infrared Fourier transform spectroscopy in the coatings industry. III. Transmission/absorption spectra

M. J. D. Low, H. Mark, *J. Paint Technol. 44* (1972) 52...7; Infrared Fourier transform spectroscopy in coatings industry. IV. Reflection/absorption spectra

S. R. Lowry, K. A. Mauritz, *J. Am. Chem. Soc. 102* (1980) 4665...7; An investigation of ionic hydration effects in perfluorosulfonate ionomers by Fourier transform infrared spectroscopy

Y. H. Mariam, K. P. W. Pemawansa, K. B. Bota, *ACS Polym. Prepr. 27*/1 (1986) 271 f.; *FT-IR* investigation of compatibility in comblike liquid crystalline polymers

P. C. Painter, M. M. Coleman, *Am. Lab. 12* (1980) 19...23, 25...9; Fourier transform infrared studies of coal and mineral matter in coal

P. C. Painter, R. E. Kessler, R. W. Snyder, *J. Polym. Sci. Polym. Phys. Ed. 18* (1980) 723...9; Fourier transform infrared study of the gel form of isotactic polystyrene

P. C. Painter et al., *J. Polym. Sci. Polym. Phys. Ed. 20* (1982) 1069...80; *FTIR* studies of calcium and sodium monomers derived from an ethylene-methacrylic acid copolymer

R. L. Pecsok, J. R. Shelton, J. L. Koenig, *Polym. Degradation Stab. 3* (1981) 161...76; Fourier transform infrared studies of inhibited autoxidation in *cis*-1,4-polybutadiene

W. Pump, D. Woltjes, *Kunststoffe 69* (1979) 317...20; Die Derivativspektroskopie in der Kunststoffanalytik am Beispiel von LDPE

B. N. Ranganathan, *Anal. Lett. 17* (1984) 2221...6; Fourier-transform infrared spectroscopy evaluation of commercial room-temperature vulcanized silicones

E. Roerdink, G. Challa, *Polymer 21* (1980) 509...13; Computerized infra-red study of the interaction of poly(vinylidene fluoride) with stereoregular poly(methyl methacrylate)

J. C. Shearer, D. C. Peters, G. Hoepfner, T. Newton, *Anal. Chem. 55* (1983) 874 A...80 A; *FTIR* in the service of art conservation

D. J. Skrovanek, S. E. Howe, P. C. Painter, M. M. Coleman, *Macromolecules 18* (1985) 1676...83; Hydrogen bonding in polymers: Infrared temperature studies of an amorphous polyamide

6.7 Combination of *CIRS* with other methods

6.7.1 Chromatographic methods and *CIRS*

L. V. Azarraga, A. C. McCall, *Environ. Prot. Technol. Ser.* (1974) EPA-660/273-034 61 pp.; *IR* Fourier transform spectrometry of gas chromatographic effluents

L. V. Azarraga, C. A. Potter, *High Resol. Chromatogr. Chromatogr. Commun. 4*/2 (1981) 60...9; An integrated *GC*/*FT-IR* system for the analysis of environmental pollutants

S. Bourne, G. T. Meedy, P. T. Cunningham, *J. Chromat. Sci. 17* (1979) 460...3; Gas chromatography/matrix isolation/infrared spectroscopy: an evalution of the performance potential

G. M. Brissey, D. E. Henry, G. N. Giss, P. W. Yang, P. R. Griffiths, C. L. Wilkins, *Anal. Chem. 56* (1984) 2002...6; Comparison of gas chromatography/Fourier transform infrared spectrometric Gram-Schmidt reconstructions from different interferometers

R. S. Brown, L. T. Taylor, *Anal. Chem. 55* (1983) 1492...7; Microbore liquid chromatography with flow cell Fourier transform infrared spectrometric detection

K. S. Chiu, K. Biemann, K. Krishnan, S. L. Hill, *Anal. Chem. 56* (1984) 1610...5; Structural characterization of polycyclic aromatic compounds by combined gas chromatography/mass spectrometry and gas chromatography/Fourier transform infrared spectrometry

P. Coffey, D. R. Mattson, J. C. Wright, *Am. Lab. 10*/5 (1978) 126...32; A programmable *GC*/*FT-IR* system

C. Combellas, H. Bayart, B. Jasse, M. Caude, R. Rosset, *J. Chromatogr. 259* (1983) 211...25; Coupling of a high-performance liquid chromatograph with a Fourier transform infrared detector

R. W. Crawford, T. Hirschfeld, R. H. Sanborn, C. M. Wong, *Anal. Chem. 54* (1982) 817...20; Organic analysis with a combined capillary gas chromatograph/mass spectrometer/Fourier transform infrared spectrometer

R. Curbelo, C. T. Foskett, G. Kneissl, *Proc. Soc. Photo. Opt. Instrum. Eng. 148* (1978) 98...111; Interactive multitasking executive (*TMX*) — a real-time multitasking Fourier spectrometer system for examination of *GC* effluents

M. F. Delaney, *J. Chromatogr. Sci. 17* (1979) 428...33; Integrated approach to automatic interpretation of vapor phase infrared spectra for gas chromatography

M. D. Erickson, E. D. Pellizzari, *4th Annual Meeting of FACSS, Detroit, MI* (1977); Application of *GC*/*FT-IR* to identification of organic components in environmental and energy-related samples

M. Erickson, S. D. Cooper, C. Sparacino, R. Zweidinger, *Appl. Spectrosc. 33* (1979) 575...7; Gas chromatography/Fourier transform infrared spectrometry analysis of semivolatile coal gasification pollutants

M. D. Erickson, *Appl. Spectrosc. Rev. 15* (1979) 261 ff.; Gas chromatography, coupled with *FTIR*-spectrometry

U. Fölster, W. Herres, *Farbe Lack 89* (1983) 417…20; Einsatz der Fourier-Transform-Infrarot-Spektroskopie zur Detektion und Identifikation in der Gelpermeationschromatographie

U. Fölster, W. Herres, *Farbe Lack 92* (1986) 13…7; Pyrolyse-Kapillar-*GC/FT-IR*-Spektroskopie zur Analyse von Makromolekülen

M. M. Gomez-Taylor, P. R. Griffiths, *Anal. Chem. 50* (1978) 422…5; On-line identification of gas-chromatographic effluents by dual-beam Fourier transform *IR* spectrometry

P. R. Griffiths, *Appl. Spectrosc. 31* (1977) 284…8; Optimized sampling in the *GC-IR* interface

P. R. Griffiths, Gas chromatography and Fourier transform infrared, in J. R. Ferraro, L. J. Basile (eds.): *Fourier Transform Infrared Spectroscopy, Applications to Chemical Systems,* Vol. 1; Academic Press, New York 1978

P. R. Griffiths, *NATO Adv. Study Inst. Ser. C57* (1980) 149…55; Chromatography and *FT-IR* spectrometry

P. R. Griffiths, J. A. de Haseth, L. V. Azarraga, *Anal. Chem. 55* (1983) 1361 A…87 A; Capillary *GC/FT-IR*

D. A. Hanna, G. Hangac, B. A. Hohne, G. W. Small, R. C. Wieboldt, T. L. Isenhour, *J. Chromatogr. Sci. 17* (1979) 423…7; A comparison of methods used for the reconstruction of *GC/FT-IR* chromatograms

A. Hanna, J. C. Marshall, T. L. Isenhour, *J. Chromatogr. Sci. 17* (1979) 434…40; A *GC/FT-IR* compound identification system

J. A. de Haseth, T. L. Isenhour, *Anal. Chem. 49* (1977) 49…81; Reconstruction of gas-chromatograms from interferometric gas chromatography/infrared spectrometry data

D. M. Hembree, A. A. Garrison, R. A. Crocombe, R. A. Yokley, E. L. Wehry, G. Mamantov, *Anal. Chem. 53* (1981) 1783…8; Matrix isolation Fourier transform infrared spectrometric detection in the open tubular column gas chromatography of polycyclic aromatic hydrocarbons

W. Herres, Capillary *GC-FTIR* analysis of volatiles: *HRGC-FTIR*, in P. Schreier (ed.): *Analysis of Volatiles*; W. de Gruyter, Berlin 1984

W. Herres, U. Fölster, *Farbe Lack 91* (1985) 6…11; Pyrolyse-Kapillar-*GC/FT-IR*-Spektroskopie zur Analyse von Makromolekülen

B. A. Hohne, G. Hangac, G. W. Small, T. L. Isenhour, *J. Chromatogr. Sci. 19* (1981) 283…9; An on-line class-specific *GC/FTIR* reconstruction from interferometric data

G. Holl, *Differenz-IR-spektrometrische und pyrolyse-gaschromatographische Charakterisierung von Acrylat-Methacrylat-Copolymeren*; Diploma thesis, Chemistry Dept., University Cologne 1984. *IR-spektroskopische Untersuchung des thermischen Abbaus von Acrylat- und Methacrylat-Copolymeren durch linear temperaturprogrammierte Pyrolyse und Pyrolyse-Gaschromatographie*; Thesis, Math. Nat. Sci. Fac., University Cologne 1988

E. Kiran, J. K. Gillham, *J. Appl. Polym. Sci. 20* (1976) 931…47; Pyrolysis-molecular weight chromatography-vapor phase infrared spectrometry: a new on-line system for analysis of polymers. I. Instrumentation

E. Kiran, J. K. Gillham, *Polym. Eng. Sci. 19* (1979) 699…708; Pyrolysis-molecular weight chromatography-vapor phase infrared spectrometry: an on-line system for analysis of polymers. A review

K. L. Kizer, *Am Lab. 5/6* (1973) 40…5; *GC/IR* on-line analysis

K. L. Kizer, A. W. Mantz, L. C. Bonar, *Am. Lab. 5* (1975) 85; Liquid chromatography/infrared spectroscopy on-line analysis

K. Krishnan, R. Curbelo, P. Chiha, R. C. Noonan, *J. Chromatogr. Sci. 17* (1979) 413…6; Design and applications of a high sensitivity gas chromatographic Fourier transform infrared system

K. Krishnan, R. H. Brown, S. L. Hill, S. C. Simonoff, M. L. Olson, D. Kuehl, *Am. Lab. 13/3* (1981) 122…9; Recent developments im *GC/FT-IR* spectroscopy

D. G. Kubler, *Arson Anal. Newsl. 4* (1980) 11…6; Gas chromatography/Fourier transform infrared spectroscopy: potential application for forensic science

D. Kuehl, P. R. Griffiths, *J. Chromatogr. Sci. 17* (1979) 471…6; Novel approaches to interfacing a high performance liquid chromatograph with a Fourier transform infrared spectrometer

D. A. Laude, Jr., G. M. Brissey, C. F. Ijames, R. S. Brown, C. L. Wilkins, *Anal. Chem. 56* (1984) 1163…8; Linked gas chromatography/Fourier transform infrared/Fourier transform mass spectrometry with integrated electron impact and chemical ionization

J. O. Lephardt, R. A. Fenner, *Appl. Spectrosc. 34* (1980) 174…85; Characterization of pyrolysis and combustion of complex systems using *FTIR* spectrometry

J. O. Lephardt, R. A. Fenner, *Appl. Spectrosc. 35* (1981) 95…101; *FTIR* evolved gas analysis: additional considerations and options

S. A. Liebman, J. H. Ahlstrom, P. R. Griffiths, *Appl. Spectrosc. 30* (1976) 355…7; On-line *FTIR* analysis of pyrolysis and combustion products

S. R. Lowry, D. A. Huppler, *Anal. Chem. 53* (1981) 889…93; Infrared spectral search system for gas chromatography/Fourier transform infrared spectrometry

D. R. Mattson, R. L. Julian, *J. Chromatogr. Sci. 17* (1979) 416…22; Programming techniques for obtaining maximum sensitivity in the real-time detection of *GC* effluents

N. N., *Eur. Spectrosc. News 26* (1979) 27…45; Kopplung spektroskopischer und chromatographischer Methoden

C. Reddmann, H. Kurz, *Labor Praxis 9* (1985) 454…6, 458, 460…1; Pyrolyse-Kapillar-*GC-FTIR*-Kopplung

G. T. Reedy, D. G. Ettinger, J. F. Schneider, *Anal. Chem. 57* (1985) 1602…9; High-resolution gas chromatography/matrix isolation infrared spectrometry

V. Rossiter, *Am. Lab. 11* (1979) 59…63, 65 f.; A system for effective *GC/IR*

V. Rossiter, *Am. Lab. 14/2* (1982) 144…52; Recent developments in *GC/IR* and *FTIR/GC*

M. Sabo, J. Gross, J.-S. Wang, I. E. Rosenberg, *Anal. Chem. 57* (1985) 1822…6; On-line high-performance liquid chromatography/Fourier transform infrared spectrometry with normal and reverse phases using an attenuated total reflectance flow cell

D. D. Saperstein, *Anal. Chem. 52* (1980) 1565…70; Analysis of the gaseous components of reactions by Fourier transform infrared spectrometry

K. H. Shafer, S. V. Lucas, R. J. Jacobsen, *J. Chromatogr. Sci. 17* (1979) 464…70; Application of the combined analytical techniques of *HPLC/FT-IR, GC/FT-IR,* and *GC/MS* to the analysis of real samples

K. H. Shafer, A. Bjoerseth, J. Tabor, R. J. Jacobsen, *High Resolut. Chromatogr. Chromatogr. Commun. 3/2* (1980) 87…8; Advancing the chromatography of *GC/FT-IR* to *WCOT* capillary columns

K. H. Shafer, M. Cooke, F. de Roos, R. J. Jacobsen, O. Rosario, J. D. Mulik, *Appl. Spectrosc. 35* (1981) 469…72;

WCOT capillary column *GC/FT-IR* and *GC/MS* for identifying toxic organic pollutants

R. H. Shaps, W. Simons, A. Varano, *Am. Lab. 9/3* (1977) 95...101; A new analytical tool *GC/IR* and *GC/NMR*

R. H. Shaps, M. J. Flanagan, A. Varano, *J. Chromatogr. Sci. 17* (1979) 454...9; Using the *CIRA GC/IR* analyser with an *FT-IR* spectrometer as alternative to interfacing a conventional gas chromatograph

S. L. Smith, S. E. Garlock, G. E. Adams, *Appl. Spectrosc. 37* (1983) 192...6; Industrial applications of a capillary gas chromatography/Fourier transform infrared system

R. C. Snyder, C. V. Breder, *J. Assoc. Off. Anal. Chem. 64* (1981) 999...1007; High-performance size exclusion chromatograph with computerized data reduction for analysis of polyethylene and oligomers

D. T. Sparks, R. B. Lam, T. L. Isenhour, *Anal. Chem. 54* (1982) 1922...6; Quantitative gas-chromatography/Fourier transform infrared spectrometry with integrated Gram-Schmidt reconstruction intensities

S. Tamura, J. K. Gillham, *J. Appl. Polym. Sci. 22* (1978) 1867...84; Pyrolysis-molecular weight chromatography-vapor phase infrared spectrophotometry: An on-line system for analysis of polymers. IV. Influence of *cis/trans* ratio on the thermal degradation of 1,4-polybutadienes

D. W. Vidrine, D. R. Mattson, *Appl. Spectrosc. 32* (1978) 502...6; A practical real-time Fourier transform infrared detector for liquid chromatography

D. W. Vidrine, *J. Chromatogr. Sci. 17* (1979) 477...82; Use of subtractive techniques in interpreting on-line *FT-IR* spectra of *HPLC* column eluates

D. L. Wall, A. W. Mantz, *Appl. Spectrosc. 31* (1977) 552...60; High sensitivity *IR* spectroscopy of *GC* peaks

R. L. White, G. N. Giss, G. M. Brissey, C. L. Wilkins, *Anal. Chem. 55* (1983) 998...1001; Effects of interferogram sampling of gas chromatography/Fourier transform infrared data on Gram-Schmidt chromatogram reconstruction

J. G. White, P. M. Owens, T. L. Isenhour, *Anal. Chem. 57* (1985) 1474...6; Effect of concentration gradients on spectra in gas chromatography/Fourier transform infrared spectrometry

R. L. White, *Anal. Chem. 57* (1985) 1819...22; Analysis of thin-layer chromatographic adsorbates by Fourier transform infrared photoacoustic spectroscopy

C. L. Wilkins, G. N. Giss, G. M. Brissey, S. Steiner, *Anal. Chem. 53* (1981) 113...7; Direct-linked gas chromatography-Fourier transform infrared-mass spectrometer system

C. L. Wilkins, G. N. Giss, R. L. White, G. M. Brissey, E. C. Onyiriuka, *Anal. Chem. 54* (1982) 2260...4; Mixture analysis by gas chromatography/Fourier transform infrared spectrometry/mass spectrometry

H. Witek, J. Knecht, *Labor Praxis 5* (1981) 1054...8; Neue Entwicklungen in der *GC-FTIR*-Spektroskopie

H. Witek, *LABO 13* (1982) 547...54; *GC-FTIR*-Spektroskopie mit Kapillarsäulen

J. D. Witt, M. K. Gabriel, R. L. Julian, *J. Chromatogr. Sci. 17* (1979) 445...8; A *GC/FT-IR* analysis of commercial divinylbenzene

6.7.2 Thermal analysis and *CIRS*, Evolved Gas Analysis (*EGA*)

G. M. Carlson, C. M. Neag, C. Kuo, T. Provder, *ACS Polym. Prepr. 25/2* (1984) 171 f.; *FT-IR* and thermal-mechanical cure characterization of blocked isocyanate containing coatings

R. G. Davidson, G. I. Mathys, *Anal. Chem. 58* (1986) 837...41; Polymer characterization by evolved-gas-infrared spectrometry using a dispersive spectrometer

A. D. English, D. B. Chase, H. J. Spinelli, *Macromolecules 16* (1983) 1422...7; Structure and degradation of an intractable polymeric system: melamine formaldehyde cross-linked acrylic coatings

R. A. Fenner, J. O. Lephardt, *J. Agricult. Food Chem. 29* (1981) 846...9; Examination of the thermal decomposition of Kraft pine lignin by Fourier transform infrared evolved gas analysis

J. F. Geibel, T. A. Giversen, J. A. Ors, R. D. Small, *Org. Coat. Appl. Polym. Sci. Proc. 44* (1981) 31; Characterization of the curing behavior of photopolymers by thermal analysis. *FT-IR* and solvent absorption/extraction techniques

J. O. Lephardt, R. A. Fenner, *Appl. Spectrosc. 34* (1980) 174...85; Characterization of pyrolysis and combustion of complex systems using Fourier transform infrared spectroscopy

J. O. Lephardt, R. A. Fenner, *Appl. Spectrosc. 35* (1981) 95...101; Fourier transform infrared evolved gas analysis: additional considerations and options

J. O. Lephardt, R. A. Fenner, *Org. Coat. Appl. Polym. Sci. Proc. 44* (1981) 588...91; Fourier transform infrared evolved gas analysis (*FT-IR-EGA*) and polymer analysis

J. O. Lephardt, *Appl. Spectrosc. Rev. 18* (1982) 265...303; Fourier transform infrared evolved gas analysis (*FT-IR-EGA*)

S. A. Liebman, D. H. Ahlstrom, P. R. Griffiths, *Appl. Spectrosc. 30* (1976) 355...7; On-line Fourier transform infrared analysis of pyrolysis and combustion products

J. M. O'Reilly, *J. Macromol. Sci. Phys. B18* (1981) 669; *FTIR* spectroscopy and calorimetry of the amorphous state

G. A. Senich, W. J. MacKnight, *Macromolecules 13* (1980) 106...10; Fourier transform infrared thermal analysis of a segmented polyurethane

P. H. Shu, D. J. Burchell, S. L. Hsu, *J. Polym. Sci. Polym. Phys. Ed. 18* (1980) 1421...31; Structure of polyethylene solid solutions from vibrational spectroscopy and thermal analysis

D. F. Varnell, J. P. Runt, M. M. Coleman, *Polymer 24* (1983) 37...42; *FTIR* and thermal analysis studies of blends of poly(ε-caprolactone) with homo-and copolymers of poly(vinylidene chloride)

6.7.3 *NMR* spectroscopy and *CIRS*

P. Cousin, R. E. Prud'homme, *Polym. Mat. Sci. Eng. 51* (1984) 291...4; *FTIR* and *NMR* studies of blends of polyvinyl chloride and polyvinyl bromide with polyesters

C. D. Eisenbach, W. Gronski, *Macromol. Chem. Rapid Commun. 4* (1983) 707...13; Hydrogen bonding and phase separation in segmented polyurethane elastomers as studied by ^{13}C *NMR* magic angle spinning and *FT-IR* spectroscopy

H. S. Fochler, J. R. Mooney, L. E. Ball, R. D. Boyer, J. G. Grasselli, *Spectrochim. Acta 41A* (1985) 271...8; Infrared and *NMR* spectroscopic studies of the thermal degradation of polyacrylonitrile

M. Gavish, A. Woodward, J. Xu, *ACS Polym. Prepr. 28/1* (1987) 15f.; ^{13}C *NMR* and *FTIR* investigations of reaction at lamellar surfaces of *trans*-1,4-polyisoprene

W. Herres, *Kunststoffe 76* (1986) 591...4; Zerstörungsfreie Methoden zur Quantifizierung des Weichmachergehalts in PVC-Folie

C. Hirst, *Rubber Chem. Technol. 55* (1982) 913...30; Applications of computerized nuclear magnetic resonance and infrared spectroscopic techniques to rubber analyses

E. Mertzel, J. L. Koenig, Application of *FT-IR* and *NMR* to epoxy resins, in K. Dusek (ed.), *Advances in Polymer Science*; Springer, Berlin 1985

D. Müller, J. Stulz, H. R. Kricheldorf, *Makromol. Chem. 185* (1984) 1739...49; Secondary structure of peptides. 14. *FT-IR* and ^{13}C *NMR CP/MAS* investigation of the helix stability of solid poly(L-proline)s

P. C. Painter et al., *Energy Res. Abstr. 9* (1984) 5690ff.; Recent *FT-IR* and ^{13}C *NMR* studies of coal structure

D. J. Patterson, J. L. Koenig, *Makromol. Chem. 188* (1987) 2325...37; A Fourier transform infrared and nuclear magnetic resonance study of cyclized natural rubber

B. C. Perry, J. L. Koenig, J. B. Lando, *Macromolecules 20* (1987) 422...7; Relaxation behaviour of the β phase of poly(butylene terephthalate)

R. W. Snyder, P. C. Painter, J. R. Havens, J. L. Koenig, *Appl. Spectrosc. 37* (1983) 497...501; The determination of hydroxyl groups in coal by *FT-IR* and C-13 *NMR*

S. A. Sojka, R. A. Wolfe, G. D. Guenther, *Macromolecules 14* (1981) 1539...43; Formation of phenolic resins: mechanism and time dependence of the reaction of phenol and hexamethylenetetramine as studied by carbon-13 nuclear magnetic resonance and Fourier transform infrared spectroscopy

J. Stulz, D. Müller, W. E. Hull, H. R. Kricheldorf, *Makromol. Chem. 184* (1983) 1311...22; Secondary structure of peptides. 10. *FT-IR* and ^{13}C *NMR CP/MAS* study on tacticity and secondary structure of poly(D,L-leucine)s

F. M. Thuillier, H. Jullien, M. F. Grenier-Loustalot, *Polym. Commun. 27* (1986) 206...8; The structure of microwave-cured epoxy resins studied by *FTIR* and ^{13}C *NMR CPMAS*

6.7.4 Mass spectrometry and *CIRS*

R. W. Crawford, T. Hirschfeld, R. H. Sanborn, C. M. Wong, *Anal. Chem. 54* (1982) 817...20; Organic analysis with a combined capillary gas chromatograph/mass spectrometer/Fourier transform infrared spectrometer

D. O. Hummel, C. Votteler, M. H. Winter, N. Wenzel, H.-J. Düssel, *IUPAC Macro 82, Amherst, Mass.,* July 12...16, 1982, Proceed. p.54; Combination of difference *IR* spectrometry and pyro-field ion mass spectrometry for the analysis of surface-coating resins and related materials

D. A. Laude, C. L. Johlman, R. S. Brown, C. L. Wilkins, *Fresenius Z. analyt. Chem. 324* (1986) 839...45; Negative chemical ionization and accurate mass measurement applications for a linked gas chromatography/Fourier transform infrared spectrometer/Fourier transform mass spectrometer

6.7.5 Other combinations with *CIRS*

K. Knutson, D. J. Lyman, *Org. Coat. Plast. Chem. 42* (1980) 621...7; *Polym. Sci. Technol. 14* (1981) 173...88; Morphology of block copolyurethanes. II. *FTIR* and *ESCA* techniques for studying surface morphology

M. G. Lazzara, *J. Coat. Techn. 56* (1984) 710, 19...27; Techniques to measure melamine/polyol reactions in a film

L. J. Mathias, *ACS Polym. Prepr. 25/2* (1984) 2; Spectroscopic characterization of polymers

D. C. Sabatelli et al., *42. Ann. Tech. Conf., Soc. Plast. Eng.* (1984) 311...5; Investigation of polymer cure with a combination of *TGA-GC-FTIR-MS* techniques

H. Seidel, *Untersuchung schneller Strukturveränderungen in teilkristallinen Polymeren durch Synchroton-Strahlung und FTIR-Spektrometrie*; Thesis, Math. Nat. Sci. Fac., University Cologne, 1988

W. Stach, H. C. Broecker, *HASYLAB Jahresbericht*, Appendix A, BMFT 1983; Dynamische Untersuchungen zur Kristallisation von Poly(i-butylen)

R. S. Stein, *Polym. J. 17* (1985) 289...305; Recent advances in rheo-optical studies of polymers in the solid state

C. Yang, J. F. Moulder, W. G. Fateley, *ACS Polym. Prepr. 28/1* (1987) 3...5; The useful combination of Fourier transform infrared photoacoustic spectroscopy and *X*-ray photoelectron spectroscopy for fiber surface analysis

6.8 Data storage and processing

R. E. Anacreon, S. C. Pattacini, *Am. Lab. 12* (1980) 97...100, 102, 104f.; Applications of an infrared data processing system

M. K. Antoon, L. D'Esposito, J. L. Koenig, *Appl. Spectrosc. 33* (1979) 351...7; Factor analysis applied to Fourier transform infrared spectra

L. V. Azarraga, R. R. Williams, J. A. de Haseth, *Appl. Spectrosc. 35* (1981) 466...9; Fourier encoded data searching of infrared spectra (*FEDS/IRS*)

E. G. Bartick, G. L. McClure, J. C. Corbett, *Org. Coat. Plast. Chem. 45* (1981) 700...5; Computerized quantitative analysis of copolymers by infrared spectroscopy

H. M. Bell, *J. Chem. Educ. 53* (1976) 26; Computer-assisted analysis of infrared spectra

R. Büchi, J. T. Clerc, C. Jost, H. Könitzer, D. Wegmann, *Analyt. Chim. Acta 103* (1978) 21...7; Compilation of computer-readable spectra libraries: general concepts

D. G. Cameron, Spectral data processing, in T. Theophanides (ed.), *Fourier Transform Infrared Spectroscopy*; Plenum Press, New York 1984

D. G. Cameron, D. J. Moffatt, *J. Testing Eval. 12* (1984) 78...85; Deconvolution, derivation and smoothing of spectra using Fourier transforms

D. G. Cameron, D. J. Moffatt, *Appl. Spectrosc. 41* (1987) 539...44; A generalized approach to derivative spectroscopy

N. S. Cartwright, P. G. Rodgers, *J. Can. Soc. Forensic. Sci. 9* (1976) 145...54; A proposed data base for the identification of automotive paint

D. B. Chase, *Appl. Spectrosc. 36* (1982) 240...4; Phase-correction in *FT-IR*

J. R. Chipperfield, G. H. Kirby, *Analyt. Chim. Acta 132* (1981) 205...8; Computer control of the *PE 580 B IR* spectrophotometer

J. T. Clerc, Spektroskopische Strukturaufklärung und Identifikation organischer Verbindungen durch computergesteuerten Vergleich von Referenzspektren, in H. Töller (ed.): *Meßtech. Autom. Int. Kongr.*; VDI Verlag, Düsseldorf 1974

J. T. Clerc, R. Knutti, H. Könitzer, J. Zupan, *Fresenius Z. analyt. Chem. 283* (1977) 177...81; Conversion of a conventional infrared library into computer-readable form

J. T. Clerc, H. Könitzer, Setting up, using, and maintaining computer-readable spectra compilations, in J. Bargon (ed.): *Computational Methods in Chemistry*; Plenum Publ. Corp., New York 1980

J. T. Clerc, *Fresenius Z. analyt. Chem. 313* (1982) 480...3; Chemische Datenbanken: Notwendig oder fragwürdig?

J. T. Clerc, G. Székely, *Trends in Anal. Chem. 2* (1983) 50...3; Spectroscopic data banks

J. T. Clerc, Automated spectra interpretation systems; *Pattern recognition methods in analytical spectroscopy*; Snowbird, Utah 1986

J. T. Clerc, E. Pretsch, M. Zürcher, *Mikrochim. Acta 1986* II, 217...42; Performance analysis of infrared library search systems

J. P. Coates, R. W. Hannah, Computer based infrared search systems, in T. Theophanides (ed.), *Fourier Transform Infrared Spectroscopy*; Reidel Publishing Comp., New York 1984

C. D. Craver, E. M. Kirby, R. N. Jones, *Proc. Int. CODATA Conf. 7* (1981) 274...7; New developments in infrared spectral data coding

J. A. de Haseth, L. V. Azarraga, *Anal. Chem. 53* (1981) 2292...6; Interferogram-based infrared search system

M. D. Erickson, *Appl. Spectrosc. 35* (1981) 181...4; Application of a search system and vapor-phase to spectral identification problems

C. L. Fisk, G. W. A. Milne, S. R. Heller, *J. Chromatogr. Sci. 17* (1979) 441...4; The status of infrared data bases

M. L. Formen, *J. Opt. Soc. Am. 1* (1966) 59; Correction of asymmetric interferograms obtained in Fourier spectroscopy

C. T. Foskett, *Appl. Spectrosc. 5* (1976) 531; Noise and finite register effects in *FTIR*

R. C. Fox, *Anal. Chem. 48* (1976) 717...21; Computer searching of infrared spectra using peak location and intensity data

B. Franke, H. Pekar, H. Schweppe, H. Wagner, *Fresenius Z. analyt. Chem. 303* (1980) 349...59; An *IR* data collection in everyday use

P. C. Gillette, J. L. Koenig, *Appl. Spectrosc. 38* (1984) 334; Objective criteria for absorbance subtraction

A. Gribov, Modern possibilities of calculations of absorption spectral coefficient distribution for vibrational spectra of non-conductive polymers, in W. E. Steger (ed.), *Progress in Polymer Spectroscopy*; Teubner, Leipzig 1986

J. Gronholz, W. Herres, *Comp. Anwend. Labor 5* (1984) 230ff., 352ff.; *ibid. 6* (1984) 418ff.; Datenverarbeitung in der *FT-IR*-Spektroskopie

J. Gronholz, W. Herres, *Instruments Computers 3* (1985) 10ff.; Understanding *FT-IR* data processing, Pt. 2: Details of the spectrum calculation

J. Gronholz, W. Herres, *Instruments Computers 4* (1985) 45ff.; Understanding *FT-IR* data processing, Pt. 3: Further useful computational methods

S. Hawkes, W. F. Maddams, W. L. Mead, M. J. Southon, *Spectrochim. Acta 38 A* (1982) 445...57; The measurement of derivative *IR* spectra. II. Experimental measurements

W. Herres, J. Gronholz, *Comp. Appl. Lab. 2* (1984) 216ff.; Understanding *FT-IR* data processing, Pt. 1: Data acquisition and Fourier transformation

Z. Hippe, A. Kerste, *Bull. Acad. Pol. Sci. Ser. Sci. Chim. 21* (1973) 395...400; Computers in polymer science. IV. Infrared identification of vinyl polymers and copolymers with the use of a computer

Z. Hippe, B. Debska, *Bull. Acad. Pol. Sci. Ser. Sci. Chim. 22* (1974) 551...7; *POLYMER*. Computer program for qualitative assignment of infrared spectra of vinyl polymers and copolymers

B. Jasse, *ACS Polym. Prepr. 25/2* (1984) 177f.; Use of curve analysis to analyze overlapping bands in the infrared spectra of polymers

J. K. Kauppinen, D. J. Moffatt, H. H. Mantsch, *Anal. Chem. 53* (1981) 1454...7; Fourier transforms in the computation of self-deconvoluted and first-order derivative spectra of overlapped band contours

J. K. Kauppinen, D. J. Moffatt, H. H. Mantsch, D. G. Cameron, *Appl. Spectrosc. 35* (1981) 271...6; Fourier self-deconvolution: a method for resolving intrinsically overlapped bands

E. M. Kirby, R. N. Jones, D. G. Cameron, *CODATA Bull. 21* (1976) 18...25; *SPIR* — a search program for the identification of infrared spectra

J. L. Koenig, *NATO Adv. Study Inst. Ser. C 57* (1980) 79...88; Modern data processing techniques for Fourier transform infrared spectroscopy

J. L. Koenig, *Pure Appl. Chem. 54* (1982) 439...46; New data processing techniques in *FTIR* spectroscopy

V. A. Koptyug, V. S. Bochkarev, B. G. Derendyaev, S. A. Nekhoroshev, V. N. Piottukh-Peletskii, M. I. Podgornaya, G. P. Ul'yanov, *Zh. Strukt. Khim. 18* (1977) 440...59 (Russ.); The use of computers for solving structured problems in organic chemistry by the methods of molecular spectroscopy

V. A. Koptyug, Computers in chemical research at the Novosibirsk scientific centre, in S. R. Heller, R. Potenzone (eds.), *Computer Applications in Chemistry*; Elsevier, Amsterdam 1983

K. S. Lebedev, V. M. Tormyshev, B. G. Derendyaev, V. A. Koptyug, *Anal. Chim. Acta 133* (1981) 517...25; A computer search system for chemical structure elucidation based on low-resolution mass spectra

W. R. Leupold, C. Domingo, W. Niggemann, B. Schrader, *Fresenius Z. analyt. Chem. 303* (1980) 337...48; Automatic reduction and evaluation of infrared and Raman spectra. I. Interpretation of characteristic bands

R. W. Liddell, P. C. Jurs, *Appl. Spectrosc. 27* (1973) 371...6; Interpretation of infrared spectra using pattern recognition techniques

C. L. Lin, J. H. Shaw, J. G. Calvert, *J. Quant. Spectrosc. Radiat. Transfer 23* (1980) 387...98; Band analysis by spectral curve fitting

S. R. Lowry, D. A. Huppler, *Anal. Chem. 53* (1981) 889...93; Infrared spectral search system for gas chromatography/Fourier transform infrared spectrometry

S. R. Lowry, D. A. Huppler, *Anal. Chem. 55* (1983) 1288...91; Boolean logic system for infrared spectral retrieval

M. McCue, E. R. Malinowski, *Anal. Chim. Acta 133* (1981) 125...36; Target factor analysis of infrared spectra of multicomponent mixtures

W. F. Maddams, *Appl. Spectrosc. 34* (1980) 245...67; The scope and limitations of curve fitting

W. F. Maddams, P. B. Tooke, *J. Macromol. Sci.-Chem. A 17* (1982) 951...68; Quantitative conformational studies on poly(vinyl chloride)

W. F. Maddams, W. L. Mead, *Spectrochim. Acta 38 A* (1982) 437...44; The measurement of derivative *IR* spectra. I. Background studies

W. F. Maddams, M. J. Southon, *Spectrochim. Acta 38 A* (1982) 459...66; III. The effect of band width and band shape on resolution enhancement by derivative spectroscopy

K. Molt, *Chemie-Technik 9* (1980) 195...200; Rechnerunterstützte Identifizierung von Infrarotspektren

P. M. Owens, T. L. Isenhour, *Anal. Chem. 55* (1983) 1548...53; Infrared spectral compression procedure for resolution independent search systems

P. C. Painter, R. W. Snyder, M. Starsinic, M. M. Coleman, D. W. Deborah, A. Davis, *Appl. Spectrosc. 35* (1981) 475...85; Concerning the application of *FT-IR* to the study of coal: a critical assessment of band assignments and the application of spectral analysis programs

E. Pretsch, J. T. Clerc, J. Bendl, *Fresenius Z. analyt. Chem.* *324* (1986) 714...9; Spectroscopic data banks

M. Razinger, M. Penca, J. Zupan, *Anal. Chem. 53* (1981) 1107...10; Digitized infrared spectra of polymers

R. Salzer, *Rozpr. Politech. Rzeszowska im. Ignacego Łukasiewicza 20* (1979) 79...96; Application of computer programs in investigation of conformations by means of *IR* and Raman spectroscopy

K. Schaarschmidt, *Anal. Chim. Acta 112* (1979) 385...96 (Fr.); Application of the information theory in the evaluation of the efficiency of a computer-aided spectra search system

K. Schaarschmidt, *Z. Chem. 22* (1982) 438...45; Stand und Entwicklungstendenzen des computergestützten Vergleichs von Infrarotspektren

B. Schrader, D. Bougeard, W. Niggemann, Determination of the structures of organic molecules by computer evaluation and simulation of infrared and Raman spectra, in J. Bargon (ed.), *Computer Methods in Chemistry (Proc. Int. Symp.)*; Plenum, New York 1980

V. V. Serov, L. A. Gribov, M. E. Elyashberg, *J. Molec. Struct. 129* (1985) 183...214; Elements of the applied theory of solving qualitative problems of molecular spectroscopy

R. H. Shaps, J. F. Sprouse, *Ind. Res. Dev. 23* (1981) 168...73; Fast matching with *IR* spectral search and display

S. C. Stinson, *Chem. Eng. News 62* (1984) 18...20; Two powerful computer programs created to analyze *FT-NMR* data

G. Szalontai, Z. Simon, Z. Csapó, M. Farkas, G. Pfeifer, *Anal. Chim. Acta 133* (1981) 31...40; Use of *IR* and carbon-13 *NMR* data in the retrieval of functional groups for computer-aided structure determination

S. A. Tomellini, D. D. Saperstein, J. M. Stevenson, G. M. Smith, H. B. Woodruff, P. F. Seelig, *Anal. Chem. 53* (1981) 2367...9; Automated interpretation of infrared spectra with an instrument based minicomputer

T. Visser, J. H. van der Maas, *Anal. Chim. Acta 122* (1980) 357...61; Systematic computer-aided interpretation of vibrational spectra

T. Visser, J. H. van der Maas, *Anal. Chim. Acta 133* (1981) 451 f.; Systematic computer-aided intepretation of vibrational spectra

H. Weitkamp, D. Wortig, *Mikrochim. Acta 1983 II*, 31...57; Vollautomatische Identitätsprüfung von Arzneimitteln durch rechnergekoppelte *IR*-Spektroskopie

R. L. White, G. N. Giss, G. M. Brissey, C. L. Wilkins, *Anal. Chem. 53* (1981) 1778...82; Comparison of methods for reconstruction of gas chromatography/infrared spectrometry data

R. C. Wieboldt, B. A. Hohne, T. L. Isenhour, *Appl. Spectrosc. 34* (1980) 7...14; Functional group analysis of interferometric data from gas chromatography Fourier transform infrared spectroscopy

S. S. Williams, R. B. Lam, T. L. Isenhour, *Anal. Chem. 55* (1983) 1117...21; Search system for infrared and mass spectra by factor analysis and eigenvector projection

H. B. Woodruff, G. M. Smith, *Anal. Chem. 52* (1980) 2321...7; Computer program for the analysis of infrared spectra

J. Zupan, M. Penca, M. Razinger, M. Janezic, *Vestn. Slov. Kem. Drus. 27* (1980) 369...84; Computer supported analysis of infrared spectra of mixtures

J. Zupan, M. E. Munk, *Anal. Chem. 57* (1985) 1609...16; Hierarchical tree based storage, retrieval, and interpretation of infrared spectra

M. Zürcher, M. Farkas, E. Pretsch, J. T. Clerc, *ARCH 87*, Budapest 1987 (submitted to *ACA*); General theory of similarity measures for library search systems

7 Other methods for analysis and structural determination of polymers

7.1 Nuclear magnetic resonance spectroscopy

7.1.1 Fundamentals

D. E. Axelson, K. E. Russell, *Progr. Polym. Sci. 11* (1985) 221...82; Characterization of polymers by means of ^{13}C *NMR* spectroscopy

F. A. Bovey, *Pure Appl. Chem. 54* (1982) 559...68; The carbon-13 *NMR* study of polymer structure and dynamics

F. A. Bovey, *Org. Coat. Appl. Polym. Sci. Proc. 48* (1983), 76...86; *NMR* and macromolecules

W. Gronski, R. Peter, Recent developments in the study of the dynamics of homo- and copolymers by high resolution *NMR* spectroscopy, in D. O. Hummel (ed.), *Proceedings of the 5th European Symposium on Polymer Spectroscopy*; Verlag Chemie, Weinheim 1979

R. K. Harris, K. J. Packer, B. J. Say, *Makromol. Chem. Suppl. 4* (1981) 117...27; Recent advances in *NMR* techniques for the study of synthetic polymers

K. J. Ivin, *J. Polym. Sci. Polym. Symp. 62* (1978) 89...116; ^{13}C *NMR* spectroscopy as a means of determining structure in some polymers containing heteroatoms in the main chain

L. W. Jelinski, *Chem. Eng. News 62* (1984) 26...30, 34...6, 41...7; Modern *NMR* spectroscopy

L. W. Jelinski, *Chemtech 16* (1986) 312...7; *NMR* of plastics. Pt. 2

D. A. Laude, C. L. Wilkins, *Macromolecules 19* (1986) 2295...2300; Application of a recycled-flow Fourier transform nuclear magnetic resonance system: molecular weight determination of siloxane polymers by ^{29}Si *NMR*

J. J. Lindberg, B. Hortling, *Adv. Polym. Sci. 66* (1984) 1...22; Cross polarization — magic angle spinning *NMR* studies of carbohydrates and aromatic polymers

M. Möller, *Adv. Polym. Sci. 66* (1985) 59...80; Cross polarization-magic angle sample spinning *NMR* studies, with respect to the rotational isomeric states of saturated chain molecules

J. C. Randall, *J. Polym. Sci. Polym. Phys. Ed. 13* (1975) 901...8; Temperature dependence among the Grant and Paul parameters as derived from ^{13}C *NMR* polymer spectra

S. C. Shit, S. Maiti, *Europ. Polym. J. 22* (1986) 1001...8; Application of *NMR* spectroscopy in molecular weight determination of polymers

H. W. Spiess, *Adv. Polym. Sci. 66* (1984) 23...58; Deuteron *NMR* — a new tool for studying chain mobility and orientation in polymers

7.1.2 Solid state *NMR*

R. S. Aujla, R. K. Harris, K. J. Packer, M. Parameswaran, B. J. Say, A. Bunn, E. A. Cudby, *Polym. Bull. 8* (1982) 253...9; Discriminatory experiments in high-resolution ^{13}C-*NMR* of solid polymers

D. E. Axelson, *J. Polym. Sci. Polym. Phys. Ed. 20* (1982) 1427...35; Crystalline order in polyethylene. A ^{13}C *NMR* CP/MAS solid-state T1 study

P. F. Barron, J. H. O'Donnell, A. K. Whittaker, *Polym. Bull. 14* (1985) 339...46; Determination of H-crosslinks in γ-irradiated polybutadiene

D. R. Bauer, R. A. Dickie, J. L. Koenig, *Polym. Mat. Sci. Eng. 50* (1984) 275...9; *Ind. Eng. Chem. Prod. Res. Dev. 24* (1984) 121; Magic angle spinning C-13 *NMR* of acrylic/melamine coatings

D. R. Bauer, R. A. Dickie, J. L. Koenig, *J. Polym. Sci. Polym. Phys. Ed. 22* (1984) 2009...20; Magic-angle ^{13}C-*NMR* of cured and degraded acrylic copolymer/melamine formaldehyd coatings

C. W. Beck, C. A. Fellows, E. MacKennan, Nuclear magnetic resonance spectrometry in archaeology, in C. W. Beck (ed.), *Archaeological Chemistry, Adv. Chem. Ser.*; ACS, Washington, DC 1974

L. A. Belfiore, F. C. Schilling, A. E. Tonelli, A. J. Lovinger, F. A. Bovey, *Macromolecules 17* (1984) 2561...5; Magic angle spinning carbon-13 *NMR* spectroscopy of three crystalline forms of isotactic poly(1-butene)

B. Blümich, C. Böffel, G. S. Harbison, Y. Yang, H. W. Spiess, *Ber. Bunsenges. Phys. Chem. 91* (1987) 1100...3; Twodimensional *MAS NMR*; New prospects for the investigation of partially oriented polymers

A. J. Brandolini, K. J. Rocco, C. R. Dybowski, *Macromolecules 17* (1984) 1455...8; Solid-state ^{19}F *NMR* investigations of annealed poly(tetrafluoroethylene)

R. L. Bryson, G. R. Hatfield, T. A. Early, A. R. Palmer, G. E. Maciel, *Macromolecules 16* (1983) 1669...72; ^{13}C *NMR* studies of solid phenolic resins using cross polarization and magic angle spinning

J. J. Cael, D. L. Kwoh, S. S. Bhattacharjee, S. L. Patt, *Macromolecules 18* (1985) 819...21; Cellulose crystallites. A perspective from solid-state ^{13}C-*NMR*

H.-J. Cantow, D. Emeis, W. Gronski, A. Hasenhindl, D. Lausberg, M. Möller, Y. Shahab, *Makromol. Chem. Suppl. 7* (1984) 63...85; Macromolecular conformation studies by variable temperature ^{13}C and ^{29}Si *NMR* magic angle spinning

A. Cholli, W. M. Ritchey, J. L. Koenig, Carbon-13 magic angle *NMR* spectroscopic studies of an epoxy resin network, in S. S. Labana, R. A. Dixkey (eds.), *Characterization of Highly Crosslinked Polymers, ACS Symp. Ser. 243*; Seattle, Wash., 1984

J. Clements, G. R. Davies, R. Jakeways, M. J. Troughton, I. M. Ward, *Polym. Mat. Sci. Eng. 52* (1985) 8...12; X-ray diffraction and *NMR* structural studies of oriented liquid crystal polymers

S. A. Curran, A. R. Padwa, *Macromolecules 20* (1987) 625...30; ^{13}C *NMR* analysis of polybutadiene via cross polarization and magic angle spinning

Y. Doi, M. Kunioka, Y. Nakamura, K. Soga, *Makromol. Chem. Rapid Commun. 7* (1986) 661...4; Conformational analysis of poly(β-hydroxybutyrate) in *Alcaligenes eutrophus* by solid-state ^{13}C *NMR* spectroscopy

D. R. Ferro, M. Ragazzi, *Macromolecules 17* (1984) 485...90; Correlation between ^{13}C *NMR* chemical shifts and conformation of polymers. 4. Solid-state spectra of poly(3-methyl-1-pentene)

C. A. Fyfe, R. L. Dudley, P. J. Stephenson, Y. Deslandes, G. K. Hamer, R. H. Marchessault, *J. Macromol. Sci. Rev. Macromol. Chem. Phys. C23* (1983) 187...216; Application of high-resolution solid-state *NMR* with cross-polarization/magic-angle spinning (*CP/MAS*) techniques to cellulose chemistry

C. A. Fyfe, M. S. McKinnon, A. Rudin, W. J. Tchir, *Macromolecules 16* (1983) 1216...9; Investigation of the mechanism of the thermal decomposition of cured phenolic resins by high-resolution ^{13}C *CP/MAS* solid-state *NMR* spectroscopy

C. A. Fyfe, M. S. McKinnon, *Macromolecules 19* (1986) 1909...12; Investigation of the thermal degradation of poly(acrylic acid) and poly(methacrylic acid) by high-resolution ^{13}C *CP/MAS NMR* spectroscopy

D. Gagnaire, J. Saint-Germain, M. Vincendon, *Polym. Bull. 13* (1985) 365...71; High resolution solid state ^{13}C-*NMR* study of heterogeneous reactions on cotton cellulose

J. R. Garbow, J. Schaefer, R. Ludicky, C. N. Matthews, *Macromolecules 20* (1987) 305...9; Detection of secondary amides in HCN polymers by dipolar rotational spin-echo ^{15}N *NMR*

A. N. Garroway, W. M. Ritchey, W. B. Moniz, *Macromolecules 15* (1982) 1051...63; Some molecular motions in epoxy polymers: a ^{13}C solid-state *NMR* study

W. V. Gerasimowicz, K. B. Hicks, P. E. Pfeffer, *Macromolecules 17* (1984) 2597...603; Evidence for the existence of associated lignin-carbohydrate polymers as revealed by carbon-13 *CPMAS* solid-state *NMR* spectroscopy

H. W. Gibson, J. M. Pochan, S. Kaplan, *J. Amer. Chem. Soc. 103* (1981) 4619f.; ^{13}C magic angle *NMR* study of the isomerization of *cis*- to *trans*-polyacetylene

A. V. Gribanov et al., *Vysokomol. Soedin. B26* (1984) 834...6 (Russ.); High-resolution *NMR* spectra of polyimide films

W. Gronski, M. Möller, H.-J. Cantow, *Polym. Bull. 8* (1982) 503...10; Micro- and macroconformation of macromolecules. 11. Glassy phase conformational analysis of semi-crystalline and amorphous polymers by variable-temperature magic-angle spinning ^{13}C-*NMR*

D. Groß, J. Kelm, *Kautsch. Gummi Kunstst. 38* (1985) 1089...92; Hochauflösende Festkörper-^{13}C-*NMR*-Spektrometrie an Elastomeren; *ibid. 40* (1987) 13...6; Part 2: Untersuchungen bei erhöhter Temperatur

G. R. Hatfield, G. E. Maciel, *Macromolecules 20* (1987) 608...15; Solid-state *NMR* study of the hexamethylene-tetramine curing of phenolic resins

J. R. Havens, H. Ishida, J. L. Koenig, *Macromolecules 14* (1981) 1327...33; High-resolution carbon-13 nuclear magnetic resonance study of conjugation in solid polyimides

J. R. Havens, J. L. Koenig, D. Kuehn, C. Rhoads, A. Davis, P. C. Painter, *Fuel 61* (1983) 936...41; Characterization of coals and coal oxidation by magic-angle ^{13}C *NMR* spectroscopy

J. R. Havens, M. Takur, J. B. Lando, J. L. Koenig, *Macromolecules 17* (1984) 1071; Study of the solid-state cross-polymerization of poly(1,11-dodecadiyne) through magic-angle carbon-13 *NMR*

G. Hempel, H. Schneider, *Pure Appl. Chem. 54* (1982) 635...46; ^{13}C-*NMR* investigations of the structure in solid polymers

J. M. Hewitt, P. M. Henrichs, M. Scozzafava, R. P. Scaronge, M. Linder, L. J. Sorriero, *Macromolecules 17* (1984) 2566...72; Structure of amorphous films containing tri-*p*-tolylamine and bisphenol-A polycarbonate as determined by high-resolution ^{13}C *NMR* of partially deuterated samples in the solid state

T. Hjertberg, W. R. Salaneck, I. Lundström, N. L. Somasiri, A. G. MacDiarmid, *J. Polym. Sci. Polym. Lett. Ed. 23* (1985) 503...8; A ^{13}C *CP-MAS NMR* investigation of polyaniline

L. W. Jelinski, J. J. Dumais, A. K. Engel, *Macromolecules 16* (1983) 403...9; Multitechnique solid-state *NMR* approach to assessing molecular motion: Poly(butylene terephthalate) and poly(butylene terephthalate)-containing segmented copolymers. 4.

L. W. Jelinski, *Chemtech. 16* (1986) 186...91; *NMR* of plastics. The achievements of recent advances in solid-state *NMR* are nowhere more apparent than in polymers

S. Kaplan, A. Dilks, *Appl. Polym. Symp. 38* (1984) 105...25; Characterization of plasma-polymerized materials by modern spectroscopic techniques

A. P. M. Kentgens, W. S. Veeman, J. van Bree, *Macromolecules 20* (1987) 1234...7; Heteronuclear *J*-resolved solid-state *NMR* of filled natural rubber

O. Kirret, E. Lippmaa, T. Pehk, *Eesti NSV Teaduste Akad. Toimetised 23* (1974) 269...71 (Russ.); ^{13}C *NMR* analysis of polyamide fibers

R. Kitamaru, F. Horii, K. Murayama, *Macromolecules 19* (1986) 636...43; Phase structure of lamellar crystalline polyethylene by solid-state high-resolution ^{13}C *NMR*: detection of the crystalline-amorphous interphase

J. L. Koenig, *Progress in Polymer Spectroscopy 9* (1986) 28; Solid state *NMR* of polymer networks

J. L. Koenig, D. J. Patterson, *Elastomers 118* (1986) 21; Vulcanization studies of elastomers using solid-state carbon-13 *NMR*

J. L. Koenig, D. J. Patterson, *Elastomers and Rubber Technology 32* (1987) 91; Application of solid state ^{13}C *NMR* spectroscopy to sulfur vulcanized natural rubber. I. The method

J. B. Lambert, J. S. Frye, *Science 217* (1982) 55...7; Carbon functionalities in amber

F. Lauprêtre, L. Monnerie, J. Virlet, *Macromolecules 17* (1984) 1397...1405; Magic-angle carbon-13 nuclear magnetic resonance study of local motions in solid poly(alkyl methacrylates)

J. J. Lindberg, B. Hortling, *Adv. Polym. Sci. 66* (1985) 1...22; Cross polarization — magic angle spinning *NMR* studies of carbohydrates and aromatic polymers

J. J. Lindberg, B. Hortling, J. Martinmaa, Magic angle spinning ^{13}C *NMR* spectroscopy of natural polymers and their derivatives, in W. E. Steger (ed.), *Progress in Polymer Spectroscopy*; Teubner, Leipzig 1986

A. J. Lovinger, F. C. Schilling, F. A. Bovey, J. M. Zeigler, *Macromolecules 19* (1986) 2657...60; Characterization of poly(di-*n*-hexylsilane) in the solid state. 1. *X*-ray and electron diffraction studies

G. E. Maciel, I.-S. Chuang, G. E. Myers, *Macromolecules 15* (1982) 1218...20; ^{13}C *NMR* study of cured furfuryl alcohol resins using cross polarization and magic-angle spinning

G. E. Maciel, N. M. Szeverenyi, T. A. Early, G. E. Myers, *Macromolecules 16* (1983) 598...604; ^{13}C-*NMR* studies of solid urea-formaldehyde resins using cross polarization and magic-angle spinning

L. Mandelkern, *Pure Appl. Chem. 54* (1982) 611...8; Carbon-13 *NMR* relaxation parameters of semi-crystalline polymers

J. Martinmaa, J. J. Lindberg, S.-L. Maunu, *Makromol. Chem. Macromol. Symp. 5* (1986) 157...66; Solid state ^{13}C *NMR* spectroscopy with special reference to proteins and their derivatives. A comparison with vibrational spectroscopic methods

V. J. McBrierty, D. C. Douglass, *J. Polym. Sci. Macromol. Rev. 16* (1981) 295...366; Recent advances in the *NMR* of solid polymers

M. Möller, H.-J. Cantow, H. Drottloff, D. Emeis, K.-S. Lee, G. Wegner, *Makromol. Chem. 187* (1986) 1237...52; Phase transitions and defect structures in the lamellar surface of polyethylene and *n*-alkane crystallites; magic angle spinning ^{13}C *NMR* studies

D. J. Patterson, J. L. Koenig, J. R. Shelton, *Rubber Chem. Technol. 56* (1983) 971...94; Vulcanization studies of elastomers using solid-state carbon-13 *NMR*

D. J. Patterson, C. M. Shields, A. Cholli, J. L. Koenig, *ACS Polym. Prepr. 25/2* (1984) 358; High resolution carbon-13 solid state *NMR* of network polymeric systems

D. J. Patterson, J. L. Koenig, Peroxide cross-linked natural rubber and *cis*-polybutadiene characterization by high-resolution solid-state carbon-13 *NMR*, in S. S. Labana, R. A. Dickey (eds.), *Characterization of Highly Crosslinked Polymers, ACS Symp. Ser. 243*; Seattle, Wash., 1984

D. J. Patterson, J. L. Koenig, *Appl. Spectrosc. 41* (1987) 949; Solid state ^{13}C *NMR* characterization of irradiation-crosslinked natural rubber

P. M. Patterson, D. J. Patterson, J. Blackwell, J. L. Koenig, A. M. Jamieson, Y. P. Carignan, E. V. Turngren, *J. Polym. Sci. Polym. Phys. Ed. 23* (1985) 483; High-resolution solid-state carbon-13 *NMR* spectroscopy of cellulose nitrates

M. C. Sacchi, P. Locatelli, L. Zetta, *Macromolecules 17* (1984) 483...5; Solid-state ^{13}C *NMR* approach to the structural investigation of racemic and optically active isotactic poly(3-methyl-1-pentene)

H. Saitô, R. Tabeta, A. Shoji, T. Osaki, I. Ando, *Macromolecules 16* (1983) 1050...7; Conformational characterization of polypeptides in the solid state as viewed from the conformation-dependent ^{13}C chemical shifts determined by the ^{13}C cross polarization/magic angle spinning method: oligo(L-alanine), poly(L-alanine), copolymers of L- and D-alanine, and copolymers of L-alanine with N-methyl- or N-benzyl-L-alanine

F. C. Schilling, F. A. Bovey, A. E. Tonelli, *Polym. Mat. Sci. Eng. 50* (1984) 256...60; The nature of the fold surface of solution-grown 1,4-*trans*-polybutadiene crystals as determined by C-13 *NMR*

F. C. Schilling, F. A. Bovey, A. E. Tonelli, S. Tseng, A. E. Woodward, *Macromolecules 17* (1984) 728...33; Solid-state carbon-13 *NMR* study of the fold surface of solution-grown 1,4-*trans*-polybutadiene crystals

F. C. Schilling, F. A. Bovey, K. Anandakumaran, A. E. Woodward, *Macromolecules 18* (1985) 2688...95; Quantitative measurement of chain folding in 1,4-*trans*-polyisoprene crystals by carbon-13 *NMR* spectroscopy

F. C. Schilling, F. A. Bovey, A. J. Lovinger, J. M. Zeigler, *Macromolecules 19* (1986) 2660...3; Characterization of poly(di-*n*-hexylsilane) in the solid state. 2. ^{13}C and ^{29}Si magic angle spinning *NMR* studies

B. Schroeter, A. Posern, *Makromol. Chem. Rapid Commun. 3* (1982) 623...8; High-resolution solid-state ^{13}C *NMR* investigations of polyethylene

T. Shibata, S. Iwayanagi, *Polym. J. 10* (1978) 599...605; *NMR* studies on poly(oxymethylene) crystals

A. Shiji, T. Ozaki, H. Saitô, R. Tabeka, I. Ando, *Macromolecules 17* (1984) 1472...79; Conformational characterization of solid polypeptides by ^{13}C *NMR* recorded by the cross polarization-magic angle spinning method: conformation-dependent ^{13}C chemical shifts of oligo- and poly(γ-benzyl L-glutamates) and sequential copolymers of γ-benzyl and γ-methyl L-glutamates and qualitative evaluation of side-chain orientation

H. Sillescu, *Pure Appl. Chem. 54* (1982) 619...26; Recent advances of ^{2}H-*NMR* for studying molecular motion in solid polymers

S. So, A. Rudin, *J. Polym. Sci. Polym. Lett. Ed. 23* (1985) 403...7; Study of the curing reactions of phenolic resins by high field carbon-13 *CP-MAS NMR* spectroscopy

J. Sohma, M. Shiotani, S. Murakami, K. Deguchi, K. Eguchi, *Polym. Degr. Stab. 9* (1984) 51...62; Application of high resolution *NMR* spectroscopy in the solid state to the degradation of polyethylene by high doses of γ-radiation

P. R. Sundararajan, G. H. Hamer, M. D. Croucher, *Macromolecules 13* (1980) 971...3; Low-temperature crystallization of poly(dimethylsiloxane) from solution

D. L. VanderHart, R. H. Atalla, *Macromolecules 17* (1984) 1465...72; Studies of microstructure in native celluloses using solid-state ^{13}C *NMR*

D. L. VanderHart, W. F. Manders, R. S. Stein, W. Herman, *Macromolecules 20* (1987) 1724...6; Proton magic-angle spinning *NMR* method for determining intimate mixing in polymer blends

R. P. Veregin, C. A. Fyfe, R. H. Marchessault, *Macromolecules 19* (1986) 2379...83; ^{13}C *CP/MAS NMR* study of the polypivalolactone polymorphs

H. Wobst, *Acta Polymer. 36* (1985) 492...4; Beitrag der hochauflösenden ^{13}C-*NMR* im Festkörper zur Aufklärung der Dynamik in PMMA

J. P. Yesinowski, H. Eckert, D. Sandman, *Polym. Mat. Sci. Eng. 54* (1986) 571...7; ^{13}C *CP-MAS NMR* studies of chemically modified polydiacetylene analogs

A. M. Zaper, A. Cholli, J. L. Koenig, *Polym. Sci. Technol.* (Plenum) *27* (1985) 299; Application of solid-state magic angle *NMR* spectroscopy to fiber reinforced composites

A. M. Zaper, J. L. Koenig, *Polym. Composites 6* (1985) 156...61; Application of solid state carbon-13 *NMR* spectroscopy to chemically modified surfaces

A. M. Zaper, J. L. Koenig, *Adv. Colloid Interface Sci. 22* (1985) 113...50; Applications of high resolution solid state nuclear magnetic resonance spectroscopy to surface studies

A. M. Zaper, J. L. Koenig, *Rubber Chem. Technol. 60* (1987) 278; Solid state carbon-13 *NMR* studies of vulcanized elastomers. II. Sulfur vulcanization of natural rubber

A. M. Zaper, J. L. Koenig, *Rubber Chem. Technol. 60* (1987) 252; Solid state carbon-13 *NMR* studies of vulcanized elastomers. III. Accelerated sulfur vulcanization of natural rubber

K. W. Zilm, R. J. Pugmire, D. M. Grant, R. E. Wood, W. H. Wiser, *Fuel 58* (1978) 11 ff.; A comparison of the carbon-13 *NMR* spectra of solid coals and their liquids obtained by catalytic hydrogenation

7.1.3 Defined polymers

7.1.3.1 CH polymers

L. Abis, G. Bacchilega, F. Milani, *Makromol. Chem. 187* (1986) 1877...86; ^{13}C-*NMR* characterization of a new ethylene-propene copolymer obtained with a high yield titanium catalyst

T. Asakura, Y. Doi, *Macromolecules 16* (1983) 786...90; ^{13}C *NMR* study of the chain dynamics of polypropylene and poly(1-butene) and the stereochemical dependance of the segmental mobility

T. Asakura, Y. Nishiyama, Y. Doi, *Macromolecules 20* (1987) 616...20; ^{13}C *NMR* chemical shift of regioirregular polypropylene

D. E. Axelson, G. C. Levy, L. Mandelkern, *Macromolecules 12* (1979) 41...52; A quantitative analysis of low-density (branched) polyethylenes by carbon-13 Fourier transform nuclear magnetic resonance at 67.9 MHz

M. Barfield, R. J. H. Chan, H. K. Hall, Y.-H. Mou, *Macromolecules 19* (1986) 1343...9; ^{13}C *NMR* studies of sequence distributions in polymers having all rings in the backbone: 1-substituted 1,3-poly(bicyclobutanes)

J. H. Bradbury, M. C. Senake Perera, *Br. Polym. J. 18* (1986) 127...34; Dichlorocarbene modified natural rubber

A. J. Brandolini, K. J. Rocco, C. R. Dybowski, *Macromolecules 17* (1984) 1455...8; Solid state ^{19}F-*NMR* investigations of annealed poly(tetrafluoroethylene)

F. Cavagna, *Macromolecules 14* (1981) 215 f.; Distinction between hexyl and longer branches in polyethylene by 67.9-MHz carbon-13 nuclear magnetic resonance

H. N. Cheng, *Polym. Bull. 14* (1985) 347...54; ^{13}C-*NMR* determination of inverted propylene units in polypropylene

H. N. Cheng, *Polym. Bull. 16* (1986) 445...52; Determination of polyethylene branching through computerized ^{13}C-*NMR* analysis

H. N. Cheng, G. H. Lee, *Macromolecules 20* (1987) 436...8; ^{13}C *NMR* assignments of the methylene carbons in polypropylene

R. Chûjô, Y. Inoue, Y. Itabashi, T. Asakura, Shan-Nong Zhu, ^{13}C-*NMR* spectra and polymerization mechanism of polypropylene, in E. Steger (ed.), *Proceedings of the 7th European Symposium of Polymer Spectroscopy*; Teubner, Leipzig 1986

F. Conti, L. Aqquaviva, E. Chiellini, F. Ciardelli, M. Delfini, A. L. Segre, *Polymer 17* (1976) 901...4; ^{13}C *NMR* study of optically active polymers: Poly(4-methyl-1-hexene)

M. Delfini, M. E. Di Cocco, M. Paci, M. Aglietto, C. Carlini, L. Crisci, G. Ruggeri, *Polymer 26* (1985) 1459...62; ^{13}C *NMR* study of poly[(S)-5-methyl-1-heptene] and poly(1-heptene) prepared by Ziegler-Natta catalyst

G. Di Silvestro, P. Sozzani, B. Savare, M. Farina, *Macromolecules 18* (1985) 928...32; Resolution of the carbon-13 nuclear magnetic resonance spectrum of hemiisotactic polypropylene at the decad and undecad level

Y. Doi, T. Koyama, K. Soga, T. Asakura, *Makromol. Chem. 185* (1984) 1827...33; Stereochemistry in "living" coordination polymerization of propene initiated by vanadium-based catalytic systems

Y. Doi, A. Yano, K. Soga, D. R. Burfield, *Macromolecules 19* (1986) 2409...12; Hydrogenation of polybutadienes. Microstructure and thermal properties of hydrogenated polybutadienes

D. E. Dorman, E. P. Otocka, F. A. Bovey, *Macromolecules 5* (1972) 574...7; Carbon-13 observations of the nature of the short-chain branches in low-density polyethylene

M. Farina, G. Di Silvestro, P. Sozzani, *Macromolecules 15* (1982) 1451 f.; Hemitactic polypropylene: an example of a novel kind of polymer tacticity

P. Frêche, M. F. Grenier-Loustalot, F. Metras, *Makromol. Chem. 182* (1981) 2305...20; Etude ^{13}C *NMR* d'alcanes ramifiés. 1. n-alkyl-12 tricosanes. Application aux polyethylenes basses densités

P. Frêche, M.-F. Grenier-Loustalot, *J. Polym. Sci. Polym. Phys. Ed. 21* (1983) 2755...62; Etude par *RMN* ^{13}C à 62,89 MHz de ramifications longues d'alcanes lourds branchés. Modèles de PE et des copolymères éthylène-α-oléfines

P. Frêche, M.-F. Grenier-Loustalot, *Eur. Polym. J. 20* (1984) 31...5; Caractérisation des branchements courts dans un polyéthylène basse densité par *RMN* ^{13}C

R. V. Gemmer, M. A. Golub, *J. Polym. Sci. Polym. Chem. Ed. 16* (1978) 2985...90; ^{13}C-*NMR* spectroscopic study of epoxidized 1,4-polyisoprene and 1,4-polybutadiene

J. G. Hamilton, K. J. Ivin, J. J. Rooney, *Br. Polym. J. 17* (1985) 11...3; ^1H-*NMR* spectra of ring-opened polymers of 1-methylbicyclo(2.2.1)hept-2-ene

H. T. Ho, K. J. Ivin, J. J. Rooney, *Makromol. Chem. 183* (1982) 1629...46; ^{13}C-*NMR* spectra of polymers made by ring-opening polymerization of optically active and racemic 5,5-dimethylbicyclo(2.2.1)hept-2-ene using metathesis catalysts

W.-D. Hoffmann, G. Eckhardt, E. Brauer, F. Keller, *Acta Polymer. 31* (1980) 233...8; Zur Bestimmung der Häufigkeit verschiedener Alkylverzweigungen in Polyethylen niederer Dichte mittels hochauflösender ^{13}C- und ^{1}H-Kernresonanz unter besonderer Berücksichtigung langkettiger Verzweigungen

B. Hortling, K. Levon, K. Soljamo, J. Pellinen, J. J. Lindberg, *Makromol. Chem. 186* (1985) 131...7; ^{13}C *NMR* investigation of crosslinked polyethylenes

Y. Inoue, Y. Kawamura, *Polymer 23* (1982) 1997...8; Configuration dependence of carbon-13 spin-lattice relaxation times of poly(α-methylstyrene)

J. Kops, H. Spangaard, *Macromolecules 15* (1982) 1225...31; Polymerization of 2,2-dimethyloxacyclobutane

T. Kuroki, T. Sawaguchi, S. Niikuni, T. Ikemura, *J. Polym. Sci. Polym. Chem. Ed. 21* (1983) 703...14; Determination of chemical structures by ^{1}H- and ^{13}C-*NMR* for thermally degraded linear high density polyethylene

L. P. Lindeman, J. Q. Adams, *Anal. Chem. 43* (1971) 1245...52; Carbon-13 nuclear magnetic resonance spectrometry. Chemical shifts for paraffins through C$_9$

P. Locatelli, M. C. Sacchi, E. Rigamonti, A. Zambelli, *Macromolecules 17* (1984) 123...5; Syndiotactic polymerization of propene: regiospecificity of the initiation step

P. Longo, A. Grassi, C. Pellecchia, A. Zambelli, *Macromolecules 20* (1987) 1015...8; ^{13}C-enriched end groups of isotactic polypropylene and poly(1-butene) prepared in the presence of ethylene-diindenyldimethyltitanium and methylalumoxane

K. Makino, M. Ikeyama, Y. Takeuchi, Y. Tanaka, *Polymer 23* (1982) 287...90; Structural characterization of 1,2-polybutadiene by ^{13}C *NMR* spectroscopy. 1. Signal assignment in hydrogenated polybutadienes

G. Moad, D. H. Solomon, S. R. Johns, R. I. Willing, *Macromolecules 15* (1982) 188...91; Structure of benzoyl peroxide initiated polystyrene: determination of the initiator-derived functionality by ^{13}C *NMR*

M. Möller, H.-J. Cantow, *Macromolecules 17* (1984) 733...40; ^{13}C-*NMR* studies on ditactic poly(α-olefins). 1. Poly(1,2-dimethyltetramethylenes) and their tetrad models

G. Müller, E. Schröder, L. Chudzynski, U. Wagnitz, *Acta Polymer. 34* (1983) 345...51; Studien zur Verzweigung von Kettenmolekülen. XXIII. Langkettenverzweigung in Polyolefinen – ein Vergleich der Ergebnisse aus ^{13}C-*NMR*-spektroskopischen Messungen und Untersuchungen zur Molekülkontraktion in Lösung

D. B. Patterson, D. H. Beebe, *Org. Coat. Appl. Polym. Sci. Proc. 46* (1982) 170...3; The microstructure of cyclized polyisoprene

D. J. Patterson, J. L. Koenig, *Org. Coat. Appl. Polym. Sci. Proc. 48* (1983) 455...8; Characterization of chemical crosslinked natural rubber and *cis*-polybutadiene

E. Pérez, D. L. VanderHart, B. Christ, P. R. Howard, *Macromolecules 20* (1987) 78...87; Morphological partitioning of ethyl branches in polyethylene by ^{13}C nuclear magnetic resonance

L. Petrakis, K. S. Seshadri, *Appl. Spectrosc. 33* (1979) 148...45; ^{13}C nuclear magnetic resonance investigation of polyethylene homopolymers, copolymers and model systems. Chemical shifts and relaxation times

J. C. Randall, *J. Appl. Polym. Sci. 22* (1978) 585...8; The identity of the amyl branch in low-density polyethylenes

J. C. Randall, F. J. Zoepfli, J. Silverman, *Org. Coat. Appl. Polym. Sci. Proc. 48* (1983) 211...5; A carbon-13 *NMR* study of radiation-induced structural changes in polyethylene

M. C. Sacchi, I. Tritto, P. Locatelli, L. Zetta, D. R. Ferro, H. Forster, *Macromolecules 19* (1986) 1634...7; Correlation between ^{13}C *NMR* chemical shifts and conformation of polymers. 5. Solution and solid-state spectra of poly[(S)-3,7-dimethyl-1-octene]

H. Sato, Y. Tanaka, *Org. Coat. Appl. Polym. Sci. Proc. 48* (1983) 196...200; *NMR* spectra of styrene oligomers and polymer

H. Sato, Y. Tanaka, K. Hatada, *J. Polym. Sci. Polym. Phys. Ed. 21* (1983) 1667...74; C-13 *NMR* analysis of polystyrene from low-molecular-weight model compounds

F. C. Schilling, F. A. Bovey, K. Anandakumaran, A. E. Woodward, *Macromolecules 18* (1985) 2688...95; Quantitative measurement of chain folding in 1,4-*trans*-polyisoprene crystals by carbon-13 *NMR* spectroscopy

H. Schütz, R. Radeglia, G. Heublein, *Acta Polymer. 36* (1985) 415...7; ^{13}C-*NMR*-spektroskopische Strukturaufklärung von Isobuten-Oligomeren mit Hilfe der *APT*-(Attached Proton Test)Technik

A. Sebenik, H. J. Harwood, *Org. Coat. Appl. Polym. Sci. Proc. 44* (1981) 449; Investigation of the structure of poly(1,4-dimethylenecyclohexane) by *pmr* and *cmr* spectroscopy

A. Segre, E. Martuscelli, Application of ^{13}C *NMR* to the study of structure properties relationship in polypropylene, in W. E. Steger (ed.), *Progress in Polymer Spectroscopy*; Teubner, Leipzig 1986

Z. Sharaby, M. Martan, J. Jagur-Grodzinski, *Macromolecules 15* (1982) 1167...73; Stereochemistry of poly(1,3-cyclohexadienes). *NMR* investigation of effects due to the solvent medium and to the mechanism of polymerization

P. Sozzani, G. Di Silvestro, M. Grassi, M. Farina, *Macromolecules 17* (1984) 2532...8; ^{13}C-*NMR* spectra of methyl-substituted 1,4-*trans*-polybutadienes. 1. Method of assignment and spectra of some homopolymers

P. Sozzani, G. Di Silvestro, M. Grassi, M. Farina, *Macromolecules 17* (1984) 2538...46; ^{13}C-*NMR* spectra of methyl-substituted 1,4-*trans*-polybutadienes. 2. Spectra of several copolymers

A. E. Tonellik, *Macromolecules 16* (1983) 604...7; Stereosequence-dependent ^{13}C-*NMR* chemical shifts in polystyrene

Y. G. Urman, M. M. Teplyakov, S. G. Alekseeva, I. A. Khotina, I. Y. A. Slonim, V. V. Korshak, *Makromol. Chem. 185* (1984) 67...74; Investigation of the structure of polymers of the polyphenylene type by ^{13}C *NMR* spectroscopy

T. Usami, S. Takayama, *Macromolecules 17* (1984) 1756...61; Fine-branching structure in high-pressure, low-density polyethylenes by 50.10-MHz ^{13}C *NMR* analysis

T. Usami, Y. Gotoh, S. Takayama, *Macromolecules 19* (1986) 2722...6; Generation mechanism of short-chain branching distribution in linear low-density polyethylenes

T. Usami, Y. Gotoh, S. Takayama, H. Ohtani, S. Tsuge, *Macromolecules 20* (1987) 1557...61; Branching structures in high-pressure low-density polyethylene as a function of molecular weight determined by ^{13}C nuclear magnetic resonance and pyrolysis-hydrogenation gas chromatography

D. L. VanderHart, E. Pérez, *Macromolecules 19* (1986) 1902...9; A ^{13}C *NMR* method for determining the partitioning of end groups and side branches between the crystalline and noncrystalline regions in polyethylene

G. van der Velden, C. Didden, T. Veermans, J. Beulen, *Macromolecules 20* (1987) 1252...6; New method for the microstructure determination of polybutadiene with *cis*-1,4, *trans*-1,4, and vinyl-1,2 units by ^{13}C *NMR*

M. I. M. Wazeer, C. P. Tsonis, *Polym. Bull. 12* (1984) 475...9; Characterization of polycyclohexene by high field carbon-13 *NMR* spectroscopy

S. Wharry, G. H. Yeh, *J. Polym. Sci. Polym. Chem. Ed. 24* (1986) 1065...7; Carbon-13 *NMR* spectroscopy of polydienes. I. Poly(2,3-dimethylbutadiene)

T. Yamanobe, I. Ando, R. Chujo, *Polymer J. 14* (1982) 827...9; ^{13}C-*NMR* chemical shifts and electronic structure of poly(*t*-butylacetylene)

T. Yamanobe, T. Sorita, I. Ando, H. Sato, *Makromol. Chem. 186* (1985) 2071...8; ^{13}C *NMR* studies of the conformation of cyclic paraffins, *n*-paraffins and polyethylen in solution

A. Zambelli, P. Locatelli, M. C. Sacchi, I. Tritto, *Macromolecules 15* (1982) 831...4; Isotactic polymerization of propene: stereoregularity of the insertion of the first monomer unit as a fingerprint of the catalytic active site

A. Zambelli, *Org. Coat. Appl. Polym. Sci. Proc. 48* (1983) 192...5; Stereospecific polymerization of α-olefins: end groups and reaction mechanism

A. Zambelli, P. Ammendola, P. Locatelli, M. C. Sacchi, *Macromolecules 17* (1984) 977...8; Ethylene units in Al(CH$_3$)$_3$-cocatalyzed polymerization of 3-methyl-1-pentene

A. Zambelli, P. Ammendola, A. Grassi, P. Longo, A. Proto, *Macromolecules 19* (1986) 2703...6; ^{13}C-Enriched end groups of polypropylene and poly(1-butene) prepared in the presence of *bis*(cyclopentadienyl)titanium diphenyl and methylalumoxane

S. N. Zhu, T. Asakura, R. Chujo, *Polym. J. 16* (1984) 895...9; Carbon-13 *NMR* analysis of stereodefects in highly isotactic polypropylene by calculation of chemical shifts

7.1.3.2 CHal and CHHal polymers

I. Ando, *Makromol. Chem. 179* (1978) 2663...5; Temperature effect of ^{1}H-*NMR* chemical shifts of poly(vinyl chloride)

D. Braun, G. Holzer, T. Hjertberg, *Polym. Bull. 5* (1981) 367...72; ^{1}H-*NMR*/^{13}C-*NMR* studies of branched structures in PVC obtained at atmospheric pressure

M. D. Bruch, F. A. Bovey, R. E. Cais, *Macromolecules 17* (1984) 2547...51; Microstructure analysis of poly(vinyl fluoride) by fluorine-19 two-dimensional *J*-correlated *NMR* spectroscopy

R. E. Cais, J. M. Kometani, *Macromolecules 14* (1981) 1346...50; Carbon-13 nuclear magnetic resonance of 2,4,6-tribromoheptane. Chemical shifts of the diastereoisomers as models of poly(vinyl bromide)

R. E. Cais, J. M. Kometani, *Org. Coat. Appl. Polym. Sci. Proc. 48* (1983) 216...20; Pure head-to-tail polyfluoroethylenes: their synthesis and characterization by *NMR*

R. E. Cais, N. J. A. Sloane, *Polymer 24* (1983) 179...87; A statistical theory of directional isomerism in polymer chains and its application to poly(vinylidenefluoride)

A. Caraculacu, E. Bezdadea, *J. Polym. Sci. Polym. Chem. Ed. 15* (1977) 611...20; Determination of unsaturated structures in poly(vinyl chloride) by means of Fourier transform ^{1}H-*NMR* spectroscopy

C. Y. Chu, R. Vukov, *Macromolecules 18* (1985) 1423...30; Determination of the structure of butyl rubber by *NMR* spectroscopy

M. M. Coleman, D. L. Tabb, E. G. Brame, *Rubber Chem. Technol. 50* (1977) 49...62; ^{13}C *NMR* characterization of polychloroprene microstructure. I. Spectral assignments

M. M. Coleman, E. G. Brame, *Rubber Chem. Technol. 51* (1978) 668...76; ^{13}C *NMR* characterization of polychlo-

roprene microstructure. II. Relaxation, *NOE*, and quantitative measurements

M. W. Crowther, N. M. Szeverenyi, G. C. Levy, *Macromolecules 19* (1986) 1333...6; Absolute tacticity assignments of poly(vinyl chloride) via the two-dimensional *NMR* spin-lock *RELAY* experiment

M. F. Darricades-Llauro, A. Michel, A. Guyot, H. Waton, R. Petiaud, Q. T. Pham, *J. Macromol. Sci. Chem. A 23* (1986) 221...69; High-field ^{1}H-*NMR* study of poly(vinylchloride) defects

R. C. Ferguson, E. G. Brame, *J. Phys. Chem. 83* (1979) 1397...1401; High resolution nuclear magnetic resonance of fluoro polymers. Fluorine-19 spectra and chain structure of poly(vinylidene fluoride)

R. C. Ferguson, D. W. Ovenall, *ACS Polym. Prepr. 25/1* (1984) 340f.; Microstructure of poly(vinylidene fluoride) by high field fluorine-19 *NMR* spectroscopy

J. T. Gerig, *Macromolecules 16* (1983) 1797...1800; Fluorine-proton chemical shift correlation in poly(*p*-fluorostyrene)

F. Keller et al., *Plaste Kautsch. 31* (1984) 187...9; Mikrostrukturuntersuchungen mit hochauflösender magnetischer Kernresonanz (^{1}H- und ^{13}C-*NMR*) an chlorhaltigen Polymeren. IX. Erweiterung des Chlorierungsmodells für chloriertes Polyvinylchlorid. 1. Ergebnisse der Teilstrukturhäufigkeitsanalyse des (−CCl$_2$−)-Teils der ^{13}C-*NMR*-Spektren lösungschlorierter Proben

J. Kelm, D. Gross, *Rubber Chem. Technol. 58* (1985) 37...44; Fluorine *NMR*. A method for investigating the decomposition of vulcanization accelerators

R. A. Komoroski, R. G. Parker, M. H. Lehr, *Macromolecules 15* (1982) 844...8; 50.3 MHz ^{13}C *NMR* study of chlorinated poly(vinyl chloride) microstructure and the mechanism of chlorination

R. A. Komoroski, R. G. Parker, J. P. Shockor, M. H. Lehr, *ACS Polym. Prepr. 25/1* (1984) 336f.; Carbon-13 *NMR* structural analysis of chlorinated poly(vinyl chloride) in terms of three-carbon sequences

P. A. Mirau, F. A. Bovey, *Macromolecules 19* (1986) 210...5; Two-dimensional nuclear magnetic resonance analysis of poly(vinyl chloride) microstructure

R. Petiaud, O. T. Pham, *J. Polym. Sci. Polym. Chem. Ed. 23* (1985) 1333...42; Polychloroprene. I. Etude de la microstructure par *RMN* ^{1}H

S. Shimokawa, E. Yamada, K. Makino, *Bull. Chem. Soc. Jap. 58* (1983) 412...5; A simple pressurized high-temperature proton *NMR* apparatus for the thermal degradation of polymers

W. H. Starnes, F. C. Schilling, I. M. Plitz, R. E. Cais, F. A. Bovey, *Polym. Bull. 4* (1981) 555...62; Detailed microstructure and concentration of the chlorinated *n*-butyl branches in poly(vinyl chloride)

W. H. Starnes, F. C. Schilling, I. M. Plitz, R. E. Cais, D. J. Freed, R. L. Hartless, F. A. Bovey, *Macromolecules 16* (1983) 790...807; Branch structures in poly(vinyl chloride) and the mechanism of chain transfer to monomer during vinyl chloride polymerization

A. E. Tonelli, F. C. Schilling, R. E. Cais, *Macromolecules 15* (1982) 849...53; ^{19}F *NMR* chemical shifts and the microstructure of fluoro polymers

7.1.3.3 CHN and CHNO polymers

J. de Abajo, H. R. Kricheldorf, *J. Macromol. Sci. Chem. A 21* (1984) 411...26; ^{13}C-*NMR* sequence analysis. 23. Synthesis and *NMR*-spectroscopic characterization of polyoxamides with alternating and statistical distribution of the aliphatic diamines

T. Asakura, H. Suzuki, Y. Watanabe, *Macromolecules 16* (1983) 1024...6; Conformational characterization of silk fibroin in intact *Bombyx mori* and *Philosamia cynthia ricini* silkworms by ^{13}C *NMR* spectroscopy

T. Asakura, Y. Watanabe, T. Itoh, *Macromolecules 17* (1984) 2421...6; *NMR* of silk fibroin. 3. Assignment of carbonyl carbon resonances and their dependence on sequence and conformation in *Bombyx mori* silk fibroin using selective isotopic labeling

T. Asakura, *Makromol. Chem. Rapid Commun. 7* (1986) 755...9; *NMR* of silk fibroin. 6. Structure of *Bombyx mori* silk fibroin in aqueous solution

D. E. Axelson, S. L. Blake, *J. Polym. Sci. Polym. Chem. Ed. 23* (1985) 2507...25; Multinuclear (^{13}C, ^{15}N) *NMR* study of polyethyleneimine-based polymers

M. Barfield, L. Kao, H. K. Hall, L. G. Snow, *Macromolecules 17* (1984) 240...8; Nitrile function as a probe of *cis/ trans* stereochemistry: ^{13}C *NMR* studies of poly(bicyclobutane-1-carbonitrile) and related model compounds

M. Barfield, R. J. H. Chan, H. K. Hall, Y.-H. Mou, *Macromolecules 19* (1986) 1350...5; ^{13}C *NMR* studies of the stereochemistry of 1,2-poly(cyclobutene-1-carbonitrile) and related oligomers

C. Chang, D. D. Muccio, T. S. Pierre, C. C. Chen, C. G. Overberger, *Macromolecules 19* (1986) 913...6; A configurational study of poly(vinylamine) by multinuclear nuclear magnetic resonance

C. Chang, F. Fish, D. D. Muccio, T. St. Pierre, *Macromolecules 20* (1987) 621...5; ^{13}C and ^{15}N *NMR* pH titration of poly(vinylamine): a two-stage process sensitive to polymer tacticity

I. Descheres, Q. T. Pham, *Makromol. Chem. 187*(1986) 1963...76; Hydroxytelechelic polybutadiene. 9. Kinetics of reactions in solution and in bulk between radically obtained hydroxytelechelic polybutadiene and propyl and phenyl isocyanate studied by ^{1}H *NMR*

A. D. English, *J. Polym. Sci. Polym. Phys. Ed. 24* (1986) 805...15; Solution and solid-state *NMR* characterization of poly(*p*-phenylene terephthalamide)

Ju. A. Fedotov, V. A. Subbotin, L. B. Sokolov, S. S. Gitis, N. I. Zotova, G. N. Trosin, *Vysokomol. Soedin. A 27* (1985) 2137...42 (Russ.); Influence of the conditions of emulsion polycondensation on the composition of aromatic copolyamides

K. Hashimoto, T. E. Hogen-Esch, *Macromolecules 16* (1983) 1805...9; Oligomerization of vinyl monomers. 12. Anionic oligomerization of 4-isopropenylpyridine. Preparation and ^{1}H-*NMR* spectroscopic analysis of stereoisomeric oligomers

K. Hashimoto, T. E. Hogen-Esch, *Macromolecules 16* (1983) 1809...13; Oligomerization of vinyl monomers. 13. Anionic oligomerization of 2- and 4-isopropenylpyridine. Stereoselectivity on monomer addition and methylation determined by end-group ^{13}C labels

B. S. Holmes, W. B. Moniz, R. C. Ferguson, *Macromolecules 15* (1982) 129...32; *NMR* study of nylon 66 in solution (^{1}H, ^{13}C, and ^{15}N *NMR* using adiabatic *J* cross polarization)

H.-H. Hörhold, J. Klee, H. Schütz, R. Radeglia, *Angew. Makromol. Chem. 144* (1986) 1...9; Unvernetzte Epoxid-Amin-Additionspolymere. 15. ^{15}N-*NMR*-Spektroskopie von DGEBA-Anilin-Additionspolymeren

W. E. Hull, H. R. Kricheldorf, *Makromol. Chem. 181* (1980) 1949...66; ^{15}N *NMR* spectroscopy. 25. Terpolymerization of glycine-NCA, leucine-NCA, and valine-NCA

J. Kelm, H.-J. Kretzschmar, H. Zimmer, *Kunststoffe 71* (1981) 514...6; Zur Identifizierung von Polyamiden

V. V. Korshak, Ya. G. Urman, S. G. Alekseeva, I. A. Slonim, S. V. Vinogradova, Ya. S. Vygodskii, Z. M. Nagiev, *Makromol. Chem. Rapid Commun. 5* (1984) 695...700; Investigation of the cyclization of poly(amic acid)s by ^{13}C *NMR* spectroscopy

H. R. Kricheldorf, E. Leppert, G. Schilling, *Makromol. Chem. 176* (1975) 81...95; ^{13}C-*NMR*-Sequenzanalyse. 2. Herstellung alternierender, aliphatischer Copolyamide aus Oligoamid-pentachlorphenylester

H. R. Kricheldorf, E. Leppert, G. Schilling, *Makromol. Chem. 176* (1975) 1629...40; ^{13}C-*NMR*-Sequenzanalyse. 3. Alternierende Copolyamide aliphatischer und aromatischer Aminocarbonsäuren

H. R. Kricheldorf, G. Schilling, *Makromol. Chem. 177* (1976) 607...19; ^{13}C-*NMR*-Sequenzanalyse. 5. Synthese von Nylon-5 und alternierenden Copolyamiden der 5-Aminovaleriansäure aus 5-Isothiocyanatovaleriansäure

H. R. Kricheldorf, W. E. Hull, *Makromol. Chem. 178* (1977) 253...9; ^{15}N *NMR* spectroscopy. 2. Detection of tacticity in polypeptides

H. R. Kricheldorf, *Makromol. Chem. 179* (1978) 2667...74; ^{15}N-*NMR* spectroscopy. 8. ^{13}C- and ^{15}N-*NMR* investigation on *cis* and *trans* amide groups in polyamides and lactams

H. R. Kricheldorf, *Makromol. Chem. 179* (1978) 2675...85; ^{15}N *NMR* spectroscopy. 9. Solvent effects on polypeptides and polyamides

H. R. Kricheldorf, *Makromol. Chem. 179* (1978) 2687...92; ^{15}N-*NMR* spectroscopy. 10. Investigation on structure/ shift relationships of Nylon-6,6 polyamides

H. R. Kricheldorf, *Makromol. Chem. 179* (1978) 247...52; ^{13}C *NMR* sequence analysis. 13. *cis/trans*-Isomerism of poly-D,L-proline

H. R. Kricheldorf, G. Schilling, *Makromol. Chem. 179* (1978) 1175...91; ^{13}C *NMR* sequence analysis. 15. Copolymerization of alanine-NCA with other α-amino acid NCAs

H. R. Kricheldorf, *Makromol. Chem. 180* (1979) 147...59; ^{15}N *NMR* spectroscopy. 13. Copolymerization of glycine-N-carboxy anhydride and β-alanine-N-carboxy anhydride

H. R. Kricheldorf, W. E. Hull, *Makromol. Chem. 180* (1979) 161...74; ^{15}N *NMR* spectroscopy. 14. Neighbouring residue effects in glycine-containing polypeptides

H. R. Kricheldorf, W. E. Hull, *Makromol. Chem. 180* (1979) 1707...14; ^{15}N *NMR* spectroscopy. 16. Stereospecificity and racemization in the course of the synthesis of (ε-Aca-D,L-Ala-D,L-Ala)$_n$

H. R. Kricheldorf, W. E. Hull, *Makromol. Chem. 180* (1979) 1715...27; ^{15}N *NMR* spectroscopy. 17. Stereospecificity of the polymerization of D,L-alanine-NCA and D,L-valine-NCA

H. R. Kricheldorf, W. E. Hull, *Makromol. Chem. 181* (1980) 507...15; ^{15}N *NMR* spectroscopy. 22. Influence of shift reagents and paramagnetic ions on the spectra of peptides and polyamides

H. R. Kricheldorf, W. E. Hull, *Makromol. Chem. 182* (1981) 1177...96; ^{15}N *NMR* spectroscopy. 27. Spectroscopic characterization of polyurethanes and related compounds

H. R. Kricheldorf, T. Mang, *Makromol. Chem. 182* (1981) 3077...98; ^{13}C *NMR* sequence analysis. 20. Stereospecificity of the polymerization of DL-Leu-NCA and DL-Val-NCA

H. R. Kricheldorf, T. Mang, *Makromol. Chem. 183* (1982) 2093...2111; ^{13}C *NMR* sequence analysis. 21. Stereoselectivity of oligopeptide syntheses

H. R. Kricheldorf, T. Mang, *Makromol. Chem. 183* (1982) 2113...29; ^{13}C *NMR* sequence analysis. 22. Stereoselectivity of the polymerization of DL-leucine and DL-valine N-thiocarboxy anhydrides

H. R. Kricheldorf, D. Müller, *Macromolecules 16* (1983) 615...23; Secondary structure of peptides. 3. ^{13}C *NMR* cross polarization/magic angle spinning spectroscopic characterization of solid polypeptides

K. Matsuzaki, T. Uryu, M. Okada, H. Shiroki, *J. Polym. Sci. A-1 6* (1968) 1475...87; The stereoregularity of polyacrylonitrile and its dependence on polymerization temperature

A. Priola, G. Gatti, S. Cesca, *Makromol. Chem. 180* (1979) 1...11; Polymerization of 1-vinylindole and its methyl derivatives. Structure of the polymers

H. Saitô, R. Tabeta, T. Asakura, Y. Iwanaga, A. Shoji, T. Ozaki, I. Ando, *Macromolecules 17* (1984) 1405...12; High-resolution ^{13}C *NMR* study of silk fibroin in the solid state by the cross-polarization-magic angle spinning method. Conformational characterization of silk *I* and silk *II* type forms of *Bombyx mori* fibroin by the conformation-dependent ^{13}C chemical shifts

G. Schilling, H. R. Kricheldorf, *Makromol. Chem. 176* (1975) 3341...52; ^{13}C-*NMR*-Sequenzanalyse. 4. Lösungsmitteleinflüsse auf die chemische Verschiebung bei Polyamiden und niedermolekularen Carbonsäurederivaten

G. Schilling, H. R. Kricheldorf, *Makromol. Chem. 178* (1977) 885...92; ^{13}C *NMR* sequence analysis. 6. Sequence polypeptides of glycine and β-alanine

A. Serra, V. Cádiz, P.-A. Martínez, A. Mantecón, *Makromol. Chem. 187* (1986) 1907...14; Some spectral and thermal contributions to the curing of new epoxy compounds with aromatic diamines

Z. Ja. Slonium, B. M. Araava, V. P. Psenicyna, N. N. Molotkova, *Vysokomol. Soedin. B27* (1985) 417f. (Russ.); Evidence of cyclic triazines in the course of curing of urea-formaldehyde masses with high-resolution ^{13}C-*NMR* spectrometry

B. Tomita, S. Hatono, *J. Polym. Sci. Polym. Chem. Ed. 16* (1978) 2509...25; Urea-formaldehyde resins. III. Constitutional characterization by ^{13}C Fourier transform *NMR* spectroscopy

H. Tomita, H. Ono, *J. Polym. Sci. Polym. Chem. Ed. 17* (1979) 3205...15; Melamine-formaldehyde resins: Constitutional characterization by Fourier transform ^{13}C-*NMR* spectroscopy

7.1.3.4 CHO polymers

P. E. Allen, G. P. Simon, D. R. Williams, E. H. Williams, *Polym. Bull. 11* (1984) 593...600; ^{13}C-*NMR* parameters of some poly(oligo (ethylene glycol)dimethacrylates)

P. E. Allen, G. P. Simon, D. R. Williams, E. H. Williams, *Eur. Polym. J. 22* (1986) 549...57; Changes of proton-enhanced, magic-angle-spinning ^{13}C-*NMR* dynamic parameters during cure of tetra(ethylene glycol) dimethacrylate

M. Andreis, Z. Meić, Z. Veksli, *Polymer 24* (1983) 611...6; ^{13}C and ^{1}H *NMR* study of the polyesterification of maleic anhydride and 1,2-propylene glycol

M. Andreis, Z. Veksli, Z. Meic, *Polymer 26* (1985) 1099...1104; Polyesterification and isomerization of maleic anhydride and 1,6-hexane diol as studied by ^{1}H and ^{13}C *NMR*

L. Banks, B. Ellis, *J. Polym. Sci. Polym. Phys. Ed. 20* (1982) 1055...67; Broad-line *NMR* studies of molecular motion in cured epoxy resins

L. A. Belfiore, P. M. Henrichs, D. J. Massa, N. Zumbulyadis, W. P. Rothwell, S. L. Cooper, *Macromolecules 16* (1983)

1744...53; Molecular dynamics of polycarbonate-diluent systems: applications of high-resolution carbon-13 solid-state *NMR*

T. L. Bluhm, G. K. Hamer, R. H. Marchessault, C. A. Fyfc, R. P. Veregin, *Macromolecules 19* (1986) 2871...6; Isodimorphism in bacterial poly(β-hydroxybutyrate-*co*-β-hydroxyvalerate)

M. D. Bruch, J.-A. K. Bonesteel, *Macromolecules 19* (1986) 1622...7; Interpretation of the proton *NMR* spectrum of poly(vinylbutyral) by two-dimensional *NMR*

S. Cholli, W. Ritchey, J. L. Koenig, *Org. Coat. Appl. Polym. Sci. Proc. 48* (1983) 450...4; Carbon-13 magic angle spectroscopy studies of the epoxy resins network

L. G. Close jr., R. E. Fornes, R. D. Gilbert, *J. Polym. Sci. Polym. Phys. Ed. 21* (1983) 1825...37; A ^{13}C *NMR* study of mesomorphic solutions of poly(*p*-phenylene terephthalamide)

J. J. Dechter, *J. Polym. Sci. Polym. Lett. Ed. 23* (1985) 261...6; ^{1}H and ^{13}C relaxation for the resolved crystalline and amorphous phases of polyethylene oxide

M. Delfini, F. Conti, M. Paci, A. L. Segre, R. Solaro, E. Chiellini, *Macromolecules 16* (1983) 1212...5; ^{13}C *NMR* study of poly(menthyl vinyl ether) obtained by different catalytic systems

Y. Doi, M. Kunioka, Y. Nakamura, K. Soga, *Macromolecules 19* (1986) 2860...4; Nuclear magnetic resonance studies on poly(β-hydroxybutyrate) and a copolyester of β-hydroxyvalerate isolated from *alcaligenes eutrophus H16*

Y. Doi, M. Kunioka, Y. Nakamura, K. Soga, *Makromol. Chem. Rapid Commun. 7* (1986) 661...4; Conformational analysis of poly(β-hydroxybutyrate) in *Alcaligenes eutropus* by solid-state ^{13}C-*NMR* spectroscopy

A. Dworak, J. Kasperczyk, Z. J. Jedlinski, *NMR* study of the microstructure of some polyethers by asymmetric synthesis and polymeranalogous reactions, in W. E. Steger (ed.), *Progress in Polymer Spectroscopy*; Teubner, Leipzig 1986

R. C. Ferguson, D. W. Ovenall, *Macromolecules 20* (1987) 1245...8; High resolution *NMR* analysis of the stereochemistry of poly(methyl methacrylate)

C. A. Fyfe, M. S. McKinnon, *Macromolecules 19* (1986) 1909...12; Investigation of the thermal degradation of poly(acrylic acid) and poly(methacrylic acid) by high-resolution ^{13}C *CP/MAS NMR* spectroscopy

L. Garrido, J. Guzmán, E. Riande, *Macromolecules 16* (1983) 1241...3; ^{13}C *NMR* spectroscopic study of the microstructure of poly(3-methyltetrahydrofuran)

G. P. Gippert, L. R. Brown, *Polym. Bull. 11* (1984) 585...92; Absolute configurational assignments for the ^{1}H-*NMR* spectrum of poly(vinyl alcohol) by use of two-dimensional *NMR* methods

D. Herrmann et al., *Acta Polymer. 35* (1984) 277...281; ^{1}H-*NMR*-spektroskopische Untersuchungen zum Glykoleinbau in gesättigte und ungesättigte Polyester

T. Hjertberg, P. Zadorecki, *Makromol. Chem. 187* (1986) 899...901; Characterization of cellulose ethers by ^{13}C *NMR*. 1. Studies of high molecular weight polymers in solution and in the solid state

F. Horii, A. Hirai, R. Kitanura, I. Sakurada, *Cellulose Chem. Techn. 19* (1985) 513...23; Cross-polarization/magic-angle spinning ^{13}C *NMR* studies of cotton and cupra rayon with different water contents

S. Hvilsted, N. U. Jørgensen, *Polym. Bull. 10* (1983) 236...43; Polyol structural elucidation in binder polyesters. 1. ^{13}C *NMR* study of fundamental polyols in aliphatic and aromatic polyesters

S. Hvilsted, N. U. Jørgensen, *Proc. IUPAC Macro Bucharest* (1983); End group identification and structural elucidation by ^{13}C *NMR* of linear diols and 2,2-disubstituted 1,3-propanediols in binder polyesters

S. Hvilsted, *XVII. Fatipec Lugano* 1984 Vol. I 347...61; Potential structural elucidation in binder polyesters

S. Hvilsted, *Xth Intern. Conf. Org. Coatings Sci. Technol. Athens,* 1984, Proc. 10. 139...62; *SPPRI* Report T7-84 M + T 1984, Structure elucidation of polyester binders for coatings

D. Judas, A. Fradet, E. Maréchal, *Makromol. Chem. 184* (1983) 1129...42; Characterization of polyesters resulting from 1,2-propanediol and phthalic anhydride and their model compounds by ^{1}H and ^{13}C *NMR* spectroscopy

D. Judas, A. Fradet, E. Maréchal, *Makromol. Chem. 185* (1984) 2583...97; ^{13}C *NMR* characterization of branched structures in polyesters resulting from the reaction of maleic and phthalic anhydride with 1,2-propanediol

K. Kamide, K. Okajima, *Polym. J. 13* (1981) 127...33; Determination of distribution of O-acetyl group in trihydric alcohol units of cellulose acetate by carbon-13 nuclear magnetic resonance analysis

J. Kasperczyk, Z. J. Jedliński, *Makromol. Chem. 187* (1986) 2215...21; ^{13}C and ^{1}H *NMR* study of polymers obtained by polymerization of styrene oxide using diethylzinc/water system as initiator

K. Kowsaka, K. Okajima, K. Kamide, *Polym. J. 18* (1986) 843...9; Further study on the distribution of substituent groups in cellulose acetate by ^{13}C/^{1}H-*NMR* analysis. Assignment of carbonyl carbon peaks

H. R. Kricheldorf, *Makromol. Chem. 179* (1978) 2133...43; ^{13}C *NMR* sequence analysis. 17. Investigation on polyesters from diacids and diols

H. R. Kricheldorf, M. Dröscher, W. E. Hull, *Polym. Bull. 4* (1981) 547...54; ^{1}H-*NMR* sequence analysis of poly(ethylene terephthalates) containing various additional diols

C. L. Lebas, P. A. Turley, *J. Cellular Plast. 20* (1984) 194...9; Primary hydroxyl content in polyols. Evaluation of two nuclear magnetic resonance (*NMR*) methods

H. Lenk, E. Klesper, *Polym. Bull. 3* (1980) 521...3; ^{13}C-*NMR* relaxation and circular dichroism of tactic polymethallylalcohol and polymethallylurethane

G. E. Maciel, I. Ssuer Chuang, G. E. Meyers, *Macromolecules 15* (1982) 1218...20; ^{13}C *NMR* study of cured furfuryl alcohol resins using cross polarization and magic-angle spinning

W. Marrs, R. H. Peters, R. H. Still, *J. Appl. Polym. Sci. 23* (1979) 1063...75; Copolyesters studies. I. Preparation and characterization of tetramethylene terephthalate-tetramethylene sebacate copolymers

K. Matsuzaki, T. Kanai, K. Yamawaki, K. P. Samre Rung, *Makromol. Chem. 174* (1973) 215...23; The microtacticity of poly(methacrylic esters)

G. Moad, E. Rizzardo, D. H. Solomon, S. R. Johns, R. I. Willing, *Macromolecules 19* (1986) 2494...7; ^{13}C-^{1}H heteronuclear chemical shift correlation spectroscopy applied to poly[methyl(*carbonyl*-^{13}C)methacrylate]: an unambiguous method for assigning resonances to configurational sequences

H. Morii, Y. Fujiwara, K. Matsuzaki, *Macromolecules 16* (1983) 1220...8; Conformational analysis of the oligomers and polymers of alkyl vinyl ethers by nuclear magnetic resonance spectroscopy

R. Nardin, M. Vincendon, *Macromolecules 19* (1986) 2452...4; Homo- and heteronuclear two-dimensional correlated nuclear magnetic resonance spectra of cellulose

I. Nehls, W. Wagenknecht, B. Philipp, *Acta Polym. 37* (1986) 610...3; ^{13}C-*NMR*-spektroskopische Untersuchungen zur Auflösung von Cellulose im System N_2O_4/DMF und anschließende Sulfatierung unter Homogenbedingungen

J. J. O'Donnell, A. K. Whittaker, *Polym. Bull. 12* (1984) 319...25; Highly resolved ^{13}C-*NMR* spectrum of poly-N,N'-*bis*(phenoxyphenyl) pyromellitic imide (Kapton) (I)

D. W. Ovenall, *Macromolecules 17* (1984) 1458...64; Microstructure of poly(vinyl alcohol) by 100-MHz carbon-13 *NMR*

M. Paci, F. Andruzzi, G. Ceccarelli, *Macromolecules 15* (1982) 835...40; Polymerization of bicyclic ethers. 3. ^{1}H *NMR* structure study of copolymers of 7-oxabicyclo[2.2.1]heptane with ethylene oxide

M. Paci, V. Crescenzi, N. Supino, F. Campana, *Makromol. Chem. 183* (1982) 377...87; Structural characterization of unsaturated polyesters

H. Pasch, P. Goetzky, E. Gründemann, H. Raubach, *Acta Polymer. 32* (1981) 14...8; ^{13}C-*NMR*-Untersuchungen an Phenol-Formaldehyd-Harzen

H. Pasch, P. Goetzky, E. Gründemann, *Acta Polymer. 36* (1985) 555...7; ^{13}C-*NMR*-Untersuchungen an Phenol-Formaldehyd-Harzen. 4. Ermittlung von quantitativen Aussagen zur Zusammensetzung von Resolen

R. A. Pethrick, B. Thomsen, *Brit. Polym. J. 18* (1986) 171...80; ^{13}C nuclear magnetic resonance studies of phenol-formaldehyde resins. 1. Model compounds

B. Philipp, J. Kunze, I. Nehls, *Das Papier 36* (1982) 571...7; Einige Anwendungsmöglichkeiten der *NMR*-Spektroskopie in der Celluloseforschung

J. W. Reynolds, R. Walker, G. W. Kirby, *Polymer 11* (1970) 333...5; Examination of oil-modified alkyds and urethanes by nuclear magnetic resonance spectroscopy

M. Rinaudo, M. Milas, F. Lambert, M. Vincendon, *Macromolecules 16* (1983) 816...9; ^{1}H and ^{13}C *NMR* investigation of xanthan gum

J. San Román, J. Guzmán, E. Riande, J. Santoro, M. Rico, *Macromolecules 15* (1982) 609...13; ^{1}H *NMR* study of low molecular weight analogues of poly(diethylene glycol terephthalate) and poly(thiodiethylene glycol terephthalate)

J. San Román, E. L. Madruga, M. A. Lavia, *Macromolecules 17* (1984) 1762...4; Stereochemical configuration of poly-(methyl-α-benzylacrylate) synthesized by radical polymerization

F. C. Schilling, F. A. Bovey, S. Tseng, A. E. Woodward, *Macromolecules 16* (1983) 808...16; Carbon-13 *NMR* of partially epoxidized 1,4-*trans*-polybutadiene crystals

F. C. Schilling, F. A. Bovey, M. D. Bruch, S. A. Kozlowski, *Macromolecules 18* (1985) 1418...22; Observation of the stereochemical configuration of poly(methyl methacrylate) by proton two-dimensional *J*-correlated and *NOE*-correlated *NMR* spectroscopy

A. L. Segre, F. Andruzzi, C. Barone, M. Paci, P. Magagnini, *J. Polym. Sci. Polym. Phys. Ed. 23* (1985) 2611...21; Studies on comblike polymers. X. Characterization of comblike polyesters by ^{13}C-*NMR*-spectroscopy

N. Spassky, A. Leborgne, W. E. Hull, *Macromolecules 16* (1983) 608...15, 1400; High-field ^{13}C and ^{1}H *NMR* analysis of α,α-disubstituted poly(β-propiolactone)

T. Terao, S. Maeda, A. Saika, *Macromolecules 16* (1983) 1535...8; High-resolution solid-state ^{13}C *NMR* of poly(vinyl alcohol): enhancement of tacticity splitting by intramolecular hydrogen bonds

A. E. Tonelli, *Macromolecules 18* (1985) 1086...90; Carbon-13 nuclear magnetic resonance chemical shifts of poly(vinyl alcohol)

S. N. Tong, K. Y. Park, H. J. Harwood, *J. Polym. Sci. Polym. Chem. Ed. 22* (1984) 1097...113; 300 MHz ¹H-NMR spectra of *p*-cresol-formaldehyde condensates having regular repeating structures

F. F. Vercauteren, W. A. Donners, *Polymer 27* (1986) 993...8; A ¹³C nuclear magnetic resonance study of the microstructure of poly(vinyl alcohol)

H. J. Yue, D. J. Nagy, R. M. Jayasuriya, M. S. El-Asser, J. M. Vanderhoff, *Polym. Mat. Sci. Eng. 52* (1985) 537...44; Structural imperfections in polyvinyl acetates

P. Zadorecki, T. Hjertberg, *Makromol. Chem. 188* (1987) 513...25; Characterization of cellulose ethers by ¹³C *NMR*. 2. Structural determination

7.1.3.5 Miscellaneous polymers, resins

M. Bardet, M. F. Foray, D. Robert, *Makromol. Chem. 186* (1985) 1495...504; Use of the *DEPT* pulse sequence to facilitate the ¹³C *NMR* structural analysis of lignins

B. B. Dambatta, J. R. Ebdon, *Br. Polym. J. 16* (1984) 69 f.; The tacticity of poly(tri-*n*-butyl tin methacrylate) determined by carbon-13 *NMR*

A. Dworak, *Makromol. Chem. Rapid Commun. 6* (1985) 665...9; *NMR* study of the tacticity of poly(epichlorohydrin) via reduction to poly(propylene oxide)

A. H. Fawcett, J. Guthrie, K. W. Lo, H. Pyszora, *Polymer 26* (1985) 1369...71; A ¹³C *NMR* study of the sulphonation of novolacs

P. Goetzky, H. Pasch, *Acta Polymer. 37* (1986) 510...2; Untersuchungen zur Synthese und Härtung von Phenol-Formaldehyd-Harzen. 1. Quantitative Aussagen zur Resolsynthese in Gegenwart von Triethylamin

B. S. Holmes, T. M. Keller, *ACS Polym. Prepr. 25* (1984) 338 f.; *NMR*-characterization of fluorinated urethanes

H.-H. Hörhold, J. Klee, H. Schütz, R. Radeglia, *Angew. Makromol. Chem. 144* (1986) 1...9; Unvernetzte Epoxid-Amin-Additionspolymere. 15. ¹⁵N-*NMR*-Spektroskopie von DGEBA-Anilin-Additionspolymeren

S. Hvilsted, Structure elucidation of polyester binders for coatings, in G. D. Parfitt, A. V. Patsis (eds.), *Organic Coatings, Science and Technology*, Vol. 8; Marcel Dekker, New York etc. 1986

S. Hvilsted, Carbon-13 *NMR* analysis of crosslinking sites in branched polyesters, in O. Kramer (ed.), *Biological and Synthetic Polymer Networks*; Elsevier Applied Science Publ., Amsterdam 1987

J. Kelm, L. Vogel, D. Groß, *Kautsch. Gummi Kunstst. 36* (1983) 274...6; Untersuchung der Aminbildung bei der Thiuramvulkanisation mit Hilfe der Fluor-*NMR*-Spektrometrie

J. Kelm, D. Groß, *Rubber Chem. Technol. 58* (1985) 37...44; Fluorine-*NMR* — a method for investigating the decomposition of vulcanization accelerators

R. A. Komoroski, J. P. Shockcor, E. C. Gregg, J. L. Savoca, *Rubber Chem. Techn. 59* (1986) 328...46; Characterization of elastomers and rubber chemicals by modern *NMR* techniques

H. R. Kricheldorf, E. Leppert, G. Schilling, *Makromol. Chem. 175* (1974) 1705...29; Über N-(Isothiocyanatoacylamino)carbonsäuren und ihre Kondensationspolymerisation zu Copolyamiden mit alternierender Sequenz

G. L. Marshall, J. A. Lander, *Eur. Polym. J. 21* (1985) 949...58; The characterisation of alkyd paint binders using ¹³C-*NMR* spectroscopy

G. L. Marshall, *Eur. Polym. J. 22* (1986) 217...30; A ¹³C-*NMR* study of stoving alkyd systems

G. L. Marshall, *Eur. Polym. J. 22* (1986) 231...41; The analysis of cured drying oils by swollen state ¹³C-*NMR* spectroscopy

M. Marshall, *J. Oil Col. Chem. Assoc. 66* (1983) 285...93; *NMR* analysis of paint media

I. Nehls, W. Wagenknecht, B. Philipp, A. Zschunke, *Acta Polymer. 36* (1985) 657...61; ¹³C-*NMR*-spektroskopische Untersuchungen an Cellulosesulfaten

C. P. Pathak, M. J. Patni, *J. Polym. Sci. Polym. Lett. Ed. 24* (1986) 389...92; Determination of tacticity of poly(hexyl α-chloroacrylate) by ¹³C *NMR* spectroscopy

C. P. Pathak, M. J. Patni, G. N. Babu, J. W. Chien, *Makromol. Chem. 187* (1986) 375...81; Investigation on the microstructure of poly(cyclohexyl-α-chloroacrylate)s using 500 MHz ¹H and 25 MHz ¹³C *NMR*

C. P. Pathak, M. J. Patni, G. N. Babu, J. C. W. Chien, *Macromolecules 19* (1986) 1035...42; *ibid.* 2672 correction; Microstructures of poly(alkyl α-chloroacrylate) determined by ¹³C and ¹H *NMR*

R. A. Pethrick, B. Thomson, *Brit. Polym. J. 18* (1986) 380...6; ¹³C-nuclear magnetic resonance studies on phenol-formaldehyde resins and related model compounds. 2. Analysis of sequence structure in resins

R. M. Rammon, *J. Adhesion 19* (1986) 115...35; The chemical structure of UF resins

J. Rybicky, *J. Appl. Polym. Sci. 23* (1979) 25...38; Fast determination of fatty acids in oil-utilizing resins by *NMR* spectroscopy

K. G. Saunders, W. J. Macknight, R. W. Lenz, *J. Polym. Sci. Polym. Chem. Ed. 24* (1986) 1389...1412; Poly(alkyl-α-bromoacrylate)s. III. Tacticity analysis from 19 MHz ¹³C-*NMR* spectroscopy

F. C. Schilling, F. A. Bovey, J. M. Zeigler, *Macromolecules 19* (1986) 2309...12; *Polym. Mat. Sci. Eng. 54* (1986) 475...9; Characterization of polysilanes by carbon-13, silicon-29, and proton *NMR*

D. D. Werstler, *Polymer 27* (1986) 750...6; Quantitative ¹³C-*NMR* characterization of aqueous formaldehyde resins. 1. Phenolformaldehyde resins; *ibid.* 757...64; 2. Resorcinol-formaldehyde resins

J. T. K. Woo, J. M. Evans, *J. Paint Technol. 49* (1977) 42...50; A method to elucidate the structure of maleinized linseed oil

7.1.4 End groups

J. C. Bevington, J. R. Ebdon, T. N. Huckerby, N. W. Hutton, *Polymer 23* (1982) 163 f; Polymer communications. Carbon-13 *NMR* study of end-groups in polymers prepared using azobisisobutyronitrile as radical initiator

J. C. Bevington, J. R. Ebdon, T. N. Huckerby, *Eur. Polym. J. 21* (1985) 685...94; An appraisal of *NMR* methods for study of end-groups derived from initiators in radical polymerizations

J. C. Bevington, T. N. Huckerby, B. J. Hunt, *Br. Polym. J. 17* (1985) 43...5; End-groups in polymers of 2-vinylnaphthalene and 4-vinylbiphenyl, prepared by polymerisations initiated by azobis(isobutyronitrile)

L. S. Bresler, E. N. Barantsevich, V. I. Polyansky, S. S. Ivantchev, *Makromol. Chem. 183* (1982) 2479...89; Mechanistic implications of the end group structure in radical telechelic polybutadienes as studied by *NMR*

J. M. Goldwasser, H. G. Adolph, *Polym. Eng. Sci. 26* (1986) 1510...3; Hydroxyl group determination in prepolymers by ¹H-*NMR*-spectroscopy

K. J. Ivin, S. Lillie, J. J. Rooney, *Makromol. Chem. 179* (1978) 2787f.; Detection of end groups in poly(1-pentenylene) by ^{13}C-*NMR* spectroscopy

7.1.5 Copolymers

J. de Abajo, H. R. Kricheldorf, *J. Macromol. Sci. Chem. A21* (1984) 411...26; ^{13}C-*NMR* sequence analysis. 23. Synthesis and *NMR* spectroscopic characterization of polyoxamides with alternating and random sequences of aliphatic diamines

L. Abis, G. Bacchilega, F. Milani, *Makromol. Chem. 187* (1986) 1877...86; ^{13}C *NMR* characterization of a new ethylene-propene copolymer obtained with a high yield titanium catalyst

S. Amiya, M. Uetsuki, *Macromolecules 15* (1982) 166...70; Microstructures in poly(vinyl alcohol-*co*-crotonic acid) studied by ^{1}H-*NMR* and ^{13}C-*NMR*

M. Avella, E. Martuscelli, G. della Volpe, A. Segre, E. Rossi, T. Simonazzi, *Makromol. Chem. 187* (1986) 1927...43; Composition-properties relationships in propene-ethene random copolymers obtained with high-yield Ziegler-Natta supported catalysts

D. B. Bailey, P. M. Henrichs, *J. Polym. Sci. Polym. Chem. Ed. 16* (1978) 3185...99; Diad, triad and pentad sequence-distribution analysis of acrylonitrile-vinylidene chloride model copolymers by ^{13}C-*NMR*

D. A. Bansleben, O. Vogl, *J. Polym. Sci. Polym. Chem. Ed. 23* (1985) 673...701; Poly(alkylene oxide) ionomers. XI. Polymerization and copolymerization of methyl ω-epoxyundecanoate and characterization of the polymers

P. F. Barron, W. K. Busfield, T. Morley-Buchanan, *Polymer 24* (1983) 1252...4; High-resolution solid state ^{13}C-*NMR* of butadiene grafted polypropylene

A. S. Brar, A. K. Saini, *J. Appl. Polym. Sci. 32* (1986) 4607...13; Sequence determination in MMA-EMA copolymers by ^{13}C *NMR*

M. D. Bruch, F. A. Bovey, *Macromolecules 17* (1984) 978...81; Proton resonance assignments in copolymer spectra by two-dimensional *NMR*

M. D. Bruch, W. G. Payne, *Macromolecules 19* (1986) 2712...21; Assignment of monomer sequences in the ^{13}C and ^{1}H *NMR* spectra of several ethylene-containing co- and terpolymers by two-dimensional nuclear magnetic resonance spectroscopy

D. Brück, D. O. Hummel, *Makromol. Chem. 163* (1973) 281...94; Copolymere aus Vinylhalogeniden und Olefinen. IV. Kernresonanzspektroskopische Untersuchungen an Vinylchlorid-Isobuten-Copolymeren

R. E. Cais, J. M. Kometani, *Macromolecules 15* (1982) 954...60; Ethylene-vinyl bromide copolymers by reductive debromination of poly(vinyl bromide). A carbon-13 *NMR* study

R. E. Cais, J. M. Kometani, N. H. Salzman, *Polym. Mat. Sci. Eng. 50* (1984) 285...9; *NMR* characterization of the chemical microstructure of vinylidene halide and vinyl halide copolymers

F. Candau, Z. Zekhnini, F. Heatley, *Macromolecules 19* (1986) 1895...1902; ^{13}C *NMR* study of the sequence distribution of poly(acrylamide-*co*-sodium acrylates) prepared in inverse micro-emulsions

C. J. Carman, R. A. Harrington, C. E. Wilkes, *Macromolecules 10* (1977) 536...44; Monomer sequence distribution in ethylene-propylene rubber measured by ^{13}C *NMR*. 3. Use of reaction probability model

H. N. Cheng, *Anal. Chem. 54* (1982) 1828...33; Markovian statistics and simplex algorithm for carbon-13 nuclear

magnetic resonance spectra of ethylene-propylene copolymers

H. N. Cheng, *J. Polym. Sci. Polym. Phys. Ed. 21* (1983) 573...81; ^{13}C-*NMR* analysis of propylene-butylene copolymers by a reaction probability model

H. N. Cheng, *Macromolecules 17* (1984) 1950...5; ^{13}C *NMR* analysis of ethylene-propylene rubbers

H. N. Cheng, M. A. Bennett, *Anal. Chem. 56* (1984) 2320...37; General analysis of the carbon-13 nuclear magnetic resonance spectra of vinyl copolymers by the spectral simulation approach

H. N. Cheng, M. A. Bennett, *Polym. Mat. Sci. Eng. 53* (1985) 668...12; General analysis of ^{13}C *NMR* spectra of ethylene and propylene polymers

H. N. Cheng, D. A. Smith, *Macromolecules 19* (1986) 2065...72; ^{13}C *NMR* studies of low-molecular-weight ethylene-propylene copolymers and characterization of the chain ends

H. N. Cheng, M. A. Bennett, *Makromol. Chem. 188* (1987) 135...48; Additive rules for the ^{13}C *NMR* shifts of methyl-substituted alkanes and ethylene-propylene copolymers

H. N. Cheng, M. A. Bennett, *Makromol. Chem. 188* (1987) 2665...77; Spectral simulation and characterization of polymers from ethene and propene by ^{13}C *NMR*

C. Corno, A. Priola, S. Cesca, *Macromolecules 15* (1982) 840...4; Cationic copolymers of isobutylene. 6. *NMR* investigation of the structure and sequence distribution of isobutylene-2,3-dimethylbutadiene copolymers

C. Corno, A. Priola, G. Spallanzani, S. Cesca, *Macromolecules 17* (1984) 37...41; Cationic copolymers of isobutylene. 7. Reactivity ratio determination by sequence distributions obtained through *NMR* analysis

C. Cosewith, *Macromolecules 20* (1987) 1237...44; Interpretation of ^{13}C *NMR* sequence distribution for ethylene-propylene copolymers made with heterogeneous catalysts

P. K. Dhal, G. N. Babu, R. K. Nanda, *Macromolecules 17* (1984) 1131...5; Microstructure elucidation of glycidyl methacrylate-alkyl acrylate copolymers by ^{13}C *NMR* spectroscopy

L. G. Ecevskaja, G. D. Bukatov, V. A. Zacharov, A. V. Nosov, *Vysokomol. Soedin. B29* (1987) 149...53; Study of molecular structure of ethylene-propylene copolymers obtained on high-effective supported Ziegler catalysts

K.-F. Elgert, W. Ritter, *Makromol. Chem. 177* (1976) 2781...5; Das ^{13}C-*NMR*-Spektrum von alternierenden Copolymeren aus Ethylen und Propylen

M.-F. Grenier-Loustalot, *J. Polym. Sci. Polym. Chem. Ed. 21* (1983) 2683...95; Etude par *RMN* [13]C à 62,89 MHz des branchements éthyles dans les copolymères éthylène-butène et polyéthylène basse densité

M.-F. Grenier-Loustalot, *Eur. Polym. J. 20* (1984) 585...8; Microstructure par *RMN*-^{13}C de terpolymères éthylène-propylène-hexadiène-1,4

F. Halverson, J. E. Lancaster, M. N. O'Connor, *Macromolecules 18* (1985) 1139...44; Sequence distribution of carboxyl groups in hydrolyzed polyacrylamide

S. A. Heffner, F. A. Bovey, L. A. Verge, P. A. Mirau, A. E. Tonelli, *Macromolecules 19* (1986) 1628...34; Two-dimensional ^{1}H and ^{13}C *NMR* spectroscopy of styrene-methyl methacrylate copolymers

P. M. Henrichs, J. M. Hewitt, L. J. Schwartz, D. B. Bailey, *J. Polym. Sci. Polym. Chem. Ed. 20* (1982) 775...82; Quantitative *NMR* measurements in copolymers of vinylidene chloride and acrylonitrile. The effects of saturation and varying nuclear Overhauser enhancements

E. T. Hsieh, J. C. Randall, *Macromolecules 15* (1982) 353...60, 1642; Ethylene-1-butene copolymers. 1. Co monomer sequence distribution

E. T. Hsieh, J. C. Randall, *Macromolecules 15* (1982) 1402...6; Monomer sequence distributions in ethylene-1-hexene copolymers

K. J. Ivin, *Pure Appl. Chem. 55* (1983) 1529...40; Characterization of copolymers by *NMR* spectroscopy

O. P. Jablonski, V. P. Konovalova, I. M. Mogilevic, V. M. Bondarenko, L. I. Salnova et al., *Vysokomol. Soedin. B 24* (1982) 648...52 (Russ.); Investigation of the structure of CP vinyl acetate-N-vinylsuccinimide by means of *NMR*

R. M. Jayasuriya, A. Klein, M. S. El-Aasser, J. W. Vanderhoff, *Polym. Mat. Sci. Eng. 51* (1984) 766...77; Prediction of the microstructure of vinyl acetate-alkyl acrylate ester emulsion copolymers based on solubility parameters

L. W. Jelinski, J. J. Dumais, P. I. Watnick, A. K. Engel, M. D. Sefcik, *Macromolecules 16* (1983) 409...15; *NMR* relaxation in poly(butylene terephthalate) and poly(butylene terephthalate)-containing copolymers

Y. S. Jo, Y. Inoue, R. Chûjô, *Makromol. Chem. Macromol. Symp. 5* (1986) 167...79; 500 MHz ^1H *NMR* studies on the configuration and conformation in the piezoelectric copolymer of vinylidene cyanide and vinyl acetate

U. Johnsen, *Ber. Bunsenges. Physik. Chem. 70* (1966) 320...34; Die Ermittlung der molekularen Struktur von sterischen und chemischen Copolymeren durch Kernspinresonanz

M. Kakugo, Y. Naito, K. Mizunuma, T. Miyatake, *Macromolecules 15* (1982) 1150...2; ^{13}C *NMR* determination of monomer sequence distribution in ethylene-propylene copolymers prepared with δ-TiCl$_3$-Al(C$_2$H$_5$)$_2$Cl

N. Kalyanam, V. G. Gandhi, S. Sivaram, I. Bhardwaj, *Macromolecules 15* (1982) 1636...8; Acrylonitrile copolymers using the cobalt acetylacetonate-triethylaluminum initiator system. 3. Monomer sequence distributions

M. Kanakavel, T. V. Sebastian, *Makromol. Chem. 186* (1985) 1313...20; Characterization of butadiene-acrylonitrile-methacrylic acid terpolymer by ^{13}C and ^1H *NMR*

K. V. Kisin, V. A. Lovcikov, V. P. Mironjuk, V. B. Romanichin, *Kautschuk Rezina 1981* (6) 5...8 (Russ.); Investigation of the microstructure of ethylene-propylene rubbers with ^{13}C-*NMR*

M. Knörgen, K. Schlothauer, H. Meyer, *Acta Polymer. 35* (1984) 490...3; Selektive *NMR* T1- und *NOE*-Messungen zur Untersuchung lokaler Molekülbewegungen in gelösten Vinylchlorid/Vinylacetat-Copolymeren

E. Kobayashi, J. Furukawa, M. Ochiai, T. Tsujimoto, *Eur. Polym. J. 19* (1983) 871...5; The microstructure of butadiene unit in the copolymer of butadiene with styrene

K. E. Koenig, *Macromolecules 16* (1983) 99...105; Structural analysis of ethylene-maleic anhydride copolymer, ammoniated ethylene-maleic anhydride copolymer, and carboxyimamidate by ^{13}C and ^1H *NMR*

H. Koinuma, T. Tanabe, H. Hirai, *Makromol. Chem. 183* (1982) 211...21; Polymer conformation and *NMR* chemical shifts. 4. Contrast of ^{13}C-*NMR* spectra between poly(methyl acrylate-*alt*-styrene) and poly(methyl methacrylate-*alt*-styrene)

H. Koinuma, K. Sato, T. Tanabe, H. Hirai, *Makromol. Chem. 183* (1982) 1533...44; Polymer conformation and *NMR* chemical shifts. 6. Alternating copolymer of α-methylene-γ-butyrolactone with styrene

R. A. Komoroski, J. P. Shockcor, *Macromolecules 16* (1983) 1539...43; ^{13}C *NMR* characterization of vinyl chloride-vinylidene chloride copolymers

J. Kops, H. Spangaard, *Macromolecules 16* (1983) 1544...6; Structural analysis by ^{13}C *NMR* of copolyethers of 2-methyloxacyclobutane and 2-methyloxacyclopentane

H. R. Kricheldorf, *Pure Appl. Chem. 54* (1982) 467...81; ^{15}N-*NMR* spectroscopic characterization of copolyamides and polypeptides

M. F. Llauro-Darricades, C. Pichot, W. Ramirez, J. Guillot, *Polym. Mat. Sci. Eng. 54* (1986) 613...7; Comparative ^{13}C *NMR* study of alkyl acrylate styrene copolymer latexes with different alkyl groups relaxation between the microstructure and the emulsion process

M. F. Llauro-Darricades, C. Pichot, J. Guillot, L. G. Rios, M. A. Cruz, C. C. Guzman, *Polymer 27* (1986) 889...98; Microstructure study of styrene/*n*-butyl acrylate emulsion copolymers by ^{13}C nuclear magnetic resonance spectroscopy

V. J. McBrierty, D. C. Douglass, T. Furukawa, *Macromolecules 15* (1982) 1063...7; Magnetic resonance and relaxation in a vinylidene fluoride/trifluoroethylene copolymer

V. J. McBrierty, D. C. Douglass, T. Furukawa, *Macromolecules 17* (1984) 1136...9; A nuclear magnetic resonance study of poled vinylidene fluoride/trifluoroethylene copolymer

M. Matlengiewicz, *Macromolecules 17* (1984) 473...8; Tetrad distribution of an aromatic copolyterephthalate by ^1H *NMR*

L. Merle, Y. Merle, *Macromolecules 5* (1982) 360...6; Synthetic ampholytes. 2. Sequence distribution in methacrylic acid-(dimethylamino)ethyl methacrylate copolymers by ^{13}C *NMR* spectroscopy

D. L. Neumann, H. J. Harwood, *Org. Coat. Appl. Polym. Sci. Proc. 44* (1981) 448; *NMR* studies of styrene-(methyl)methacrylate copolymers derived from styrene-methacrylic anhydride copolymers

R. A. Newmark, *J. Polym. Sci. Polym. Chem. Ed. 18* (1980) 559...63; Sequence distribution in polyethylene/tetramethylene terephthalate copolyesters by ^{13}C-*NMR*

M. K. Niknam, R. N. Majumdar, F. A. Blouin, H. J. Harwood, *Makromol. Chem. Rapid Commun. 3* (1982) 825...33; ^{13}C-*NMR* spectra of alternating copolymers of α-methylstyrene with methyl methacrylate and methyl acrylate

T. Okada, K. Hashimoto, T. Ikushige, *J. Polym. Sci. Polym. Chem. Ed. 19* (1981) 1821...34; Sequence distributions of vinyl chloride-vinyl acetate and vinyl chloride-vinyl propionate copolymers

G. Opitz, *Acta Polymer. 36* (1985) 439...43; Zur Bestimmung der Mikrostruktur von Trioxan-1,3-Dioxolan-Copolymeren. V. Sequenzanalyse der Struktureinheiten Oxymethylen und 1,4-Dioxapentamethylen zur Charakterisierung von Transacetylisierungsreaktionen

J. C. Randall, *J. Polym. Sci. Polym. Phys. Ed. 11* (1973) 275...87; Carbon-13 *NMR* of ethylene-1-olefin copolymers: extension to the short-chain branch distribution in a low-density polyethylene

J. C. Randall, *Macromolecules 11* (1978) 33...6; Methylene sequence distributions and number average sequence lengths in ethylene-propylene copolymers

J. C. Randall, E. T. Hsieh, *Macromolecules 15* (1982) 1584...6; ^{13}C *NMR* tetrad assignments in ethylene-propylene copolymers

M. Rätzsch, S. Zschoche, V. Steinert, K. Schlothauer, *Makromol. Chem. 187* (1986) 1669...79; Structural analysis of alkene/maleic anhydride copolymers

G. J. Ray, P. E. Johnson, J. R. Knox, *Macromolecules 10* (1977) 773...8; Carbon-13 nuclear magnetic resonance determination of monomer composition and sequence distribution in ethylene-propylene copolymers prepared with a stereoregular catalyst system

B. S. R. Reddy, R. Arshady, M. H. George, *Macromolecules 16* (1983) 1813...7; Copolymerization of 2,4,5-trichlorophenyl acrylate with styrene: reactivity ratios, molecular weights, and ^{13}C *NMR* spectra

G. A. Russell, P. M. Henrichs, J. M. Hewitt, H. R. Grashof, M. A. Sandhu, *Macromolecules 14* (1981) 1764...70; *ibid. 15* (1982) 1642; Monomer sequence distribution in four-component polyesters as determined by ^{13}C and ^{1}H *NMR*

F. C. Schilling, A. E. Tonelli, M. Valenciano, *Macromolecules 18* (1985) 356...60; Carbon-13 nuclear magnetic resonance characterization of random ethylene-vinyl chloride copolymers

K. Schlothauer et al., *Plaste Kautsch. 31* (1984) 183...6; ^{13}C-*NMR*-Untersuchungen der Sequenzverteilung und Taktizität von Vinylchlorid-Vinylacetat-Copolymeren

K. Schlothauer, H. Herold, *Acta Polymer. 36* (1985) 200...3; ^{13}C-*NMR*-Untersuchungen der Mikrostruktur von Vinylchlorid-Vinylidenchlorid-Copolymeren

K. Schlothauer, F. Keller, H. Schneider, B. Wandelt, *Polym. Bull. 13* (1985) 473...9; Compositional sequence distribution and second-order Markov statistics in vinyl chloride-vinylidene chloride copolymers by carbon-13 *NMR*

A. Sebenik, S. Guhaniyogi, E. R. Santee, H. J. Harwood, *ACS Polymer. Prepr. 27*/2 (1986) 138 f.; ^{13}C-*NMR* investigation of chlorotrifluoroethylene-isobutylene copolymers

A. L. Segre, M. Delfini, M. Paci, A. M. Raspolli-Galletti, R. Solaro, *Macromolecules 18* (1985) 44...8; Optically active hydrocarbon polymers with aromatic side chains. 13. Structural analysis of (S)-4-methyl-1-hexene/styrene copolymers by ^{13}C *NMR* spectroscopy

G. Sielaff, D. O. Hummel, *Makromol. Chem. 175* (1974) 1561...78; Kernresonanzspektroskopische Mikrostrukturanalyse von Vinylchlorid-Propen-Copolymeren. I. *NMR*-spektroskopische Bestimmung der Bruttozusammensetzung und der kompositiven Triaden von Vinylchlorid-Propen-Copolymeren; *ibid.* 1579...96; II. *NMR*-spektroskopische Bestimmung der Taxieparameter aus den Häufigkeiten konfigurativer Triaden

P. Sozzani, G. Di Silvestro, M. Grassi, M. Farina, *Macromolecules 17* (1984) 2538...46; ^{13}C *NMR* spectra of methyl-substituted 1,4-*trans*-polybutadienes. 2. Spectra of several copolymers

D. Strasilla, M. C. Berg-Feld, V. Barth, E. Klesper, *Eur. Polym. J. 19* (1983) 85...94; Assignments for the ^{1}H-*NMR* of alkoxy groups in syndiotactic methacrylate copolymers. I. Methyl methacrylate-methacrylic acid copolymers and methyl methacrylate-diphenylmethyl methacrylate copolymers

M. Świtała, Z. Wojtczak, *Makromol. Chem. 187* (1986) 2411...8; Microstructure of styrene-methacrylic acid and styrene-acrylic acid copolymers, 1. ^{1}H *NMR* study of methylated styrene-methacrylic acid copolymers; *ibid.* 2419...26: 2. ^{1}H *NMR* study of methylated styrene-acrylic acid copolymers; *ibid.* 2433...7: 4. ^{1}H *NMR* study of phenyl rings in methylated styrene-methacrylic acid and styrene+acrylic acid copolymers

A. E. Tonelli, F. C. Schilling, *Macromolecules 17* (1984) 1946...9; ^{13}C *NMR* chemical shifts and the microstructure of propylene-vinyl chloride copolymers with low propylene content

S. Toppet, P. J. Lemstra, G. van der Velden, *Polymer 24* (1983) 507...12; Nuclear magnetic resonance studies on sequence distributions in vinyl alcohol-vinyl acetate copolymers

J. J. Uebel, F. J. Dinan, *J. Polym. Sci. Polym. Chem. Ed. 21* (1983) 1773...83; ^{1}H-*NMR* study of structure and tacticity in *p-t*-butylstyrene/methyl methacrylate copolymers

G. van der Velden, J. Beulen, *Macromolecules 15* (1982) 1071...5; 300-MHz ^{1}H *NMR* and 25-MHz ^{13}C *NMR* investigations of sequence distributions in vinyl alcohol-vinyl acetate copolymers

G. van der Velden, *Macromolecules 16* (1983) 85...9; ^{13}C *NMR* study of the nonconjugated diene incorporated in ethylene-propylene-diene terpolymers

H. Yue, W. Daniels, R. M. Jayasuriya, M. S. Al-Aasser, J. W. Vanderhoff, *Polym. Mat. Sci. Eng. 50* (1984) 261...70; Implementation of multiphase sequences in *NMR* spectroscopy for copolymer characterization

A. Zambelli, B. Bajo, E. Rigamonti, *Makromol. Chem. 179* (1978) 1249...59; Model compounds and ^{13}C *NMR* investigation of isolated ethylene/propene copolymers

7.1.6 Polymer blends

B. Albert, R. Jérôme, P. Teyssié, G. Smyth, V. J. McBrierty, *Macromolecules 17* (1984) 2552...6; A nuclear magnetic resonance study of poly(ε-caprolactone) and its blends with poly(vinyl chloride)

B. Albert, R. Jérôme, P. Teyssié, G. Smyth, N. G. Boyle, V. J. McBrierty, *Macromolecules 18* (1985) 388...94; Investigation of compatibility in syndiotactic poly(methyl methacrylate)/poly(vinyl chloride) blends

L. A. Belfiore, *ACS Polym. Mat. Sci. Eng. 51* (1984) 223...7; Compatibility studies of polymer-diluent blends and segmented block copolymers using ^{1}H-^{13}C intermolecular cross-polarization magic-angle-spinning *NMR*

P. Caravatti, P. Neuenschwander, R. R. Ernst, *Macromolecules 19* (1986) 1889...95; Characterization of polymer blends by selective proton spin-diffusion nuclear magnetic resonance measurements

J. M. Hewitt, P. M. Henrichs, M. Scozzafava, R. P. Scaringe, M. Linder, L. J. Sorriero, *Macromolecules 17* (1984) 2566...72; Structure of amorphous films containing tri-*p*-tolylamine and bisphenol-A-polycarbonate as determined by high-resolution ^{13}C *NMR* of partially deuterated samples in the solid state

R. Kosfeld, L. Zumkley, *Colloid Polym. Sci. 260* (1982) 198...204; Zur Verträglichkeit von Polyamid-6 und Hochdruckpolyethylen in Abhängigkeit von Temperatur und Mischungsverhältnis (*NMR*-Relaxationszeitmessungen)

R. A. Newmark, B. C. Copley, *Macromolecules 17* (1984) 1973...80; High-resolution *NMR* spectra of solid poly(dimethylsiloxane) gums, silicone resins, and incompatible resin/gum blends

T. Nishi, *Rubber Chem. Technol. 51* (1978) 1075...82; Application of pulsed *NMR* to elastomeric composite systems

U. D. Standt, J. Klein, *Angew. Makromol. Chem. 99* (1981) 171...5; The analysis of ^{13}C-*NMR* spectra of mixtures containing isotactic and atactic polystyrene

P. Tekely, F. Laupretre, L. Monnerie, *Polymer 26* (1985) 1981...6; Local composition heterogeneities occurring during crystallization in PVF$_2$/PMMA blends as studied by high-resolution solid-state ^{13}C *NMR*

T. C. Ward, T. S. Lin, *Adv. Chem. Ser. 206* (1984) 59...75; Compatibility studies of poly(vinylidene fluoride) blends using carbon-13 *NMR*

R. Zhbankov, O. A. Pupko, D. D. Grinshpan, R. E. Teejaer, F. N. Kaputskii, T. A. Savitskaya, E. T. Lipmaa, *Acta Polymer. 36* (1985) 486...9; Structural features and some physico-chemical properties of materials prepared from non-aqueous solutions of cellulose-synthetic polymer blends. 2. High resolution ^{13}C-*NMR* study of cellulose synthetic polymer blends in the solid state

7.2 Miscellaneous spectrometric methods

7.2.1 *UV/VIS* and fluorescence spectroscopy, circular dichroism and optical rotary dispersion

J. L. Acosta, R. Sastre, *Rev. Plast. Mod. 26* (205) (1973) 67...73; Determination of copolymer composition. II. *UV* spectrometry

M. Aglietto, C. Carlini, E. Chiellini, F. Ciardelli, *Gazz. Chim. Ital. 110* (1980) 449...55; Synthesis and stereochemistry of alternating copolymers of maleic anhydride with chiral olefins

N. S. Allen, *Polym. Photochem. 1* (1981) 43...55; A study of the light absorption properties of polymer films using *UV*-visible derivative spectroscopy

N. S. Allen, K. O. Fatinikun, T. J. Henman, *Chem. Ind. London 1981* 4; Analysis of polymer films by ultraviolet-visible derivative spectroscopy

N. S. Allen, A. Parkinson, *Polym. Degr. Stab. 4* (1982) 239...244; Ultraviolet derivative absorption spectra of nylon 6,6. Effect of photolysis versus photoinduced oxidation

H. Anders, H. Zimmermann, J. Behnisch, Application of *UV/VIS*-spectroscopy to kinetic investigation of thermal degradation of PVC, in W. E. Steger (ed.), *Progress in Polymer Spectroscopy*; Teubner, Leipzig 1986

S. W. Beavan, J. S. Hargreaves, D. Phillips, *Adv. Photochem. 11* (1979) 207 ff.; Photoluminescence methods in polymer science

A. J. M. van Bejnen, R. J. M. Nolte, A. J. Naaktgeboren, J. W. Zwikker, W. Drenth, A. M. F. Hezemans, *Macromolecules 16* (1983) 1679...89; Helical configuration of poly-(iminomethylenes). Synthesis and *CD* spectra of polymers derived from optically active isocyanides

R. Beltschewa, M. Jantschewa, *Plaste Kautsch. 28* (1981) 385 f.; Bestimmung von Antioxidanzien des Phenoltyps in Synthesekautschuk

C. Bertucci, P. Salvadori, F. Ciardelli, G. Fatti, *Polym. Bull. 13* (1985) 469...72; Vacuum-*UV* circular dichroism of optically active isotactic poly-α-olefins

D. Bloor, D. J. Ando, J. S. Obhi, S. Mann, M. R. Worboys, *Makromol. Chem. Rapid Commun. 7* (1986) 665...70; Metastable intermediate structures in polydiacetylene solutions

D. Braun, D. Sonderhof, *Polym. Bull. 14* (1985) 39...43; Assignment of *UV*-absorption maxima of degraded PVC

R. G. Brown, J. E. Glass, *Polym. Mat. Sci. Eng. 54* (1986) 690...4; Ultraviolet spectroscopic determination of copolymer composition in IEM containing copolymers

R. J. Brüssau, D. J. Stein, *Angew. Makromol. Chem. 12* (1970) 59...71; Abhängigkeit der *UV*-Absorption binärer Styrol-Copolymerisate von der Länge der Styrolsequenzen

F. Ciardelli, P. Salvadori (eds.), *Fundamental Aspects and Recent Developments in Optical Rotatory Dispersion and Circular Dichroism*; Heyden, London etc. 1973

F. Ciardelli, C. Carlini, E. Chiellini, P. Salvadori, L. Lardicci, O. Pieroni, Circular dichroism and optical rotatory dispersion in polymer structure analysis, in D. O. Hummel (ed.), *Proceedings of the 5th European Symposium on Polymer Spectroscopy*; Verlag Chemie, Weinheim 1979

F. Ciardelli, O. Pieroni, *Chimia 34* (1980) 301...7; Chiral synthetic macromolecules as models for biopolymers

F. Ciardelli, M. Aglietto, C. Carlini, E. Chiellini, R. Solaro, *Pure Appl. Chem. 54* (1982) 521...32; Structural analysis of optically active copolymers by *CD*

F. Ciardelli, P. Salvadori, *Pure Appl. Chem. 57* (1985) 931 ff.; Conformational analysis of chiral polymers in solution

O. Faix, W. Schweers, *Holzforschung 28* (1974) 94...8; Vergleichende Untersuchungen an polymeren Modellverbindungen für Lignine. 4. *UV*-spektroskopische Untersuchungen

L. Fanghaenel, H. G. Moslé, *Kunststoffe 63* (1973) 324...6; Unterscheidung von schmelz- und lösungspolykondensierten Polycarbonaten durch deren *UV*-Spektren

D. Fornasiero, T. Kurucsev, *Chem. Phys. Lett. 117* (1985) 176...80; Analysis of the visible-near ultraviolet spectrum of 9-aminoacridine using dichroic spectra in stretched polymer films

B. M. Gallo, S. Russo, *Adv. Chem. Ser. 142* (1974) 85...91; Structure and properties of random alternating and block copolymers. The *UV*-spectra of styrene-methylmethacrylate copolymers

B. M. Gallo, S. Russo, *J. Macromol. Sci. Chem. A 8* (1974) 521...31; Ultraviolet absorption spectra of styrene copolymers

L. H. Garcia-Rubio, *J. Appl. Polym. Sci. 27* (1982) 2043...52; The effect of composition, sequence length, and tacticity on the *UV* absorption analysis of styrene copolymers in solution

L. H. Garcia-Rubio, N. Ro, R. D. Patel, *Macromolecules 17* (1984) 1998...2005; Ultraviolet analysis of benzoyl peroxide initiated styrene polymerizations and copolymerizations. 1.

L. H. Garcia-Rubio, *Polym. Mat. Sci. Eng. 52* (1985) 489...94; Recent advances in ultraviolet spectroscopy of polymers and copolymers

L. H. Garcia-Rubio, N. Ro, *Can. J. Chem. 63* (1985) 253...63; Detailed copolymer characterization using ultraviolet spectroscopy

K. Gosa, D. Donescu, N. Carp, *Makromol. Chem. 182* (1981) 1725...34; Study of conformational transitions of graft copolymers by *UV* spectrophotometry

D. N. Goswami, N. Prasad, *J. Oil Colour Chem. Ass. 65* (1982) 223...6; Spectrophotometric studies on hard and soft lac resins

E. Gruber, W. L. Knell, *Makromol. Chem. 179* (1978) 733...46; Bestimmung der chemischen Heterogenität statistischer Copolymerer anhand von Untersuchungen an Poly(styrol-*co*-butylacrylat) und Poly(styrol-*co*-butylmethacrylat). 1.

L. A. Harrah, J. M. Zeigler, *Macromolecules 20* (1987) 601...8; Electronic spectra of polysilanes

M. Hennecke, J. Fuhrmann, *Makromol. Chem. Macromol. Symp. 5* (1986) 181...6; Polarized fluorescence spectra of poly(ethylene terephthalate) films

G. R. Kelly, T. Kurucsev, *Eur. Polym. J. 11* (1975) 581...3; Ultraviolet-visible spectroscopy of polymer films. Reduction of scattering losses

G. R. Kelly, T. Kurucsev, *Biopolymers 15* (1976) 1481...90; Geometry of DNA-dye intercalation complexes from the study of linear dichroic spectra of stretched films

W. Klöpffer, *Chem. Tech. (Amsterdam) 32* (1977) 459...62; Spectroscopic study of polymers. II. *VIS, UV, FUV, ESCA,* and Moessbauer effect

W. Klöpffer, Energy transfer, in J. Mort, G. Pfister (ed.), *Electronic Properties of Polymers*; John Wiley, New York 1982

W. Klöpffer, G. Rippen, J. Kowal, *Makromol. Chem. Macromol. Symp. 5* (1986) 187...96; Electronic spectra of dilute solutions of cationic and radicalic poly(N-vinylcarbazole)

M. Kusakawa, Y. Tsujita, A. Takizawa, *Polymer 26* (1985) 848...52; Optical rotatory dispersion and circular dichroism studies of copolyaspartates with long alkyl side chain

M. LeClerc, R. E. Prud'Homme, *J. Polym. Sci. Polym. Phys. Ed. 23* (1985) 2021...30; Conformational analysis of substituted polyacetylenes

H. C. Lee, W. H. Waddell, F. E. Casassa, *Macromolecules 14* (1981) 1021...4; Ultraviolet absorbance of dilute and semidilute polymer solutions

S. R. Leijenaar, C. J. van den Heuvel, W. G. Huysmans, *Makromol. Chem. 186* (1985) 1549...53; Polyene formation and crosslinking during the thermal degradation of poly(vinyl chloride)

T. Lesiak, H. Orlikowska, *Chem. Anal. (Warsaw) 23* (1978) 111...8 (Pol.); *UV* spectrophotometric determinations of tolylenediamine (TDA) isomers in the products of hydrolytic degradation of selected polyurethanes after separation by thin-layer chromatography

N. I. Lytkina, T. M. Egorova, L. N. Mizerovskij, *Plast. Massy 1983* (3) 58 (Russ.); Direct determination of the plasticizer content of polyvinyl chloride by means of *UV* spectrophotometry

K. Maruyama, H. Akahoshi, M. Kobayashi, Y. Tanizaki, *Bull. Chem. Soc. Jap. 58* (1985) 2923...8; Assignment of conjugate double bond system produced in heated PVA film by absorption and excitation spectra

H. Masuhara, *Makromol. Chem. Suppl. 13* (1985) 75...90; Laser photochemistry of polymers

J. E. Moore, *Org. Coat. Plast. Chem. 42* (1980) 576...81; Differential ultraviolet spectroscopy as an aid in studying polycarbonate photodegradation

S. Mori, *J. Appl. Polym. Sci. 33* (1987) 1923...31; Derivative ultraviolet and visible spectrophotometry. Applications to polymer analysis

M. Nencioni, S. Russo, *J. Macromol. Sci. Chem. A 17* (1982) 1255...61; Ultraviolet absorption spectra of styrene copolymers. II. Studies on model compounds

O. Nuyken, G. Talsky, *Polym. Bull. 2* (1980) 719...26; Polymer analysis by higher-order *UV/VIS*-derivative spectrophotometry

S. Onari, *J. Phys. Soc. Jap. 26* (1969) 500...4; Vacuum ultraviolet absorption spectra of synthesized polymer films

C. M. Patel, V. M. Patel, *Staerke 25* (1973) 47...50; Characterization of amylose-styrene graft copolymer

C. Salom, A. Horta, I. Hernández-Fuentes, I. F. Pierola, *Macromolecules 20* (1987) 696...8; Poly(phenylsiloxanes) electronic spectra

R. Sastre, G. Martinez, F. Castillo, J. L. Millan, *Makromol. Chem. Rapid Commun. 5* (1984) 541...6; The *UV*-visible second derivation spectroscopy as a useful tool for studying the PVC degradation mechanisms

G. Schulz, G. Lenz, R. Gnauck, *Plaste Kautsch. 28* (1981) 383f.; *UV*-spektroskopische Konzentrationsbestimmung von Polyurethanen in Dimethylformamid

M. Sisido, A. Okamoto, S. Egusa, Y. Imanishi, *Polym. J. 17* (1985) 1253...61; One-dimensional aromatic crystals in solution. VI. Synthesis and spectroscopic characterization of poly(β-9-anthryl methyl L-aspartate)

B. Stuetzel, T. Miyamoto, H.-J. Cantow, *Polym. J. 8* (1976) 247...53; Hypochromic effects in *UV* spectra of polymers in solution

C. S. P. Sung, E. Pyun, H.-L. Sun, *Macromolecules 19* (1986) 2922...32; Characterization of epoxy cure by *UV*-visible and fluorescence spectroscopy

G. Talsky, J. Gerum, O. Nuyken, *Makromol. Chem. 180* (1979) 513...6; *UV*-Derivativspektrometrie höherer Ordnung an azogruppenhaltigen Polycarbonaten

G. Talsky, M. Glasbrenner, S. Götz-Mahler, *IUPAC Macro Florence 1980*, Preprints Vol. 2, 441...4; Higher-order *UV/VIS* derivative spectrophotometry for the studying and characterization of proteins and other macromolecules

W. H. Waddell, C. H. Lee, *ACS Polym. Prepr. 21/2* (1980) 199...201; Absorption spectral studies of dilute solutions of flexible polymers

A. Winston, P. Wichacheewa, *Macromolecules 6* (1973) 200...5; Sequence distribution in 1-chloro-1,3-butadiene-styrene copolymers

Z. Wojtczak, M. Świtała, *Makromol. Chem. 187* (1986) 2427...31; Microstructure of styrene-methacrylic acid and styrene-acrylic acid copolymers. 3. *UV* absorption study of methylated styrene-methacrylic acid and styrene-acrylic acid copolymers

7.2.2 *X*-Ray-photoelectron spectroscopy

7.2.2.1 Fundamentals

D. T. Clark, *Polym. Sci. Technol. 5 A* (1974) 241...314; The application of *ESCA* to studies of structure and bonding in polymers

D. T. Clark, The application of *ESCA* to studies of structure and bonding in polymers, in K. J. Ivin (ed.), *Structural Studies of Macromolecules by Spectroscopic Methods*; John Wiley, London etc. 1976

D. T. Clark, A. Dilks, J. Peeling, H. R. Thomas, *Faraday Discuss. Chem. Soc. 60* (1976) 183...95; Application of *ESCA* to studies of structure and bonding in polymers

D. T. Clark, *ESCA* applied to organic and polymeric systems, in D. Briggs (ed.), *Handbook of X-Ray and Ultraviolet Photoelectron Spectroscopy*; Heyden, London etc. 1977

D. T. Clark, *Adv. Polym. Sci. 24* (1977) 125...88; *ESCA* applied to polymers

D. T. Clark, *Phys. Scr. 16* (1977) 307...28; Some experimental and theoretical aspects of structure, bonding and reactivity polymeric systems as revealed by *ESCA*

D. T. Clark, *CRC Crit. Rev. Solid State Mater. Sci. 8* (1978) 1...51; Structure, bonding, and reactivity of polymer surfaces studied by means of *ESCA*

D. T. Clark, H. R. Thomas, D. Shuttleworth, *J. Polym. Sci. Polym. Lett. Ed. 16* (1978) 465...71; Electron mean free paths in polymers: a critique on the current state of the art

D. T. Clark, *Pure Appl. Chem. 54* (1982) 415...38; Advances in *ESCA* applied to polymer characterization

M. Delamar, M. Chehimi, S. Zeggane, C. P. Minh, J. E. Dubois, *Ann. Phys. (Paris) 11 (Suppl.)* (1986) 75...8 (Fr.); *ESCA* in analysis of thin polymer coatings

A. Dilks, *Dev. Polym. Charact. 2* (1980) 145...82; Characterization of polymers by *ESCA*

T. M. Duc, *Ann. Phys. (Paris) 11 (Suppl.)* (1986) 65...9 (Fr.); Photoelectron spectroscopy (*XPS* or *ESCA* and *UPS*) applied to polymers

D. W. Dwight, J. E. McGrath, J. P. Wightman, *J. Appl. Polym. Sci. Appl. Polym. Symp. 34* (1978) 35...47; *ESCA* analysis of polymer structure and bonding

C. B. Duke, *Int. J. Quantum Chem. Quantum Chem. Symp. 13* (1979) 267...81; Electronic structure of large molecules: *CNDO/S3* model

C. B. Duke, A. Paton, W. R. Salaneck, *Mol. Cryst. Liq. Cryst. 83* (1982) 177...97; Dependence of polymer electronic structure on molecular architecture

C. B. Duke, W. K. Ford, *Int. J. Quantum Chem. Quantum Chem. Symp. 17* (1983) 597...608; The electronic structure of polymers: relation to molecular architecture

D. W. Dwight, H. R. Thomas, *ACS Org. Coat. Plast. Chem. 44* (1981) 641...7; Developments in *ESCA* analysis of polymers

L. A. Harris, *Anal. Chem. 40* (1968) 24A...34A; Auger electron emission analysis

L. A. Harris, *J. Appl. Phys. 39* (1968) 1419...27; Analysis of materials by electron-excited Auger electrons

G. Hohlneicher, *Ber. Bunsenges. physik. Chem. 78* (1974) 1125...40; Entwicklungen und Tendenzen in der Photoelektronenspektroskopie

G. Hohlneicher, Photoelectron Spectroscopy, in *Encyclopedia of Physical Science and Technology*, Vol. 2; Academic Press, New York etc. 1987

R. Holm, L. Morbitzer, S. Storp, *Kunststoffe 67* (1977) 717...24; Anwendungsmöglichkeiten von *ESCA* im Polymerbereich

R. Holm, S. Storp, *Surf. Interface Anal. 2* (1980) 96...160; Surface and interface analysis in polymer technology: a review

R. Holm, S. Storp, *ESCA*. Eine Methode zur Bestimmung von Elementen und ihren Bindungszuständen in der Oberfläche von Festkörpern, in Fresenius et al. (Hrsg.), *Analytiker-Taschenbuch*, Vol. 4; Springer, Berlin etc. 1984

J. J. Pireux, J. Riga, R. Caudano, J. J. Verbist, J. Delhalle, S. Delhalle, J. M. Andre, Y. Gobillon, *Phys. Scr. 16* (1977) 329...38; Polymer primary structures studied by *ESCA* and *EHCO* methods

K. Richter, G. Kley, J. Robbe, J. Gähde, I. Löschke, *Z. Chem. 18* (1978) 390f.; Röntgenphotoelektronenspektroskopische Untersuchung der Metall-Polymer-Phasengrenzen in Verbundmaterialien

K. Siegbahn et al., *ESCA Applied to Free Molecules*; Elsevier, Amsterdam 1971

S. Suzuki, Y. Inoue, I. Ando, R. Chûjô, K. Seto, K. Hoshino, *Polym. J. 7* (1975) 8...13; Correlation between *ESCA* [electron spectroscopy for chemical analysis] and *NMR* chemical shifts of carbons in linear polymers

7.2.2.2 Investigation of surface modification

D. T. Clark, A. Dilks, *J. Electron Spectrosc. Relat. Phenom. 11* (1977) 225...30; Difference *ESCA* spectra as a convenient probe for surface modification of polymers

D. T. Clark, *Pure Appl. Chem. 57* (1985) 941...4; Synthesis, characterization, modification and degradation of polymer surfaces as revealed by *ESCA* (electron spectroscopy for chemical analysis)

P. Denison, F. R. Jones, J. F. Watts, *J. Phys. Appl. Phys. 20* (1987) 306...10; The use of *XPS* and labelling techniques to study the surface chemistry of carbon fibres

D. W. Dwight, B. R. Beck, *ACS Org. Coat. Plast. Chem. 40* (1979) 494...9; Ion beam polymer surface modification: characterization by *ESCA* and *SEM*

D. S. Everhart, C. N. Reilley, *Anal. Chem. 53* (1981) 665...76; Chemical derivatization in electron spectroscopy for chemical analysis of surface functional groups introduced on low-density polyethylene film

D. S. Everhart, C. N. Reilley, *Surf. Interf. Anal. 3* (1981) 126...33; The effects of functional group mobility on quantitative *ESCA* of plasma modified polymer surfaces

C. N. Reilley, D. S. Everhart, *Chem. Anal. (N.Y.) 63* (1982) 105...33; *ESCA* analysis of functional groups on modified polymer surfaces

A. Tóth, I. Bertóti, T. Székely, M. Mohai, *Surf. Interf. Anal. 7* (1985) 282...8; *XPS* study of ion-induced changes on the surface of an organosilicon model polymer

S. J. Valenty, J. J. Chera, G. A. Smith, W. Katz, R. Argani, H. Bakhru, *J. Polym. Sci. Polym. Chem. Ed. 22* (1984) 3367...81; Monitoring polymer surface derivatization by *RBS* and *ESCA*

H. Yasuda, H. C. Marsh, S. Brandt, C. N. Reilley, *J. Polym. Sci. Polym. Chem. Ed. 15* (1977) 991...1019; *ESCA* study of polymer surfaces treated by plasma

S. C. Yoon, B. D. Ratner, *Macromolecules 19* (1986) 1068...79; Surface structure of segmented poly(ether urethanes) and poly(ether urethane ureas) with various perfluoro chain extenders. An *X*-ray photoelectron spectroscopic investigation

7.2.2.3 Investigation of oxidation and degradation

D. T. Clark, A. Dilks, H. R. Thomas, *Dev. Polym. Degr. 1* (1977) 87...135; The application of *ESCA* to polymer degradation

D. T. Clark, H. S. Munro, *Polym. Degr. Stab. 8* (1984) 195...211; Surface and mass aspects during natural and artificial photo-ageing of bisphenol-A polycarbonate, revealed by *ESCA* and difference *UV* spectroscopy

D. T. Clark, H. S. Munro, *Polymer 25* (1984) 826...34; *ESCA* investigation of the surface oxidation of bisphenol-A polycarbonate films induced by reactive oxygen carriers

A. Dilks, *J. Polym. Sci. Polym. Chem. Ed. 19* (1981) 1319...27; The identification of peroxy-features at polymer surfaces by *ESCA* (electron emission spectroscopy)

A. Dilks, D. T. Clark, *J. Polym. Sci. Polym. Chem. Ed. 19* (1981) 2847...60; *ESCA* studies of natural weathering phenomena at selected polymer surfaces

A. Dilks, Surface degradation of polymers studied by *ESCA*, in H. H. G. Jellinek (ed.), *Polymer Degradation and Stabilization*, Vol. 1; Elsevier, Amsterdam 1983

A. H. Fowler, H. S. Munro, D. T. Clark, *Polym. Degr. Stab. 11* (1985) 287...96; *ESCA* studies of the thermal degradation of cellulose nitrates

D. N.-S. Hon, *J. Appl. Polym. Sci. 29* (1984) 2777...84; *ESCA* study of oxidized wood surfaces

H. S. Munro, D. T. Clark, J. Peeling, *Polym. Degr. Stab. 9* (1984) 185...91; Surface aspects of the photo-oxidation of polystyrene films as revealed by *ESCA*. Part III. Natural weathering

H. S. Munro, D. T. Clark, *Polym. Degr. Stab. 11* (1985) 211...24; The surface photo-oxidation of bisphenol-A polysulfone films as studied by *ESCA*

H. S. Munro, D. T. Clark, *Polym. Degr. Stab. 11* (1985) 225...31; An *ESCA* investigation of the surface photo-oxidation of polyethersulphone

H. S. Munro, R. S. Allaker, *Polym. Degrad. Stab. 15* (1986) 367...73; An *ESCA* study of the thermal oxidation of low density polyethylene

J. Peeling, D. T. Clark, *Polym. Degr. Stab. 3* (1981) 97...105; An *ESCA* study of the photooxidation of the surface of polystyrene film

J. Peeling, D. T. Clark, *Polym. Degr. Stab. 3* (1981) 177...85; *ESCA* study of the surface photooxidation of some non-aromatic polymers

A. Tóth, I. Bertóti, T. Székely, J. N. Sazanov, T. A. Antonova, A. V. Shchukarev, A. V. Gribanov, *Surf. Interf. Anal. 8* (1986) 261...6; *XPS* study on the thermal degradation of poly-N,N′/4,4′-diphenylether/pyromellitimide

7.2.2.4 CHal and CHHal polymers

D. Adams, D. Clark, A. Dilks, J. Peeling, H. R. Thomas, *Makromol. Chem. 177* (1976) 2139...48; Some observations on the interpretation of *ESCA* spectra of fluorine containing polymers and their relation to the degree of crystallinity, to the surface tension, and to the content of absorbed gas

R. Chûjô, K. Maeda, K. Okuda, N. Murayama, K. Hoshino, *Makromol. Chem. 176* (1975) 213...23; *ESCA* spectra of fluorine containing polymers and their relation to the degree of crystallinity, to the surface tension, and to the content of absorbed gas

D. T. Clark, W. J. Feast, D. Kilcast, W. K. R. Musgrave, *J. Polym. Sci. Polym. Chem. Ed. 11* (1973) 389...411; Applications of *ESCA* [electron spectroscopy for chemical analysis] to polymer chemistry. III. Structures and bonding in homopolymers of ethylene and the fluoroethylenes and determination of the compositions of fluoro copolymers

D. T. Clark, W. J. Feast, W. K. R. Musgrave, I. Ritchie, *Polym. Sci. Technol. 5 A* (1974) 373...407; Structure, bonding and dynamics of surface and sub-surface polymer films produced by direct fluorination as revealed by *ESCA*

D. T. Clark, W. J. Feast, I. Ritchie, W. K. R. Musgrave, M. Modena, M. Ragazzini, *J. Polym. Sci. Polym. Chem. Ed. 12* (1974) 1049...63; Applications of *ESCA* to polymer chemistry. IV. Composition and structure of copolymers of ethylene with tetrafluoroethylene

D. T. Clark, W. J. Feast, W. K. R. Musgrave, I. Ritchie, *J. Polym. Sci. Polym. Chem. Ed. 13* (1975) 857...90; Applications of *ESCA* [electron spectroscopy for chemical analysis] to polymer chemistry. VI. Surface fluorination of polyethylene. Application of *ESCA* [electron spectroscopy for chemical analysis] to the examination of structure as a function of depth

D. T. Clark, D. Shuttleworth, *J. Polym. Sci. Polym. Chem. Ed. 17* (1979) 1317...29; Plasma polymerization: an *ESCA* investigation of polymers synthesized by excitation of inductively coupled RF plasma in isomeric difluoroethylenes

D. T. Clark, W. J. Feast, P. J. Tweedale, H. R. Thomas, *J. Polym. Sci. Polym. Chem. Ed. 18* (1980) 1651...64; *ESCA* applied to polymers. XXVI. Investigation of a series of aliphatic, aromatic, and fluorine-containing polycarbonates

D. T. Clark, D. Shuttleworth, *J. Polym. Sci. Polym. Chem. Ed. 18* (1980) 27...46; Plasma polymerization. II. An *ESCA* investigation of polymers synthesized by excitation of inductively coupled RF plasma in perfluorobenzene and perfluorocyclohexane

D. T. Clark, D. Shuttleworth, *J. Polym. Sci. Polym. Chem. Ed. 18* (1980) 407...25; *ESCA* applied to polymers. Part XXVIII. Plasma polymerization. III. An *ESCA* investigation of polymers synthesized by excitation of inductively coupled RF plasmas in perfluorocyclohexa-1,3- and 1,4-dienes, and in perfluorocyclohexene

D. T. Clark, M. Z. Abrahman, *J. Polym. Sci. Polym. Chem. Ed. 19* (1981) 2689...703; *ESCA* applied to polymers. XXXII. Plasma polymerization. V. A systematic investigation of the inductively coupled RF plasma polymerization of the isomeric tetrafluorobenzenes

D. T. Clark, M. Z. Abrahman, *J. Polym. Sci. Polym. Chem. Ed. 20* (1982) 1717...28; *ESCA* applied to polymers. XXXIV. Plasma polymerization. VII. An *ESCA* investigation of the RF plasma polymerization of perfluorobenzene and perfluorobenzene/hydrogen mixtures

D. T. Clark, M. Z. Abrahman, *J. Polym. Sci. Polym. Chem. Ed. 20* (1982) 1729...44; *ESCA* applied to polymers. XXXV. Plasma polymerization. VIII. A comparative study of the plasma polymers produced from inductively coupled plasmas excited in the fluorobenzenes

D. T. Clark, H. S. Munro, A. Recca, J. K. Stille, *Macromolecules 17* (1984) 1871...3; *ESCA* characterization of perfluoroalkylene-linked polyquinolines

H. S. Munro, C. Till, *J. Polym. Sci. Polym. Chem. Ed. 22* (1984) 3833...42; *ESCA* studies of metal-containing plasma polymers. Part I. Incorporation of mercury into plasma-polymerized perfluorobenzene

H. S. Munro, C. Till, *J. Polym. Sci. Polym. Chem. Ed. 23* (1985) 1621...9; An *ESCA* investigation of the inductively coupled RF plasma polymerization of fluoronaphthalene and fluoronaphthalene/hydrogen mixtures

S. Nagarajan, Z. H. Stachurski, M. E. Hughes, F. P. Larkins, *J. Polym. Sci. Polym. Phys. Ed. 20* (1982) 1001...12; A study of the PE-PTFE system. II. *ESCA* measurements

M. Waesche, T. Gross, I. von Lampe, *Polym. Bull. 14* (1985) 147...51; Radiation chemical reactions of poly-*p*-chlorophenylmethacrylate by *ESCA*

7.2.2.5 CHN and CHNO polymers

D. T. Clark, D. Kilcast, W. J. Feast, W. K. R. Musgrave, *J. Polym. Sci. A-1 10* (1972) 1637...54; Applications of *ESCA* [electron spectroscopy for chemical analysis] to polymer chemistry

D. T. Clark et al., *J. Macromol. Sci. Rev. Macromol. Chem. Phys. C 23* (1983) 217...46; Application of modern analytical techniques for the investigation of cellulose nitrates

J. Gähde, I. Löschcke, K. H. Richter, *Acta Polymer. 34* (1983) 260...4; Röntgen-photoelektronenspektroskopische Untersuchungen zur Ermittlung der Schwachstelle in Polyamid-6/Silan/Glas-Verbundmodellen

H. Hiraoka, W. Lee, *Macromolecules 11* (1978) 622...4; *ESCA* studies of structural changes of poly(acrylonitrile) and poly(chloroacrylonitrile). High-temperature-, electron-impact-, and ultraviolet-light-induced changes

T. Takahaki, I. Shimada, M. Fukuhura, K. Morita, A. Ishitani, *J. Polym. Sci. Polym. Chem. Ed. 24* (1986) 3101...7; *XPS* studies on the chemical structure of the stabilized polyacrylonitrile fiber in the carbon fiber production process

7.2.2.6 CHO polymers

D. T. Clark, H. R. Thomas, *J. Polym. Sci. Polym. Chem. Ed. 14* (1976) 1671...700; Applications of *ESCA* to polymer chemistry. X. Core and valence energy levels of a series of polyacrylates

D. T. Clark, H. R. Thomas, *J. Polym. Sci. Polym. Chem. Ed. 14* (1976) 1701...13; Applications of *ESCA* to polymer chemistry. XI. Core and valence energy levels of a series of polymethacrylates

D. T. Clark, M. M. Abu-Shbak, *Polym. Degr. Stab. 9* (1984) 225...37; Surface aspects of the heat treatment of poly(ethylene terephthalate) as revealed by *ESCA*

G. A. Efremov, Yu. P. Kostikov, *Vysokomol. Soedin. B 24* (1982) 813...5 (Russ.); *ESCA* investigation of the surface of epoxy resins

D. R. Miller, N. A. Peppas, *Macromolecules 20* (1987) 1257...65; Surface analysis of poly(vinyl alcohol-*co*-N-vinyl-2-pyrrolidone) copolymers by *X*-ray photoelectron spectroscopy

P. J. Mjoeberg, *Cellulose Chem. Technol. 15* (1981) 481...6; Chemical surface analysis of wood fibers by means of *ESCA*

A. P. Pijpers, W. A. B. Donners, *J. Polym. Sci. Polym. Chem. Ed. 23* (1985) 453...62; Quantitative determination on the surface composition of acrylate copolymer latex films by *XPS (ESCA)*

Z. Song, B. Rånby, A. Gupta, E. Borsig, O. Vogl, *Polym. Bull. 12* (1984) 245...51; Functional polymers. 31. *ESCA* spectroscopy of polyesters stabilized with polymer-bound ultraviolet stabilizers

A. J. Varma, *Polym. Test. 6* (1986) 79 f.; *ESCA* features of lignins

7.2.2.7 Miscellaneous polymers and resins

D. T. Clark, J. Peeling, J. M. O'Malley, *J. Polym. Sci. Polym. Chem. Ed. 14* (1976) 543...51; Application of *ESCA* to polymer chemistry. VIII. Surface structures of AB block copolymers of polydimethylsiloxane and polystyrene

D. T. Clark, H. S. Munro, P. Finocchiaro, E. Libertini, A. Recca, *Polym. Commun. 25* (1984) 5...9; Surface aspects of metal complexed polymeric Schiff bases as studied by means of *ESCA*

H. S. Munro, J. G. Eaves, *J. Polym. Sci. Polym. Chem. Ed. 23* (1985) 507...15; *ESCA* studies of metal-containing plasma polymers. II. Plasma polymerization of ferrocene, vinylferrocene and dimethylaminomethylferrocene

A. K. Sha'aban, S. McCartney, N. Patel, I. Yilgor, J. S. Riffle, D. W. Dwight, J. E. McGrath, *ACS Polym. Prepr. 24/2* (1983) 130...3; *ESCA* studies on poly(dimethylsiloxane)-urethane copolymers and their blends with segmented polyether-urethanes

D. Shuttleworth, *J. Phys. Chem. 84* (1980) 1629...34; Preparation of metal-polymer dispersions by plasma techniques. An *ESCA* investigation

A. Tóth, N. K. Gladkova, I. Bertóti, S. G. Dourgarian, T. Székely, V. G. Filippova, *ESCA* study on organosilicon block copolymeric membranes, in B. Sedláček (ed.), *Synthetic Polymeric Membranes*; Walter de Gruyter, Berlin etc. 1987

K. Waltersson, *Fibre Sci. Technol. 17* (1982) 289...302; *ESCA* studies of carbon fibres. Part I. The chemical composition of a carbon fibre subsurface

H. M. Wu, S. A. Chen, *Polym. Commun. 28/3* (1987) 75...8; *X*-ray photoelectron spectroscopic studies on WCl$_6$ and MoCl$_5$-doped polyacetylene. An occurrence of electron back-donation

7.2.3 Electron spin resonance spectrometry *(ESR)*

M. Azori, F. Tüdős, A. Rockenbauer, P. Simon, *Eur. Polym. J. 14* (1978) 173...6; Investigation of the macromolecular stable free nitroxide radical

M. Azori, F. Tüdős, A. Rockenbauer, P. Simon, *React. Kinet. Catal. Lett. 8* (1978) 137...42; Inhibition effect of polymeric nitroxide on radical polymerization

M. Azori, F. Tüdős, A. Rockenbauer, P. Simon, *Prepr. IUPAC Macromol. Symp. Mainz 1* (1979) 500...2; Investigation of polymeric nitroxide radical

G. Bálint, A. Rockenbauer, T. Kelen, F. Tüdős, L. Jókay, *Polym. Photochem. 1* (1981) 139...52; *ESR* study of polypropylene photostabilisation by sterically hindered piperidine derivatives

M. J. Ballard, R. G. Gilbert, D. H. Napper, P. J. Pomery, J. H. O'Donnell, *Macromolecules 17* (1984) 504...6; Application of electron spin resonance spectroscopy to emulsion polymerization

L. J. Berliner, X. Wan, H. Fujii, *J. Polym. Sci. Polym. Lett. Ed. 24* (1986) 587...95; Non-invasive visualization of solvent swelling and diffusion into solid polymers by electron spin resonance *(ESR)* imaging

I. M. Brown, T. C. Sandreczki, *Macromolecules 16* (1983) 1890...5; Nitroxide spin labelling of epoxy resins

I. M. Brown, T. C. Sandreczki, *Macromolecules 18* (1985) 1041...3; Fracture-induced free radicals in amine-cured epoxy resins

J. R. Brown, D. K. Hodgeman, *Polymer 23* (1982) 365...8; An *ESR* study of the thermal degradation of Kevlar 49 Aramid

A. T. Bullock, G. G. Cameron, *ESR* studies of spin-labeled synthetic polymers, in K. J. Ivin (ed.), *Structural Studies of Macromolecules by Spectroscopic Methods*; John Wiley, London etc. 1976

A. T. Bullock, G. G. Cameron, I. S. Miles, *Polymer 23* (1982) 1536...9; Segment size in synthetic polymers by the spin-probe method

A. T. Bullock, G. G. Cameron, I. S. Miles, *Polym. Commun. 24* (1983) 22...4; Electron spin resonance studies of spin-labelled polymers: 17. A spin probe study of the compatibility limit of poly(vinyl acetate) and dinonyl phthalate

W. K. Busfield, T. Morley-Buchanan, P. J. Pomery, *J. Polym. Sci. Polym. Chem. Ed. 24* (1986) 3089...99; Post-gamma-irradiation grafting of polypropylene. Part 2. Butadiene. *ESR* experiments

G. G. Cameron, *Pure Appl. Chem. 54* (1982) 483...92; *ESR* studies for polymers in the bulk phase

G. G. Cameron, A. T. Bullock, I. S. Miles, *Eur. Polym. J. 21* (1985) 695...9; Anisotropy of spin-probe rotation in poly(vinyl acetate)

G. G. Cameron, I. S. Miles, A. T. Bullock, *Brit. Polym. J. 19* (1987) 129...34; Distribution in correlation times for rotational diffusion of spin probes in polymers

D. J. Carlsson, C. J. Dobbin, D. M. Wiles, *Macromolecules 18* (1985) 2092...4; Direct observation of macroperoxyl radical propagation and termination by electron spin resonance and infrared spectroscopies

J. C. W. Chien, G. E. Wnek, F. E. Karasz, J. W. Warakomski, L. C. Dickinson, A. J. Heeger, A. G. MacDiarmid, *Macromolecules 15* (1982) 614...21; Electron paramagnetic resonance saturation characteristics of pristine and doped polyacetylenes

K. L. DeVries, M. Igarashi, An *ESR* investigation of environmental effects on Nylon fibers, in A. E. Woodward, F. A. Bovey (eds.), *Polymer Characterization by ESR and NMR, ACS Symp. Ser. 142*; Washington DC 1980

N. M. Dvoreckaja, R. A. Erochina, A. M. Solovev, V. A. Ogarkov, *Izv. Vyssh. Ucheb. Zav. Khim. Khim. Tekhnol. 25* (1982) 996...9 (Russ.); Application of the paramagnetic sonde method to the investigation of the structure of the adhesive layers in composite materials

A. S. Fialkov, L. S. Tjan, R. N. Sibgatullina, *Dokl. Akad. Nauk SSSR 267* (1982) 422...5; Einfluß von Sauerstoff auf die Form der *ESR*-Kurven in Systemen Ruß/Polymer

H. Fischer, G. Giacometti, *J. Polym. Sci. C 16* (1967) 2763...71; *ESR* studies on transient free radicals during redox polymerization of some monomers

H. Fischer, *Fortschr. Hochpolym. Forsch. — Adv. Polym. Sci. 5* (1967) 463 ff.; *ESR*-Spektroskopie makromolekularer Systeme

H. Fischer, *Proc. Roy. Soc. (London) A 302* (1968) 321...7; Applications of electron spin resonance in polymer chemistry

H. Fischer, D. O. Hummel, Electron spin resonance, in D. O. Hummel (ed.), *Polymer Spectroscopy*; Verlag Chemie, Weinheim 1974

J. L. Gerlock, D. R. Bauer, L. M. Briggs, *Polym. Degr. Stab. 14* (1986) 53...71; Photo-stabilisation and photo-degradation in organic coatings containing a hindered amine light stabilizer. Part I. *ESR* measurements of nitroxide concentration

M. Győr, A. Rockenbauer, L. Jókay, F. Tüdős, *Polym. Bull. 15* (1986) 525...30; Plasticizer diffusion into PVC particles as studied by *ESR* spin probe method

M. Győr, A. Rockenbauer, F. Tüdős, *Tetrahedron Lett. 27* (1986) 4795...8; Spin trapping reactions with nitric oxides. V. Reactions with unsaturated macromolecular chains — a new spin labeling method

D. J. Hill, J. H. O'Donnell, P. W. O'Sullivan, P. J. Pomery, A. K. Whittaker, *J. Macromol. Sci. Chem. A 22* (1985) 403...14; An *ESR* study of the *UV* photolysis of styrene and maleic anhydride at 90 K

J. S. Hwang, C. P. Tsonis, *Macromolecules 16* (1983) 736...9; *EPR* application to polymers. 2. Spin probing of poly-(phenylacetylene)

T. V. Ivanova, B. P. Nikolaev, L. N. Petrov, D. K. Toropov, *Vysokomol. Soedin. A 27* (1985) 2281...5 (Russ.); Investigation of gel cations by spin labelling

M. T. Jones, S. Jansen, J. Roble, *Polym. Mat. Sci. Eng. 54* (1986) 578...81; *ESR* studies of polydiacetylene and its reaction with bromine

H. Kaczmarek, F. Rozpłoch, A. Kamińska, *Angew. Makromol. Chem. 118* (1983) 183...90; Effect of copolymers modifying PVC on its physical and mechanical properties and its *UV*-radiation resistance. I. *ESR* investigation of *UV*-irradiated PVC films containing MNA/MA, VC/VAC, MBS or ABS

M. Kamachi, M. Kohno, Y. Kuwae, S. I. Nozakura, *Polymer J. 14* (1982) 749...52; *ESR* observation of methacrylate propagating radicals in stationary state

T. Kelen, F. Tüdős, G. Bálint, A. Rockenbauer, *ACS Polym. Prepr. 25/1* (1984) 28 f.; *ESR* study of hindered piperidine derivatives in polypropylene matrix in presence of other additives

T. Kelen, F. Tüdős, G. Bálint, A. Rockenbauer, Electron spin resonance study of hindered piperidine derivatives in polypropylene matrix in the presence of other additives, in *Polymer Degradation and Stabilization*; American Chemical Soc., Washington DC 1985

S. S. Kim, R. H. Liang, F.-D. Tsay, A. Gupta, *Macromolecules 19* (1986) 1930...5; Electron-spin resonance study of the photooxidation mechanism in poly(*n*-butyl acrylate): Photochemical processes in polymeric systems. 11.

Y. Kuwae, M. Kamachi, S.-I. Nozakura, *Macromolecules 19* (1986) 2912...5; Kinetic and electron-spin resonance studies on radical polymerization of isopropenyl acetate

F. Lembicz, *Makromol. Chem. 186* (1985) 665...9; Spin probe study of relaxation in poly(oxytetramethylen)

J. Linke, P. Wuensche, H. K. Roth, *Polym. Photochem. 2* (1982) 367...81; Intermolecular interactions on photolytically generated anion radicals of maleic anhydride measured by *ESR*

H. Loelinger, B. Gilg, *Angew. Makromol. Chem. 137* (1985) 163...74; *UV*-stabilization of ABS with sterically hindered amines. Results of an *ESR*-study

J. Menczel, J. Varga, G. Hardy, *Period. Polytechn. Chem. Eng. (Budapest) 22* (1978) 231...8 (Russ.); *ESR* investigation of N-vinylphthalimide, irradiated with X-rays

J. Menczel, J. Varga, K. Juhász, M. Binett, *Period. Polytech. Chem. Eng. (Budapest) 22* (1978) 289...96; *ESR* study of thermal degradation of PVC

P. Meurisse, C. Friedrich, M. Dvolaitzky, F. Laupretre, C. Noel, L. Monnerie, *Macromolecules 17* (1984) 72...83; *ESR* investigation of molecular motion in thermotropic liquid crystalline polyesters containing nitroxide spin probes

I. S. Miles, G. G. Cameron, A. T. Bullock, *Polymer 27* (1986) 190...4; *ESR* and saturation transfer *ESR* spectroscopy of spin-probed poly(vinyl acetate): A new spectral transition correlating with glass transition temperature

F. M. Mitte, P. L. Buwalda, J. B. Engberts, *Colloid Polym. Sci. 265* (1987) 42...44; Micelle-polymer complexes as studied by *ESR* spin probe technique

D. L. Patel, R. D. Gilbert, *J. Polym. Sci. Polym. Phys. Ed. 20* (1982) 1019...28; Investigation of molecular order in liquid-crystalline solutions of cellulose triacetate using *ESR* spectroscopy

C. W. Paul, A. T. Bell, D. S. Soong, *Macromolecules 19* (1986) 1436...42; Initiation of methyl methacrylate polymerization by the nonvolatile products of a methyl methacrylate plasma. 4. An *ESR* study of the initiating radicals

A. Rockenbauer, L. Jókay, B. Pukánszky, F. Tüdős, *Macromolecules 18* (1985) 918...23; Electron paramagnetic resonance investigation of orientation produced by mechanical processing in the fillers of polymer composites

A. Rockenbauer, Electron paramagnetic resonance investigation of orientation produced by mechanical processing in the fillers of polymer composites. II. Computer analysis of oriented spectra, in W. E. Steger (ed.), *Progress in Polymer Spectroscopy*; Teubner, Leipzig 1986

H.-K. Roth, P. Wünsche, *Acta Polymer. 32* (1981) 491...511; *EPR* studies during radical polymerization in the liquid state. Review

T. C. Sandreczki, I. M. Brown, *Macromolecules 17* (1984) 1789...94; Electron paramagnetic resonance studies of amine-cured epoxy resins: dependence of nitroxide spin-probe mobility on cross-link density, free volume, and temperature

M. Shiotani, J. Sohma, J. H. Freed, *Macromolecules 16* (1983) 1495...9; Anisotropic molecular motion of spin-labeled poly(methyl methacrylate) detected by *ESR*

P. Simon, A. Rockenbauer, M. Azori, F. Tüdős, *Eur. Polym. J. 13* (1977) 189...92; *ESR* study of γ-irradiated nylon-6; conformational isomerism of free radicals

P. Simon, A. Rockenbauer, M. Azori, F. Tüdős, *Polym. Bull. 5* (1981) 425...7; *ESR* study of the spin labeled polyethylene crosslinking system

P. Simon, L. Sümegi, A. Rockenbauer, F. Tüdős, J. Csekő, K. Hideg, *Macromolecules 18* (1985) 1137...39; Effect of main chain double bond on dynamics of polystyrene: An *ESR* study of macromolecules spin labeled by copolymerization

P. Simon, A. Rockenbauer, F. Tüdős, *Macromolecules 19* (1986) 2454...6; *ESR* study of polystyrene chain scission induced by 2,6-dichloronitrosobenzene: observation of chiral nitroxide radical pair

V. P. Striguckij, I. I. Listvan, Ju. Ju. Navosa, L. S. Ljubcenko, B. I. Liogonskij, *Dokl. Akad. Nauk Belorus. SSR 27* (1983) 240...3 (Russ.); Concerning the paramagnetism of the organic components of natural high molecular weight substances

J. Tino, F. Szöcs, Z. Hlouskova, *Polymer 23* (1982) 1443...5; Study of radical products of mechanically destructed poly(N-vinylene carbazole)

A. Torikai, K. Fucei, *Polym. Degrad. Stab. 13* (1985) 183...9; Elementary processes in the radiation-induced degradation of poly(ethylene terephthalate). A note

H. Toriumi, R. A. Weiss, H. A. Frank, *Macromolecules 17* (1984) 2104...7; Electron spin resonance studies of ionic interactions in sulfonated polystyrene ionomers: Manganese(II) salts

G. Vancsó, A. Rockenbauer, *Chemica Scripta 17* (1981) 153f.; Saturation and line width studies of the *ESR* spectra in polyacetylene

J. Varga, K. Belina, J. Menczel, F. Olajos, *Magyar Kémiai Folyóirat 88* (1982) 165...9 (Hung.); Preparation and investigation of polyimides. V. The investigation of the mutual influence of dianhydride and solvent

O. Watanabe, M. Tabata, J. Sohma, *Macromolecules 17* (1984) 1139...45; *ESR* study on local conformations of polystyrene spin adducts produced by chlorinated nitrosobenzene as a chain-scission inducer

J. Yamauchi, S. Yano, *Macromolecules 15* (1982) 210; *ESR* studies of structure in ethylene-acrylic acid copolymers neutralized with manganese(II) acetate

N.-L. Yang, J. Liutkus, H. Haubenstock, An *ESR* study of initially formed intermediates in the photodegradation of poly(vinyl chloride), in A. E. Woodward, F. A. Bovey (eds.), *Polymer Characterization by ESR and NMR, ACS Symp. Ser. 142*; Washington DC 1980

K.-H. Wassmer, E. Ohmes, M. Portugall, H. Ringsdorf, G. Kothe, *J. Am. Chem. Soc. 107* (1985) 1511...9; Molecular order and dynamics of liquid-crystal side-chain polymers: an electron spin resonance study employing rigid nitroxide spin probes

P. Wünsche, K. Pfeiffer, H.-J. Lorkowski, J. Reinhardt, *Acta Polymer. 36* (1985) 268...72; *ESR*-Untersuchungen an γ-bestrahltem Polymethylmethacrylat und an einem Copolymerisat mit Methacrylsäure

N. D. Zacharov, V. I. Izjumova, M. Ja. Melnikov, A. M. Sachparonjanc, G. I. Kostrikina, *Vysokomol. Soedin. A 26* (1984) 2082...7 (Russ.); *ESR* investigation of the interaction between the surface of rubber powder and p-nitrosodiphenylamine

7.2.4 Miscellaneous spectroscopic methods

G. Allen, A review of neutron scattering with special reference to the measurement of the unperturbed dimensions in macromolecules, in K. J. Ivin (ed.), *Structural Studies of Macromolecules by Spectroscopic Methods*; John Wiley, London etc. 1976

F. Ciardelli, C. Carlini, E. Chiellini, P. Salvadori, L. Lardicci, Circular dichroism and optical rotatory dispersion in polymer structure analysis, in D. O. Hummel (ed.), *Proceedings of the 5th European Symposium on Polymer Spectroscopy*; Verlag Chemie, Weinheim 1979

J. Comyn, Inelastic tunnelling spectroscopy of polymeric adhesives and coupling agents, in W. E. Steger (ed.), *Progress in Polymer Spectroscopy*; Teubner, Leipzig 1986

G. C. Corfield, J. S. Brooks, S. Plimley, *Org. Coat. Appl. Polym. Sci. Proc. 44* (1981) 443; Mössbauer studies of polymers from 1,1-divinylferrocene

C. J. Edwards, S. Bantle, W. Burchard, R. F. Stepto, J. A. Semlyen, *Polymer 23* (1982) 873...6; Studies of cyclic and linear poly(dimethylsiloxanes). 9. Quasi-elastic light scattering and concentration dependences of diffusion coefficients

D. M. Hercules, S. W. Graham, J. A. Gardella jr., *Org. Coat. Appl. Polym. Sci. Proc. 44* (1981) 648...51; Structural analysis of polymeric materials by laser microprobe mass analysis (*LAMMA*)

K.-J. Liu, J. S. Lignowski, R. Ullman, *Makromol. Chem. 105* (1967) 18...42; Optical rotatory dispersion studies of poly(1-α-methylbenzyl methacrylate) and poly(methyl methacrylate) in solution

G. D. Patterson, P. J. Carroll, J. R. Stevens, *J. Polym. Sci. Polym. Phys. Ed. 21* (1983) 605...11; Photon correlation spectroscopy of polystyrene as a function of temperature and pressure

G. D. Patterson, P. J. Carroll, J. R. Stevens, *J. Polym. Sci. Polym. Phys. Ed. 21* (1983) 613...23; Photon correlation spectroscopy of poly(methyl methacrylate) near the glass transition

B. Rodmacq, M. Pineri, J. M. Coey, A. Meagher, *J. Polym. Sci. Polym. Phys. Ed. 20* (1982) 603...21; Moessbauer spectroscopy of Nafion polymer membranes exchanged with Fe(2+), Fe(3+), and Eu(3+)

C. H. Wang, G. Fytas, T. Dorfmüller, *Macromolecules 16* (1983) 68...71; Light beating spectroscopy of branched poly(propylene glycol)

J. W. White, Studies of phonons in polymer crystals (by neutron scattering), in K. J. Ivin (ed.), *Structural Studies of Macromolecules by Spectroscopic Methods*; John Wiley, London etc. 1976

7.3 Non-destructive chromatographic methods

J. H. van den Berg, N. L. Meijerink, T. G. Scholte, R. Konigsveld, G. Glöckner, *Macromolecules 17* (1984) 962...7; Size exclusion and high-performance precipitation liquid chromatography of styrene-acrylonitril copolymers

L. Birkofer, W. Pauly, *Brennstoff-Chemie 50* (1969) 2...8; Gaschromatographische und massenspektroskopische Untersuchung von Kohleextrakten

G.-P. Blümer, R. Thoms, M. Zander, *Erdöl Kohle Erdgas Petrochemie 31* (1978) 197; Kombination Hochdruck-Flüssigkeits-Chromatographie/*UV*-Spektroskopie

D. Braun, G. Vorendohre, *Kunststoffe 57* (1967) 821...4; Dünnschichtchromatographische Analyse von Polyamiden

W. Dankelman, J. M. H. Daemen, A. J. J. de Breet, J. L. Mulder, W. G. B. Huysmans, J. de Wit, *Angew. Makromol. Chem. 54* (1976) 187...201; Modern methods for the analysis of urea formaldehyde resins

R. Denig, *Kunststoffe 75* (1985) 491...5; Chromatographische Methoden bei der Analyse von Kunststoffen

H. Feuerberg, W. Kretschmer, H. Weigel, *Kautsch. Gummi 14* (1961) WT 218...21; Beitrag zur Analyse von Elastomeren in Vulkanisaten. Papierchromatographische Identifizierung von Elastomer-Pyrolysaten

G. Glöckner, *Pure Appl. Chem. 55* (1983) 1553...62; Characterization of copolymers by means of liquid chromatography

G. Glöckner, V. Albrecht, F. Francuskiewicz, *Angew. Makromol. Chem. 127* (1984) 153...69; Charakterisierung von Styrol-Acrylnitril-Copolymeren durch Ausschlußchromatographie und turbidimetrische Titration der dabei erhaltenen Fraktionen. I. Testgemische

E. Haeffner, *Isolierung und Strukturaufklärung der C_{20}- und C_{22}-Polyensäuren aus Rüböl (Oleum Rapae)*; Thesis, Math. Nat. Sci. Fac., Univ. Cologne 1966

H. Inagaki, *Adv. Polym. Sci. 24* (1977) 190...237; Polymer separation and characterization by thin-layer chromatography

H. Inagaki, T. Kotaka, T.-I. Min, *Pure Appl. Chem. 46* (1976) 61...70; Separation and characterization of block and graft copolymers by thin-layer chromatography

J. Klee, H.-H. Hörhold, W. Tänzer, M. Fedtke, *Angew. Makromol. Chem. 147* (1987) 71...81; Unvernetzte Epoxid-Amin-Additionspolymere. 16. *HPLC*-Analyse und ^{13}C-*NMR*-Spektroskopie von telechelen (Diglycidylether-Bisphenol A)-Anilin-Prepolymeren

E. Knappe, D. Peteri, *Z. analyt. Chem. 188* (1962) 184; Dünnschichtchromatographie der Dicarbonsäuren. I. Trennungen in der homologen Reihe von Oxal- bis Sebacinsäure

E. Knappe, D. Peteri, *Z. analyt. Chem. 188* (1962) 352; Dünnschichtchromatographie der Dicarbonsäuren. II. Trennung von carbocyclischen Dicarbonsäuren

E. Knappe, D. Peteri, *Z. analyt. Chem. 190* (1962) 380; Dünnschichtchromatographie der Dicarbonsäuren. III. Identifizierung von einfach ungesättigten aliphatischen Dicarbonsäuren mit Hilfe der Hydrier-Differenz-Methode

E. Knappe, D. Peteri, *Z. analyt. Chem. 199* (1964) 270; Dünnschichtchromatographische Identifizierung technisch wichtiger Polyalkohole

E. Knappe, I. Rohdewald, *Z. analyt. Chem. 200* (1964) 9; Die dünnschichtchromatographische Identifizierung der niederen Phenole über ihre Kupplungsprodukte mit Echtrotsalz AL

E. Knappe, I. Rohdewald, *Z. analyt. Chem. 210* (1965) 183; Dünnschichtchromatographie der Dicarbonsäuren. IV. Kombination von dünnschichtchromatographischen Anordnungen zur Identifizierung von Einzelkomponenten in umfassenden Dicarbonsäuregemischen

E. Knappe, K. G. Yekundi, *Z. analyt. Chem. 203* (1964) 87; Imprägnierung chromatographischer Dünnschichten mit Polyestern. II. Trennung und Identifizierung von niederen und mittleren Fettsäuren über ihre Hydroxamsäuren

G. Pastuska, H.-J. Petrowitz, *Chemiker-Ztg. 86* (1962) 311; Dünnschicht-Chromatographie der Phenole

V. Preussler, K. Šlais, J. Hanuš, *Angew. Makromol. Chem. 150* (1987) 179...87; The use of micro-*HPLC* with gradient elution for the characterization of phenol-formaldehyde resins

S. E. Prince, G. D. McGinnis, *Polym. Mat. Sci. Eng. 53* (1985) 196...202; Characterization of phenol-formaldehyde resins using reverse-phase chromatography

H. Schindlbauer, J. Schuster, *Kunststoffe 71* (1981) 508...13; Fortschritte in der chromatographischen Auftrennung von Harnstoff-Formaldehyd-Kondensaten

H. Schmidt, *Fette Seifen Anstrichmittel 73* (1971) 586...90; Über eine dünnschicht-chromatographische Identifizierung genuiner Naturwachse

F. Scholl, *Dtsch. Farben-Z. 16* (1962) 93, 146; Die Gaschromatographie und ihre Anwendung auf dem Anstrichmittelgebiet

U.-D. Standt, *Angew. Makromol. Chem. 150* (1987) 13...9; Characterization of low molecular compounds in dashboard foils by extraction, preparative high performance liquid chromatography, and *IR*-spectroscopy

E. G. Tsatsaroni, A. H. Kehayoglou, *Angew. Makromol. Chem. 147* (1987) 35...40; Identification of nylons by thin layer chromatography

L. H. Tung, A. L. Gatzke, *J. Polym. Sci. Polym. Phys. Ed. 21* (1983) 1839...49; Determination of long-chain branching in model polystyrene samples by the *GPC*-sedimentation method

S. S. Zislina, P. P. Nefedov, S. D. Julcevskaja, L. M. Terman, *Acta Polymer. 35* (1984) 729...32 (Russ.); Investigation of the products of hydrolytic copolycondensation of methylvinyl and methylphenyldichlorosilanes by means of exclusion liquid chromatography

7.4 Thermal analysis

B. K. Appelt, *Polym. Eng. Sci. 23* (1983) 125...8; Characterizing photoresists by thermal analysis

I. M. Barkalov, D. P. Kirjuchin, *Vysokomol. Soedin. A 2* (1980) 723...37 (Russ.); Calorimetric investigation of polymerization in solid or viscous medium

D. J. Blundell, D. R. Beckett, P. H. Willcocks, *Polymer 22* (1981) 704...7; Routine crystallinity measurements of polymers by *DSC*

R. F. Boyer, *Macromolecules 17* (1984) 1803...11; Pressure dependence of secondary transitions. 6. $T_{\alpha c}$ and $T_{\alpha a}$ in polyethylenes

D. W. Brazier, G. H. Nickel, Z. Szentgyörgyi, *Rubber Chem. Technol. 53* (1980) 160...75; Enthalpic analysis of vulcanization by calorimetry. Thiuram monosulfide/sulfur vulcanization of NR, BR and SBR

H. J. Bressers, J. G. Kloosterboer, *Polym. Bull. 2* (1980) 201...4; Thermally and light-induced polymerization of ethyl acrylate and methyl methacrylate, studied by *DSC*

G. G. Cameron, A. Rudin, *J. Polym. Sci. Polym. Phys. Ed. 19* (1981) 1799f.; Comments on the interpretation of kinetic parameters from dynamic thermogravimetric experiments

B. Cassel, *Polymer News 6* (1980) 108...15; Characterization of thermosets

B. Čerič, S. Jeler, P. Bukovec, *Acta Polymer. 32* (1981) 546...51; Thermogravimetry, differential thermal analysis and oxygen index of untreated and flame-resistant treated wool-polyester blends

A. V. Chabenko, Z. L. Titkova, V. S. Volkov, V. S. Levsanov, S. A. Dolmatov, *Vysokomol. Soedin. A 23* (1981) 1135...40 (Russ.); Investigation of the thermal degradation of poly-*bis*-maleinimidamides by thermogravimetry

J. C. Chien, J. K. Kiang, *Macromolecules 12* (1979) 1088...92; Polymer reaction. 11. Oxidative pyrolysis of poly(isoprene)

J. Clements, G. Capaccio, I. M. Ward, *J. Polym. Sci. Polym. Phys. Ed. 17* (1979) 693...703; Melting behavior of ultra-high modulus linear polyethylene

L. Costa, G. Camino, L. Trossarelli, *J. Anal. Appl. Pyrol. 8* (1985) 15...24; A study of the thermal degradation of polystyrene-chloroalkyne mixtures by thermogravimetry-high resolution gas chromatography

J. S. Crighton, Characterization of textile materials by thermal degradation: a critique of pyrolysis *GC* and thermogravimetry, in C. E. Ronald Jones, C. A. Cramers (eds.), *Analytical Pyrolysis*; Elsevier, Amsterdam 1977

P. Cukor, M. Rubner, *J. Polym. Sci. Polym. Phys. Ed. 18* (1980) 909...13; Effect of heating on the relative molecular weight distribution of isomers of polyphenylacetylene

C. De Rosa, G. Guerra, R. Napolitano, V. Petraccone, B. Pirozzi, *Eur. Polym. J. 20* (1984) 937...41; Conditions for the $\alpha_1 \rightarrow \alpha_2$ transition in isotactic polypropylene samples

F. W. Evans, H. Frey, *Chimia (Ch) 34* (1980) 247...49; Reaktionskinetik aus kalorimetrischen Untersuchungen, ein Beispiel der industriellen Verwendung

J. H. Flynn, B. Dickens, *US Government Reports AD-A063060* (1978) Sep. 1...24; Application of new kinetic techniques to the lifetime prediction of polymers from weight-loss data

J. H. Flynn, *ACS Polym. Prepr. 26/1* (1985) 6 f.; The kinetics of cure of resins and varnishes by differential scanning calorimetry

B. G. Frushour, *Polym. Bull. 4* (1981) 305...14 (jap.); A new thermal analytical technique for acrylic polymers

S. Gabbay, S. S. Stivala, P. R. Reed, *Anal. Chem. Acta 78* (1975) 359; Application of thermal and mass chromatography to thermal oxidative degradation of polymers

K. D. Gauler, H. Möhler, *Farbe Lack 86* (1980) 507...15; Quantitative Differenzmikrokalorimetrie zur Untersuchung der Lackhärtung. 4. Melamin-Alkyd-Harze

U. W. Gedde, J. F. Jansson, *Polym. Test. 1* (1980) 303...12; Determination of thermal oxidation of high density polyethylene pipes using differential scanning calorimetry

A. Ghijsels, F. M. Waals, *Polym. Test 1* (1980) 149...60; Differential scanning calorimetry: A powerful tool for the characterization of thermoplastics

I. J. Goldfarb, E. G. Jones, *ACS Polym. Prepr. 26/1* (1985) 17 f.; Characterization of high temperature polymers by *TGA/MS*

N. Grassie, K. F. Francey, *Polym. Degr. Stab. 2* (1980) 53...66; The thermal degradation of polysiloxanes. Part 3. Poly(dimethyl/methyl phenyl siloxane)

N. Grassie, K. F. Francey, I. G. MacFarlane, *Polym. Degr. Stab. 2* (1980) 67...83; The thermal degradation of polysiloxanes. Part 4. Poly(dimethyl/diphenyl siloxane)

J. N. Hay, *Brit. Polym. J. 11* (1979) 137...45; Crystallisation kinetics and melting studies

J. N. Hay, P. L. Mills, *Polymer 23* (1982) 1380...4; The use of differential scanning calorimetry to study polymer crystallization kinetics

A. Henig, M. Jaeth, H. Möhler, *Farbe Lack 86* (1980) 313...9; Quantitative Differenzmikrokalorimetrie zur Untersuchung der Lackhärtung. 2. Pulverlacke auf Epoxidharzbasis

T. R. Hesketh, J. V. van Bogart, S. L. Cooper, *Polym. Eng. Sci. 20* (1980) 190...7; Differential scanning calorimetry analysis of morphological changes in segmented elastomers

C. J. Hilado, P. A. Huttlinger, *J. Elastomers Plast. 12* (1980) 150...4; Weight loss of plastics at various temperatures

F. Horkay, *Farbe Lack 81* (1975) 189...203; Untersuchungen von Lacken und Farben

C. Ibbotson, R. P. Sheldon, *Brit. Polym. J. 11* (1979) 146...50; Heterogeneous crystallization of polyethylene terephthalate

K.-H. Illers, H. Haberkorn, *Makromol. Chem. 142* (1971) 31...67; Schmelzverhalten, Struktur und Kristallinität von 6-Polyamid

K.-H. Illers, *Progr. Colloid Polym. Sci. 58* (1975) 61...76; Die Änderung der Dichte und der Schmelzwärme beim Tempern von 6,6-Polyamid

G. Janik, H. Möhler, *Farbe Lack 86* (1980) 425...9; Quantitative Differenzmikrokalorimetrie zur Untersuchung der Lackhärtung. 3. Isocyanatvernetzende Polyesterharze

F. E. Karasz, W. J. MacKnight, *Pure Appl. Chem. 52* (1980) 409...17; Heats of polymer mixing

K. Kimura et al., *J. Appl. Polym. Sci. 29* (1984) 3161...70; Characterization of ethylene-1-butene copolymers by differential scanning calorimetry and ^{13}C-*NMR* spectroscopy

W. Kunze, H. Möhler, *Thermochim. Acta 83* (1985) 47...58; Characterization of processing for injection molding of thermoplastics using thermal analysis

E. G. Lovering, D. C. Wooden, *J. Polym. Sci. A-2 7* (1969) 1639...49; Transitions in *trans*-1,4-polyisoprene

J. R. MacCallum, W. W. Wright, *Polym. Degr. Stab. 3* (1981) 397...401; Weight change caused by accumulation of volatiles during thermogravimetry of polymers

J. S. Mayer, R. B. Cassel, *Elastomerics 113* (1981) 21...6; Thermal analysis test methods for characterizing elastomers

H. Möhler, R. Wellert, *Farbe Lack 88* (1982) 722...30; Einsatzmöglichkeiten der Thermoanalyse in der Lacktechnik

H. Nishizaki, K. Yoshida, H. H. Wang, *J. Appl. Polym. Sci. 25* (1980) 2869...77; Comparative study of various methods for thermogravimetric analysis of polystyrene degradation

H. Nishizaki, K. Yoshida, *J. Appl. Polym. Sci. 26* (1981) 3503 f.; Effect of molecular weight on various *TGA* methods in polystyrene degradation

H. Noemayr, H. Rothbaecher, *Thermochim. Acta 83* (1985) 131...8; Importance of thermoanalytical methods for quality control in the car building industry

K. L. Paciorek, W. G. Lajiness, C. T. Lenk, *J. Polym. Sci. 60* (1962) 141...8; Differential thermal analysis of fluoroelastomer systems

R. Patel, R. Patel, K. C. Patel, R. D. Patel, *Makromol. Chem. Rapid Commun. 1* (1980) 503...6; Thermal degradation of a *p*-hydroxybenzoic acid-formaldehyde condensation product

F. Paulik, J. Paulik, *Hungarian Scientific Instruments 1980*(50) 19...30; Simultaneous thermoanalytical examinations under conventional and quasi isothermal − quasi isobaric conditions

N. S. Pesocinskaja, M. V. Vinogradov, E. N. Sotnikov, N. P. Apuchtina, *Izv. Vysskh. Ucheb. Zaved. Khim. Khim. Thekh. 23* (1980) 1295...9 (Russ.); The behavior of amorphous polyurethane elastomers on the influence of high temperatures

R. B. Prime, *ACS Polym. Prepr. 26/1* (1985) 15 f.; Thermogravimetric analysis/mass spectroscopy of a phenolic resole resin

P. L. Privalov, *Pure Appl. Chem. 52* (1980) 479...97; Scanning microcalorimeters for studying macromolecules

G. Radhakrishnan, T. Nagabhushanam, K. T. Joseph, *Makromol. Chem. 180* (1979) 2923...8; Thermal analysis of oxidized poly(acrylonitrile-*co*-methyl methacrylate)

M. J. Richardson, N. G. Savill, *Brit. Polym. J. 11* (1979) 123...9; What information will differential scanning calorimetry give on glassy polymers?

W. Roth, *Plaste Kautsch. 27* (1980) 132...6; Ermittlung der Reaktivität von Epoxidharzmassen nach differentialthermoanalytischen Methoden

T. P. Russell, J. T. Koberstein, *J. Polym. Sci. Polym. Phys. Ed. 23* (1985) 1109...15; Simultaneous differential scanning calorimetry and small-angle *X*-ray scattering

Ju. N. Sazanov, F. S. Florinskij, G. N. Fedorova, M. M. Koton, *Vysokomol. Soedin. B 21* (1979) 463...7 (Russ.); Thermal and thermal oxidative degradation of rigid-chain polyimides

Y. N. Sazanov, F. S. Florinsky, M. M. Koton, *Eur. Polym. J. 15* (1979) 781...6; Investigation of thermal and thermooxidative degradation of some polyimides containing oxyphenylene groups in the main chain

M. Savov, C. Bechev, Y. Georgiev, K. Dimov, *Angew. Makromol. Chem. 127* (1984) 7...26; *DSC* studies on polyester-polyamide biconstituent fibers

H. A. Schneider, *Polym. Bull. 2* (1980) 551...3; The influence of the volatility of reaction products on thermogravimetric results of polymer degradation

H. A. Schneider, *Thermochim. Acta 83* (1985) 59...70; The quantitative evaluation of *TG*-curves of polymers

N. S. Schneider, J. K. Gillham, *Org. Coat. Plast. Chem.* *38* (1978) 491...6; *DSC* and *TBA* studies of the curing behavior of two dicy-containing epoxy resins

N. M. Seidov, R. M. Aliguliev, F. O. Gusejnov, Ch. D. Ibragimov, G. S. Ovanesova, T. N. Talybova, *Vysokomol. Soedin. B 22* (1980) 254...7 (Russ.); Investigation of the vulcanization of poly(ethylene-*co*-propylene-*co*-hexene) with the aid of differential thermal analysis

J. Sickfeld, *Kautsch. Gummi Kunstst. 36* (1983) 760...5; Die Thermogravimetrie von Vulkanisaten

K. W. Smalldon, R. E. Ardrey, L. R. Mullings, *Analytica Chim. Acta 107* (1979) 327...34; The characterization of closely related polymeric materials by thermogravimetry-mass spectrometry

R. Sonninen, L. Niinistö, O. Kirret, *Kemia-Kemi 8* (1981) 89...91; Thermal decomposition of selected polymer fibres in vacuum

H. Springer, U. Brinkmann, G. Hinrichsen, *Colloid Polym. Sci. 259* (1981) 38...46; Differential thermal analysis of drawn PET-films

E. B. Stark, J. C. Seferis, *ACS Polym. Prepr. 26/1* (1985) 23...25; Kinetic information from multiple thermal analysis techniques

R. H. Still, *Brit. Polym. J. 11* (1979) 101...14; Some problems associated with the application of thermal methods to polymers

M. Tomescu, I. Demetrescu, E. Segal, *J. Appl. Polym. Sci. 26* (1981) 4103...16; Study of the thermal degradation of acrylic copolymers

E. Torchon, *Rev. Gen. Caoutch. Plast. 60* (1983) 121...4; Thermogravimetry applied to elastomers

B. L. Treherne, *Kunststoffberater 26* (1981) 28f.; Thermo-analyse, ein Verfahren zur Gütekontrolle. Für Anwendung in der Kunststoff- und Gummiindustrie

W. D. Varnell, I. R. Harrison, D. R. Roberts, *J. Appl. Polym. Sci. 27* (1982) 3591...5; The utilization of *DSC* in studies of oligomers

I. Wadsoe, *Pure Appl. Chem. 52* (1980) 465...77; Calorimetric instrumentation for studies of biopolymer model compounds

H. Wyden, *Kunststoffe — Plastics 29* (1982) 9...16; Thermogravimetrische Bestimmung der Hauptkomponenten in technologischen Elastomersystemen

7.5 Thermal degradation, analytical pyrolysis

7.5.1 Fundamentals

E. M. Andersson, I. Ericsson, *J. Anal. Appl. Pyrol. 3* (1981) 35...47; Thermal degradation of organic polymers using different metals as the pyrolysis filament

R. K. Bansal, R. Agarwal, *Angew. Makromol. Chem. 127* (1984) 43...7; Studies on thermal stability of epoxy resins

D. C. de Jongh, Pyrolytic reaction mechanisms, in C. E. Roland Jones, C. A. Cramers (eds.) *Analytical Pyrolysis*; Elsevier, Amsterdam 1977

G. F. L. Ehlers, K. R. Fisch, W. R. Powell, *J. Polymer Sci. A-1 7* (1969) 2931...53; Thermal degradation of polymers with phenylene units in the chain. I. Polyphenylenes and poly(phenylene oxides); *ibid.* 2955...67; II. Sulfur-containing polyarylenes; *ibid.* 2969...81; III. Polyarylates

G. F. L. Ehlers, K. R. Fisch, W. R. Powell, *J. Polymer Sci. A-1 8* (1970) 3511...27; Thermal degradation of polymers with phenylene units in the chain. IV. Aromatic polyamides and polyimides

J. L. Fan, J. C. Chien, *Polym. Degr. Stab. 12* (1985) 43...63; Thermal degradation studies of segmented thermoplastic elastomers

E. Fitzer, *Angew. Chem. 92* (1980) 375...86; Thermischer Abbau von Polymeren bis zum elementaren Kohlenstoff — ein Weg zu Werkstoffen der Zukunft

I. R. Gelling, M. J. Loadman, B. D. Sidek, *J. Polym. Sci. Polym. Chem. Ed. 17* (1979) 1383...92; Pyrolysis of polyisoprenes. I. Differentiation between natural and synthetic *cis*-1,4-polyisoprenes

N. Grassie, M. I. Guy, *Polym. Degr. Stab. 12* (1985) 65...91; Degradation of epoxy polymers. 1. Products of thermal degradation of bisphenol-A diglycidyl ether

T. Hirata, T. Kashiwagi, J. E. Brown, *Macromolecules 18* (1985) 1410...18; Thermal and oxidative degradation of poly(methyl methacrylate). Weight loss

D. O. Hummel, H.-J. Düssel, G. Czybulka, N. Wenzel, G. Holl, *Spectrochim. Acta 41 A* (1985) 279...90; Analytical pyrolysis of copolymers

D. Kumar, G. M. Fohlen, J. A. Parker, *J. Polym. Sci. Polym. Chem. Ed. 21* (1983) 245...67; High-temperature resins based on aromatic amine-terminated bisaspartimides

D. H. MacKerron, R. P. Gordon, *Polym. Degr. Stab. 12* (1985) 277...85; Minor products from the pyrolysis of thin films of poly(hexamethylene adipamide)

L. Michajlov, P. Zugenmeier, H.-J. Cantow, *Polymer 9* (1968) 325...43; Structural investigations on polyethylenes and ethylene-propylene copolymers by reaction gas chromatography and *X*-ray diffraction

G. Montaudo, C. Puglisi, Thermal degradation mechanisms in condensation polymers, in N. Grassie (ed.), *Developments in Polymer Degradation*, Vol. 7; Applied Science, London 1986

J.-M. Rigo, O. Riveros-Ravelo, H. Dieu, *J. Anal. Appl. Pyrol. 8* (1985) 123...34; Degradative transition of pyrolysis to combustion of a polyurethane at the analytical level

M. B. Roller, *Polym. Eng. Sci. 19* (1979) 692...8; Thermoset and coatings technology: The challenge of interdisciplinary chemistry

M. Seeger, H.-J. Cantow, *Makromol. Chem. 176* (1975) 2059...78; Thermische Spaltungsmechanismen in Homo- und Copolymeren aus α-Olefinen. 2. Polypropylen mit bekannter Taktizität, Polyisobutylen und Poly(1-buten)

R. Sonninen, L. Niinistö, O. Kirret, *Kemia-Kemi 8/3* (1981) 89...91; Thermal decomposition of selected polymer fibers in vacuum

G. J. Sutton, B. J. Tighe, *J. Polym. Sci. Polym. Chem. Ed. 11* (1973) 1069...77; Poly-α-ester degradation studies. I. Introduction: Design and construction of equipment

T. Székely, M. Blazsó, Analytical pyrolysis of inorganic and thermostable polymers, in C. E. Roland Jones, C. A. Cramers (eds.), *Analytical Pyrolysis*; Elsevier, Amsterdam 1977

L. J. Taylor, *ACS Polym. Prepr. 13/1* (1972) 113...7; A survey of practical applications of polymer-degradation processes

P. C. Uden, D. E. Henderson, R. J. Lloyd, An interfaced vapor phase instrumental system for thermal analysis and pyrolysis, in C. E. Roland Jones, C. A. Cramers (eds.), *Analytical Pyrolysis*; Elsevier, Amsterdam 1977

E. Urbas, A. Kogerman, E. Kullik, O. Kirret, E. Heinsoo, Yu. D. Andrichenko, T. V. Druzhinina, *Acta Polymer. 31* (1980) 264...6; Über die quantitative Zusammensetzung der Pyrolyseprodukte beim thermischen Abbau halogenhaltiger Polyamidfasern

C. T. Vijayakumar, J. K. Fink, K. Lederer, *Angew. Makromol. Chem. 113* (1983) 121...8; Primary processes of the thermal degradation of HET acid containing unsaturated polyester cured with styrene

B. A. Zubanov, G. M. Mirkarimova, M. B. Leonova, Ju. N. Sazanov et al., *Vysokomol. Soedin. B 27* (1985) 358...61 (Russ.); Thermal analysis of polyimides of aryl-alicyclic composition

7.5.2 Pyrolysis-mass spectrometry
(see also 6.7.3 and 7.5.3.9)

7.5.2.1 Fundamentals, methodology, general investigations of polymers

R. E. Adams, *Anal. Chem. 55* (1983) 414...6; Positive and negative chemical ionization pyrolysis mass spectrometry of polymers

A. Ballistreri, D. Garozzo, M. Giuffrida, G. Montaudo, A. Filippi, C. Guaita, P. Manaresi, F. Pilati, *Macromolecules 20* (1987) 1029...32, *ibid.* 2991...7; Fast atom bombardment mass spectrometry identification of oligomers contained in poly(ε-caprolactam) and poly(butylene isophthalate)

H. D. Beckey, H.-R. Schulten, *Z. analyt. Chem. 273* (1975) 345...58; Felddesorptions-Massenspektrometrie biologisch wichtiger Substanzen

I. V. Bletsos, D. M. Hercules, D. van Leyen, A. Benninghoven, *Macromolecules 20* (1987) 407...13; Time-of-flight secondary ion mass spectrometry of polymers in the mass range 500 – 10000

C. E. Brown, P. Kovacic, C. A. Wilkie, R. B. Cody, R. E. Hein, J. A. Kinsinger, *Polym. Mat. Sci. Eng. 54* (1986) 307...11; Laser desorption/Fourier transform mass spectral analysis of polymers

R. S. Brown, D. A. Weil, C. L. Wilkins, *Macromolecules 19* (1986) 1255...60; Laser desorption-Fourier transform mass spectrometry for the characterization of polymers

D. C. Conway, R. Marak, *J. Polym. Sci. Polym. Chem. Ed. 20* (1982) 1765...75; Analysis of polymers by pyrolysis/chemical ionization mass spectrometry

R. J. Cotter, J. P. Honovich, J. K. Olthoff, R. P. Lattimer, *Macromolecules 19* (1986) 2996...3001; Laser desorption time-of-flight mass spectrometry of low molecular weight polymers

P. J. Derrick, *Fresenius Z. Anal. Chem. 324* (1987) 486...91; Mass spectroscopy at high mass

M. Doerr, I. Luederwald, H.-R. Schulten, *J. Anal. Appl. Pyrol. 8* (1985) 109...21; Investigations of polymers by field desorption and fast atom bombardment mass spectrometry

D. M. Hercules, S. W. Graham, J. A. Gardella jr., *Org. Coat. Appl. Polym. Sci. Proc. 44* (1981) 648...5; Structural analysis of polymeric materials by laser microprobe mass analysis (*LAMMA*)

D. M. Hercules, I. V. Bletses, A. Benninghoven, D. Griefendorf, *Polym. Mat. Sci. Eng. 54* (1986) 302...6; Characterization of polymers using time-of-flight secondary ion mass spectrometry

D. A. Hickman, I. Jane, *Analyst 104* (1979) 334...47; Reproducibility of pyrolysis-mass spectrometry using three different pyrolysis systems

D. O. Hummel, Structure and degradation behaviour of synthetic polymers using pyrolysis in combination with field ion mass spectrometry, in C. E. Roland Jones, C. A. Cramers (eds.), *Analytical Pyrolysis*; Elsevier, Amsterdam 1977

D. O. Hummel, H.-J. Düssel, H. Rosen, Decomposition behaviour of thermostable polymers as studied by pyrofield ion mass spectrometry, in Z. Jedlinski (ed.), *Advances in the Chemistry of Thermally Stable Polymers*; Warszawa 1977

D. O. Hummel, H.-J. Düssel, K. Rübenacker, T. Schweren, *Makromol. Chem. 145* (1971) 259...65; Feldionen- und Elektronenstoß-Massenspektrometrie von Polymeren und Copolymeren. I. Fortschritte in der Methodik der Pyro-Feldionenmassenspektrometrie

D. O. Hummel, H.-J. Düssel, P. Manshausen, Pyrolysis mass spectrometry of multicomponent polymeric systems, in W. E. Steger (ed.), *Progress in Polymer Spectroscopy*; Teubner, Leipzig 1986

S. C. Israel, M. J. Bechard, M. Abbot, *ACS Polym. Prepr. 24/1* (1983) 159f.; Polymer characterization by direct pyrolysis/chemical ionization mass spectrometry

G. A. Kleineberg, D. L. Geiger, W. T. Gormley, *Makromol. Chem. 175* (1974) 483...95; Rapid determination of kinetic parameters for the thermal degradation of high polymers utilizing a computerized thermogravimetric analyzer-mass spectrometer system

I. Lüderwald, Recent results and new techniques in pyrolysis-electron impact mass spectrometry of synthetic polymers, in D. O. Hummel (ed.), *Proceedings of the 5th European Symposium on Polymer Spectroscopy*; Verlag Chemie, Weinheim 1979

I. Lüderwald, *Pure Appl. Chem. 54* (1982) 255...65; Mass spectrometry of synthetic polymers

I. Lüderwald, H.-R. Schulten, Investigation of synthetic polymers by field desorption and fast atom bombardment mass spectrometry; in W. E. Steger (ed.), *Progress in Polymer Spectroscopy*; Teubner, Leipzig 1986

H. L. C. Meuzelaar, H. G. Ficke, H. C. den Harink, *J. Chromatogr. Sci. 13* (1975) 12...7; Fully automated Curie-point pyrolysis gas-liquid chromatography

H. L. C. Meuzelaar, W. Windig, A. M. Harper, S. M. Huff, W. H. McClennen, J. M. Richards, *Science 226* (1984) 268...74; Pyrolysis mass spectrometry of complex organic materials

G. Montaudo, *Brit. Polym. J. 18* (1985) 577...621; Application of mass spectrometry to synthetic polymers

J. B. Pausch, R. P. Lattimer, H. L. C. Meuzelaar, *Rubber Chem. Technol. 56* (1983) 1031...44; A new look at direct compound analysis using pyrolysis mass spectrometry

R. Saferstein, J. J. Manura, *J. Forens. Sci. 22* (1977) 748...56; Pyrolysis mass spectrometry — A new forensic science technique

R. D. Sedgwick, *Dev. Polym. Charact. 1* (1978) 41...69; Mass spectrometry

Y. Shimizu, B. Munson, *J. Polym. Sci. Polym. Chem. Ed. 17* (1979) 1991...2001; Pyrolysis/chemical ionization mass spectrometry of polymers

G. P. Shulman, *J. Polymer Sci. B 3* (1965) 911; Thermal degradation of polymers. 1. Mass spectrometric thermal analysis

G. Várhegyi, F. Till, T. Székely, *Thermochim. Acta 102* (1986) 115...24; Software for a mass spectrometer-thermobalance system

R. H. Wiley, *Macromol. Rev. 14* (1979) 379...417; The mass spectral characterization of oligomers

W. Windig, P. Kistemaker, J. Haverkamp, H. L. C. Meuzelaar, *J. Anal. Appl. Pyrol. 1* (1979) 39...52; The effects of sample preparation, pyrolysis and pyrolyzate transfer conditions on pyrolysis mass spectra

A. Zeman, *Angew. Makromol. Chem. 31* (1973) 1...24; Die Identifizierung einiger handelsüblicher Polymerer durch thermischen Abbau im Massenspektrometer

7.5.2.2 CH, CHal and CHHal polymers

T. W. Allen, R. J. Hurtubise, H. F. Silver, *Anal. Chem. 57* (1985) 666...71; Comparison of hydrocarbon composi-

tion in complex coal-liquid samples by liquid chromatography and field-ionization mass spectrometry
C. E. Brown, P. Kovacic, C. A. Wilkie, R. B. Cody, jr., J. A. Kinsinger, *J. Polym. Sci. Polym. Lett. Ed. 23* (1985) 453...63; Laser desorption Fourier-transform mass-spectral analysis of molecular weight distribution and end-group composition of poly(*p*-phenylene)s synthesized by various routes
C. E. Brown, P. Kovacic, C. A. Wilkie, J. A. Kinsinger, R. E. Hein, S. I. Yaniger, R. B. Cody, *J. Polym. Sci. Polym. Chem. Ed. 24* (1986) 255...67; Polynuclear and halogenated structures in polyphenylenes synthesized from benzene, biphenyl, and *p*-terphenyl under various conditions. Characterization by Laser desorption/Fourier transform mass spectrometry
D. O. Hummel, H.-J. Düssel, K. Rübenacker, *Makromol. Chem. 145* (1971) 267...87; Feldionen- und Elektronenstoß-Massenspektrometrie von Polymeren und Copolymeren. II. Polyisobuten, Polystyrol, Polypropen, Polystyrolperoxid, Polyvinylchlorid
R. P. Lattimer, J. B. Pausch, H. L. C. Meuzelaar, *Macromolecules 16* (1983) 1896...1900; Pyrolysis studies of chlorinated poly(vinyl chloride)
D. E. Mattern, F.-T. Lin, D. M. Hercules, *Anal. Chem. 56* (1984) 2762...9; Laser mass spectrometry of poly(fluoroethylenes)
H.-D. R. Schüddemage, *Charakterisierung von Hochpolymeren durch Pyrolyse im Feldionen-Massenspektrometer*; Thesis, University of Cologne, Math. Nat. Sci. Fac., 1967

7.5.2.3 CHN and CHNO polymers

A. Ballistreri, S. Foti, P. Maravigna, G. Montaudo, E. Scamporrino, *J. Polym. Sci. Polym. Chem. Ed. 18* (1980) 1923...31; Mechanism of thermal degradation of polyurethanes investigated by direct pyrolysis in the mass spectrometer
A. Ballistreri, S. Foti, P. Maravigna, G. Montaudo, E. Scamporrino, *Macromol. Chem. 181* (1980) 2161...73; Thermal degradation of polyurethanes investigated by direct pyrolysis in the mass spectrometer
A. Ballistreri, M. Giuffrida, P. Maravigna, G. Montaudo, *J. Polym. Sci. Polym. Chem. Ed. 23* (1985) 1145...61; Direct mass spectrometry of polymers. XII. Thermal fragmentation processes in poly-α-aminoacids
A. Ballistreri, M. Giuffrida, P. Maravigna, G. Montaudo, *J. Polym. Sci. Polym. Chem. Ed. 23* (1985) 1731...47; Direct mass spectrometry of polymers. XIII. Thermal fragmentation processes in copoly-α-amino acids
A. Ballistreri, D. Garozzo, M. Giuffrida, P. Maravigna, G. Montaudo, *Macromolecules 19* (1986) 2693...9; Thermal decomposition processes in aliphatic-aromatic polyamides investigated by mass spectrometry
A. Ballistreri, D. Garozzo, M. Giuffrida, G. Montaudo, *Polym. Degrad. Stab. 16* (1986) 337...46; Thermal degradation processes of polyamides investigated by collision activated decomposition mass spectrometry/mass spectrometry
A. Ballistreri, D. Garozzo, M. Giuffrida, G. Montaudo, A. Filippi, C. Guaita, P. Manaresi, F. Pilati, *Macromolecules 20* (1987) 1029...32, *ibid.* 2991...7; Fast atom bombardment mass spectrometry identification of oligomers contained in poly(ε-caprolactam) and poly(butylene isophthalate)
A. Ballistreri, D. Garozzo, M. Giuffrida, P. Maravigna, G. Montaudo, *J. Polym. Sci. Polym. Chem. Ed. 24* (1986)

331...6; Direct mass spectrometry of polymers. XIV. Thermal fragmentation processes in poly-Schiff bases
S. Caruso, S. Foti, P. Maravigna, G. Montaudo, *J. Polym. Sci. Polym. Chem. Ed. 20* (1982) 1685...96; Mass spectral characterization of polymers. Primary thermal fragmentation processes in polyureas
M. Chaigneau, *Analysis 5* (1977) 223...7; Mass spectrometric analysis of compounds formed by pyrolysis of polyacrylonitrile and copolymers
H.-J. Düssel, H. Rosen, D. O. Hummel, *Makromol. Chem. 177* (1976) 2343...68; Feldionen- und Elektronenstoß-Massenspektrometrie von Polymeren und Copolymeren. 5. Aliphatische und aromatische Polyamide und Polyimide
H.-J. Düssel, N. Wenzel, D. O. Hummel, *Angew. Makromol. Chem. 106* (1982) 107...41; Segmented copolyetherurethane-ureas and semicarbazides for blood circulation systems. III. Mass spectrometric investigations. 1. Pyrofield ion mass spectrometry
H.-J. Düssel, A. Recca, J. Kolb, D. O. Hummel, J. K. Stille, *J. Analyt. Appl. Pyrol. 3* (1982) 307...25; Pyrolysis-field ionization mass spectrometric investigation of polymeric heterocycles. I. Polyquinolines and polyquinoxalines
H.-J. Düssel, N. Wenzel, D. O. Hummel, *Angew. Makromol. Chem. 129* (1985) 121...41; Segmented copolyetherurethane-ureas and semicarbazides for blood circulation systems. III. Mass spectrometric investigations. 2. Linear-temperature programmed pyrolysis electron-impact mass spectrometry
J. L. Fan, J. C. Chien, *Polym. Degr. Stab. 12* (1985) 43...63; Thermal degradation studies of segmented thermoplastic elastomers
S. Foti, P. Maravigna, G. Montaudo, *J. Polym. Sci. Polym. Chem. Ed. 19* (1981) 1679...87; Mechanisms of thermal decomposition in totally aromatic polyurethanes
S. Foti, A. Liguori, P. Maravigna, G. Montaudo, *Anal. Chem. 54* (1982) 674...7; Characterization of poly(carboxypiperazine) by mass analyzed ion kinetic energy spectrometry
S. Foti, P. Maravigna, G. Montaudo, *Macromolecules 15* (1982) 883...5; Mass spectrometric detection of cyclic oligomers in polyurethanes and polyureas
S. Foti, P. Maravigna, G. Montaudo, *Polym. Degr. Stab. 4* (1982) 287...92; Effects of N-methyl substitution on the thermal stability of polyurethanes and polyureas
S. Foti, M. Giuffrida, P. Maravigna, G. Montaudo, *J. Polym. Sci. Polym. Chem. Ed. 21* (1983) 1583...98; Direct mass spectrometry of polymers. VIII. Primary thermal fragmentation processes in polyurethanes
D. O. Hummel, J. Kolb, H.-J. Düssel, *Angew. Makromol. Chem. 109/110* (1982) 89...99; Pyro-Feldionenmassenspektrometrie und *IR*-Spektrometrie von Cardopoly(phenylchinolin)en
G. L. Marshall, *Eur. Polym. J. 19* (1983) 439...44; Pyrolysis-mass spectrometry of polymers. II. Polyurethanes
G. Montaudo, E. Scamporrino, D. Vitalini, *J. Polym. Sci. Polym. Chem. Ed. 21* (1983) 3321...31; The effect of ammonium polyphosphate on the mechanism of thermal degradation of polyureas
H.-R. Schulten, H.-J. Düssel, *J. Analyt. Appl. Pyrol. 2* (1980/1981) 293...308; Pyrolysis field-desorption mass spectrometry of polymers. II. Pyrolysis field ionization and field desorption mass spectrometry of aliphatic and aromatic poly(4,4′-dipiperidylamides)
N. Wenzel, *Linear temperaturgesteuerte Pyrolyse von Polyurethanen*; Thesis, Math. Nat. Sci. Fac., University of Cologne 1984

7.5.2.4 CHO and CHS polymers

R. E. Adams, *J. Polym. Sci. Polym. Chem. Ed. 20* (1982) 119...29; Pyrolysis mass spectrometry of terephthalate polyesters using negative ionization

C. Aguilera, I. Lüderwald, *Makromol. Chem. 185* (1984) 1449...54; Investigation of polyesters of adipic acid and sebacinic acid with hydroquinone by pyrolysis-mass spectrometry

S. Foti, M. Giuffrida, P. Maravigna, G. Montaudo, *J. Polym. Sci. Polym. Chem. Ed. 21* (1983) 1567...81; Direct mass spectrometry of polymers. VII. Primary thermal fragmentation processes in polycarbonates

S. Foti, M. Giuffrida, P. Maravigna, G. Montaudo, *J. Polym. Sci. Polym. Chem. Ed. 22* (1984) 1201...16; Direct mass spectrometry of polymers. X. Primary thermal fragmentation processes in totally aromatic polyesters

S. Foti, M. Giuffrida, P. Maravigna, G. Montaudo, *J. Polym. Sci. Polym. Chem. Ed. 22* (1984) 1217...29; Direct mass spectrometry of polymers. XI. Primary thermal fragmentation processes in aromatic-aliphatic polyesters

W. E. Franklin, *Anal. Chem. 51* (1979) 992...6; Direct pyrolysis of cellulose derivatives in a mass spectrometer with a data system

D. Garozzo, M. Giuffrida, G. Montaudo, *Polym. Bull. 15* (1986) 353...8; Mixtures of cyclic oligomers of poly(lactic acid) analyzed by negative chemical ionization and thermospray mass spectrometry

D. Garozzo, G. Montaudo, *Polym. Degrad. Stab. 16* (1986) 143...9; Primary thermal fragmentation processes in poly-(lactic acid) investigated by positive and negative chemical ionization mass spectrometry

M. Giuffrida, P. Maravigna, G. Montaudo, E. Chiellini, *J. Polym. Sci. Polym. Chem. Ed. 24* (1986) 1643...56; Thermal decomposition mechanism of sequential bipolyesters based on propeneglycol and hydroxybenzoic/phthalic diacid derivatives

D. O. Hummel, H.-J. Düssel, H. Rosen, K. Rübenacker, *Makromol. Chem. Suppl. 1* (1975) 471...84; Field ionization and electron impact mass spectrometry of polymers and copolymers. 4. Aromatic polyethers

G. H. Irzl, C. T. Vijayakumar, J. K. Fink, K. Lederer, *Polym. Degrad. Stab. 16* (1986) 53...71; Pyrolysis studies on an unsaturated polyester based on HET-acid, maleic anhydride and 1,2-propandiol. Qualitative analysis of the products of degradation and mechanistic aspects

J. Jachowicz, M. Kryszewski, M. Mucha, *Macromolecules 17* (1984) 1315...21; Thermal degradation of the blend poly(2,6-dimethyl-1,4-phenylene oxide)-polystyrene

E. Jacobi, I. Lüderwald, R. C. Schulz, *Makromol. Chem. 179* (1978) 429...36; Strukturuntersuchung von Polyestern durch direkten Abbau im Massenspektrometer. 4. Polyester und Copolyester der Milchsäure und Glycolsäure

H. R. Kricheldorf, I. Lüderwald, *Makromol. Chem. 179* (1978) 421...7; Strukturuntersuchung von Polyestern durch direkten Abbau im Massenspektrometer. 3. Poly-β-propiolacton, Poly-β-pivalolacton, Poly-δ-valerolacton

I. Lüderwald, H. Urrutia, Direct pyrolysis of aromatic and aliphatic polyesters in the mass spectrometer, in C. E. Roland Jones, C. A. Cramers (eds.), *Analytical Pyrolysis*; Elsevier, Amsterdam 1977

D. E. Mattern, D. M. Hercules, *Anal. Chem. 57* (1985) 2041...6; Laser mass spectrometry of polyglycols: comparison with other mass spectral techniques

R. Milina, G. Laufenberg, H. Budzikiewicz, *Makromol. Chem. Macromol. Symp. 5* (1986) 197...212; The composition of an antioxidant obtained by styrylation of phenol

G. Montaudo, C. Puglisi, E. Scamporrino, D. Vitalini, *Macromolecules 19* (1986) 870...82; Thermal degradation of aromatic-aliphatic polyethers. 1. Direct pyrolysis-mass spectrometry

G. Montaudo, C. Puglisi, E. Scamporrino, D. Vitalini, *Macromolecules 19* (1986) 2157...60; Mass spectrometric analysis of the thermal degradation products of poly(*o*-, *m*- and *p*-phenylene sulfide) and of the oligomers produced in the synthesis of these polymers

L. Prokai, *J. Polym. Sci. Polym. Lett. Ed. 24* (1986) 223...7; Investigation of phenol-formaldehyde condensates by field desorption mass spectrometry

7.5.2.5 Fibers

A. Ballistreri, M. Giuffrida, P. Maravigna, G. Montaudo, *J. Polym. Sci. Polym. Chem. Ed. 23* (1985) 1731...47; Direct mass spectrometry of polymers. XIII. Thermal fragmentation processes in copoly-α-amino acids

J. C. Hughes, B. B. Wheals, M. J. Whitehouse, *Analyst 103* (1978) 482...91; Pyrolysis-mass spectrometry of textile fibers

E. Urbas, A. Kogerman, E. Küllik, O. Kirret, E. Heinsoo, Yu. D. Andrichenko, T. V. Druszinina, *Acta Polymer. 31* (1980) 264...6; Über die quantitative Zusammensetzung der Pyrolyseprodukte beim thermischen Abbau halogenhaltiger Polyamidfasern

7.5.2.6 Rubbers

A. Ballistreri, D. Garozzo, G. Montaudo, *Macromolecules 17* (1984) 1312...5; Mass spectral characterization and thermal decomposition mechanism of poly(dimethylsiloxane)

G. Czybulka, H. Dunker, H.-J. Düssel, H. Logemann, D. O. Hummel, *Angew. Makromol. Chem. 100* (1981) 1...21; Pyro-feldionenmassenspektrometrische Untersuchungen an unvulkanisierten und vulkanisierten Kautschuken mit Komponenten geringer Konzentration (Comonomere, Beschleuniger, Metalloxide, Antioxidantien)

H. Dunker, *Anwendung der Pyro-Feldionenmassenspektrometrie zur Untersuchung der Struktur und des thermischen Abbauverhaltens von unvulkanisierten und vulkanisierten Kautschuken*; Diploma thesis, Chemistry Dept., University Cologne 1977

R. P. Lattimer, R. E. Harris, D. B. Ross, H. E. Diem, *Rubber Chem. Technol. 57* (1984) 1013...22; Identification of rubber additives by field desorption and fast atom bombardment mass spectroscopy

W. H. McClennen, J. M. Richards, H. L. Meuzelaar, J. B. Pausch, R. P. Lattimer, *ACS Polym. Mater. Sci. Eng. 53* (1985) 203...7; Direct characterization of solid rubber samples by laser pyrolysis mass spectrometry (*Py-MS*)

7.5.2.7 Copolymers and polymer blends

A. Ballistreri, G. Montaudo, R. W. Lenz, *Macromolecules 17* (1984) 1848...54; Mass spectral characterization and thermal decomposition mechanism of alternating silarylene-siloxane polymers

G. Czybulka, *Anwendung der Pyrolyse-Feldionenmassenspektrometrie zur Untersuchung des thermischen Abbaus von Copolymeren und Polymermischungen sowie zur Identifizierung von Zusatzstoffen*; Thesis, Math. Nat. Sci. Fac., University of Cologne 1985

S. Foti, M. Giuffrida, P. Maravigna, G. Montaudo, *J. Polym. Sci. Polym. Chem. Ed. 21* (1983) 1599...1615; Direct mass spectrometry of polymers. IX. Copoly(carbonate-urethanes) prepared by reorganization of polycarbonates with piperazine

D. O. Hummel, H.-J. Düssel, *Makromol. Chem. 175* (1974) 655...65; Feldionen- und Elektronenstoß-Massenspektrometrie von Polymeren und Copolymeren. III. Copolymere des α-Methylstyrols mit Methylmethacrylat und Acrylnitril

D. O. Hummel, H.-J. Düssel, G. Czybulka, N. Wenzel, G. Holl, *Spectrochim. Acta 41 A* (1985) 279...90; Analytical pyrolysis of copolymers

D. O. Hummel, F. H. J. Sadowski, D. Widdershoven, H.-J. Düssel, *Quad. Ric. Sci. 84* (1973) 23...41; Pyro-field ion mass spectrometry, gas chromatography, and infrared spectroscopy to investigate degradation behaviour and structure of polymaleic anhydride as well as maleic anhydride-isobutene copolymers

E. Jacobi, I. Lüderwald, R. C. Schulz, *Makromol. Chem. 179* (1978) 277...80; Über die massenspektrometrische Bestimmung des Einbauverhältnisses in Copolymeren. 2. Copolyester der Milchsäure und Glykolsäure

R. P. Lattimer, K. M. Schur, W. Windig, H. L. C. Meuzelaar, *J. Anal. Appl. Pyrol. 8* (1985) 95...107; Quantitative analysis of rubber triblends by pyrolysis-mass spectrometry

I. Lüderwald, H. R. Kricheldorf, *Angew. Makromol. Chem. 56* (1976) 173...91; Über den thermischen Abbau von alternierenden Copolyamiden im Massenspektrometer

W. H. McClennen, J. M. Richards, H. L. C. Meuzelaar, J. B. Pausch, R. P. Lattimer, *Polym. Mat. Sci. Eng. 53* (1985) 203...7; Direct characterization of solid rubber samples by Laser pyrolysis mass spectrometry

M. Ryska, H.-D. R. Schüddemage, D. O. Hummel, *Makromol. Chem. 126* (1969) 32...41; Strahlenchemische Copolymerisation des Styrols mit Vinylchlorid. II. Pyrolyse der Styrol-Vinylchlorid-Copolymeren im Feldionen-Massenspektrometer

G. G. Wanless, *J. Polym. Sci. 62* (1962) 263; Analysis of copolymers by pyrolysis and mass spectrometry

7.5.2.8 Resins, miscellaneous macromolecular systems

A. Ballistreri, D. Garozzo, G. Montaudo, *Macromolecules 17* (1984) 1312...5; Mass spectral characterization and thermal decomposition mechanism of poly(dimethyl-siloxane)

C. E. Carraher, G. G. Hess, H. M. Molloy, T. O. Tiernan, M. L. Taylor, K. B. Tomer, *Polym. Mat. Sci. Eng. 50* (1984) 204...8; Characterization of organometallic polymers employing mass spectrometry and coupled mass spectrometry

C. E. Carraher, H. M. Molloy, M. L. Taylor, T. O. Tiernan, J. Schroeder, *Polym. Mat. Sci. Eng. 54* (1986) 316...20; Characterization of polymers employing coupled thermogravimetric-mass spectroscopy programmed pyroprobe-mass spectroscopy and infrared spectroscopy: uranium-containing polymers

P. K. Dhal, G. N. Babu, J. C. Chien, *Polym. Degrad. Stab. 16* (1986) 135...45; Resist polymers. Part VII. Thermolysis of fluoroalkyl methacrylates

H.-J. Eichhoff, G. Mischer, *Z. Naturforsch. 27b* (1972) 380...6; Massenspektrometrische und Emissionsspektroskopische Untersuchungen an Bernstein zur Herkunftsbestimmung

J. K. Fink, *Thermochim. Acta 71* (1983) 377...80; Investigation of the thermal degradation of an HET acid containing unsaturated polyester resin by flash pyrolysis in a mass spectrometer

D. A. Hickman, I. Jane, *Analyst (London) 104* (1979) 334...47; Reproducibility of pyrolysis-mass spectrometry using three different pyrolysis systems

D. O. Hummel, H.-D. R. Schüddemage, U. Pohl, *Kolloid-Z. Z. Polymere 210* (1966) 103...11; Thermischer Abbau von Polysulfonen. III. Pyrolyse verzweigter aliphatischer Polysulfonen im Massenspektrometer

D. R. Jardine, S. Nekula, N. Than-Trong, P. R. Haddad, P. J. Derrick, E. Grespos, J. H. O'Donnell, *Macromolecules 19* (1986) 1770...2; Field desorption mass spectrometry of poly(olefin sulfones)

J. Kolb, *Massenspektrometrische Analyse von Kohlen, ihren Chloroformextrakten und Extraktrückständen*; Thesis, Math. Nat. Sci. Fac., Cologne 1984

L. M. Lucht, M. E. Hill, N. A. Peppas, *Angew. Makromol. Chem. 150* (1987) 123...36; Macromolecular structure of coals. 7. Mass spectrometry of pyridine extracts and depolymerized coal

I. M. Lukashenko, R. A. Khmel'nitskii, Ye. S. Brodskii, G. A. Kalikevich, N. M. Kovalena, R. P. Batizat, *Vysokomol. Soedin. A 18* (1976) 1133...40 (Russ.); Pyrolysis-mass spectrometry for investigating liquid epoxy resins

R. M. Lum, C. W. Wilkins, M. Robbins, A. M. Lyons, R. P. Jones, *Org. Coat. Plast. Chem. 46* (1982) 17...21; Thermal analysis of graphite and carbon-phenolic composites by pyrolysis-mass spectrometry

G. Mischer, H.-J. Eichhoff, T. E. Haevernick, *Jahrbuch Röm.-Germ. Zentralmuseum Mainz 17* (1970) 111...22; Herkunftsuntersuchungen an Bernstein mit physikalischen Analysenmethoden

J. Pierre, J. van Bree, *Kunststoffe 73* (1983) 319...24; Analyse von Kunststoff-Formmassen mit Hilfe von Massenspektrometrie und Kernresonanzspektroskopie

M. A. Posthumus, A. J. H. Boerboom, H. L. C. Meuzelaar, *Adv. Mass Spectr. 6* (1974) 397...402; Analysis of biopolymers by Curie-point pyrolysis in direct combination with low voltage electron impact ionization mass spectrometry

H. Rosen, H.-J. Düssel, D. O. Hummel, *J. Appl. Polym. Sci. Appl. Polym. Symp. 35* (1979) 193...206; Thermal degradation mechanism of polymeric heterocycles as studied by pyro-field ion mass spectrometry

R. C. A. Rottländer, *Acta praehist. archaeol. 11/12* (1980) 21...34; Neue Beiträge zur Kenntnis des Bernsteins

H.-D. R. Schüddemage, D. O. Hummel, *Kolloid Z. Z. Polymere 210* (1966) 103...6; *ibid. 220* (1967) 133...45; Thermischer Abbau von Polysulfonen. II. Pyrolyse von Polystyrolsulfonen im Massenspektrometer. — IV. Pyrolyse von Polydiensulfonen und Polybutadien im Feldionen-Massenspektrometer

H.-R. Schulten, H. D. Beckey, H. L. C. Meuzelaar, A. J. H. Boerboom, *Anal. Chem. 45* (1973) 191...5; High resolution field ionization mass spectrometry of bacterial pyrolysis products

H.-R. Schulten, H. D. Beckey, A. J. H. Boerboom, H. L. C. Meuzelaar, *Anal. Chem. 45* (1973) 2358...62; Pyrolysis field desorption mass spectrometry of dezoxyribonucleic acid

H.-R. Schulten, N. Simmleit, R. Müller, *Fresenius Z. analyt. Chem. 323* (1986) 450...4; Distinction of coals and their extracts by field ionization mass spectrometry and pattern recognition

D. A. Scola, *ACS Polym. Prepr. 24/1* (1983) 231f.; *ISS/SIMS* analysis of graphite fiber surfaces

G. P. Shulman, H. W. Lochte, *J. Polym. Sci. C4* (1966) 619; Thermal degradation of polymers. 2. Mass spectrometric thermal analysis of phenolformaldehyde polycondensates

C. T. Vijayakumar, J. K. Fink, *Intern. J. Mass Spectrom. Ion Phys. 48* (1983) 59...62; Investigations on the mechanism of flame retardancy in HET acid containing unsaturated polyester resins. − Discussion of mass spectra of the flame retardants

C. T. Vijayakumar, J. K. Fink, K. Lederer, *Angew. Makromol. Chem. 113* (1983) 121...8; Primary processes of the thermal degradation of HET acid containing unsaturated polyester cured with styrene

7.5.3 Pyrolysis-gas chromatography

7.5.3.1 Fundamentals, methodology

K. V. Alekseeva, *Zh. Analit. Khim. 30* (1975) 594...603 (Russ.); Analysis of nonvolatile high-molecular-weight compounds by pyrolysis gas chromatography

V. R. Alishoev, V. G. Berezkin, A. I. Malyshev, *Zh. Analit. Khim. 27* (1972) 1035...49 (Russ.); Pyrolysis gas chromatography of polymers

E. M. Andersson, I. Ericsson, *J. Anal. Appl. Pyrol. 1* (1979) 27...38; Determination of the temperature-time profile of the sample in pyrolysis-gas chromatography

E. M. Andersson, I. Ericsson, *J. Anal. Appl. Pyrol. 2* (1980) 97...107; Samples from ng to mg in pyrolysis-gas chromatography

M. Blazsó, E. Jakab, *J. Anal. Appl. Pyrol. 8* (1985) 189...94; Study of thermal decomposition reactions in coals by pyrolysis-gas chromatography-mass spectrometry

G. M. Brauer, *J. Polym. Sci. C 8* (1965) 3...26; Pyrolytic techniques

I. Ericsson, *J. Anal. Appl. Pyrol. 8* (1985) 73...86; Influence of pyrolysis parameters on results in pyrolysis-gas chromatography

W. G. Fischer, *G-I-T Fachz. Lab. 11* (1967) 562...70, 775...80, 1086...95; Pyrolyse-Gaschromatographie

W. G. Fischer, *G-I-T Fachz. Lab. 13* (1969) 13...6; Curiepunkt-Pyrolyse zur gas-chromatographischen Analyse

W. G. Fischer, *G-I-T Fachz. Lab. 24* (1980) 666, 668f.; Neuer Curie-Punkt Pyrolyse-Reaktor für Pyrolyse Kapillar-Gaschromatographie

W. G. Fischer, *G-I-T Fachz. Lab. 16* (1972) 37...51; Methoden der Pyrolyse und ihre Anwendung zur gaschromatographischen und massenspektrometrischen Untersuchung

O. Heisz, *G-I-T Fachz. Lab. 19* (1975) 729...832; Einsatzmöglichkeiten der Curie-Punkt-Pyrolyse bei der Untersuchung von Polymeren und anderen nicht flüchtigen Verbindungen

J. W. de Leeuw, W. L. Maters, D. v. d. Meent, P. A. Schenck, H. L. C. Meuzelaar, Curie-point evaporation: A new and simple technique for splitless injection of open tubular capillary columns, in C. E. Roland Jones, C. A. Cramers (eds.), *Analytical Pyrolysis*; Elsevier, Amsterdam 1977

S. A. Liebman, T. P. Wampler, E. J. Levy, *J. High Resol. Chromatogr. Chromatogr. Commun. 7* (1984) 172...84; Developments in pyrolysis capillary *GC*

J. P. Schmid, P. P. Schmid, W. Simon, Application of Curiepoint pyrolysis gas chromatography using high-resolution glass open-tubular columns, in C. E. Roland Jones, C. A. Cramers (eds.), *Analytical Pyrolysis*; Elsevier, Amsterdam 1977

S. Tsuge, Y. Matsushima, N. Watanabe, A. Shintai, K. Nishimura, Y. Hoshika, *Analyt. Sciences 3* (1987) 101...7; New automated thermal desorption system for gas chromatography of volatile components in environmental and polymeric samples

I. Tyden-Ericsson, *Chromatographia 6* (1973) 353...8; A new pyrolyzer with improved control of pyrolysis conditions

7.5.3.2 Polymers general, plastics

K. V. Alekseeva, *J. Anal. Appl. Pyrol. 2* (1980) 19ff.; Gas chromatographic identification of polymers using individual pyrolysis products

A. Barlow, R. S. Lehrle, J. C. Robb, *Polymer 2* (1961) 27...40; Direct examination of polymer degradation by gas chromatography. I. Applications to polymer analysis and characterization

C. N. Caşcaval, I. A. Schneider, I. C. Poinescu, *J. Polym. Sci. Polym. Chem. Ed. 13* (1975) 2259...68; PGC of polymers obtained by Friedel-Crafts reactions of poly(vinyl chloride) with aromatic compounds

E. W. Cieplinski, L. S. Ettre, B. Kolb, G. Kemmner, *Z. analyt. Chem. 205* (1964) 357...71; Pyrolysis-gas chromatography with linearly programmed temperature packed and open tubular columns. The thermal degradation of polyolefins

A. Davis, J. H. Golden, *J. Gas Chromatogr. 5* (1967) 81...5; The application of gas chromatography to the characterisation and thermal degradation of a polycarbonate

D. Deur-Šiftar, *J. Gas Chromatogr. 5* (1967) 72...6; Application of pyrolysis-gas chromatography for characterization of polyolefins

H. Eustache, N. Robin, J. C. Daniel, M. Carrega, *Eur. Polym. J. 14* (1978) 239...43; Determination of multipolymer structure using pyrolysis gas chromatography

R. O. Gardner, R. F. Browner, *Anal. Chem. 52* (1980) 1360...4; Determination of polymer pyrolysis products by gas chromatography and gas chromatography/mass spectrometry

T. A. Gough, C. E. Roland Jones, *Chromatographia 8* (1975) 696ff.; Precision of *PGC* of polymers

K.-G. Häusler et al., *Plaste Kautsch. 30* (1983) 617...9; Lichtstrahl- und Curiepunktpyrolyse von Polymeren. 17. Charakterisierung von nachvernetzten Styrol-Divinylbenzol-Copolymeren

M. Henkel, I. Lüderwald, *Fresenius Z. analyt. Chem. 321* (1985) 252...6; Bestimmung von synthetischen Polymeren in Humangewebe durch Pyrolyse-Gaschromatographie (*Py-GC*). 3. Polymethylmethacrylat und Polyethylene

N. Iglauer, F. F. Bentley, *J. Chromatogr. Sci. 12* (1974) 23...33; *PGLC* for the rapid identification of organic polymers

E. Kiran, J. K. Gillham, *J. Appl. Polym. Sci. 20* (1976) 2045...68; Pyrolysis-molecular weight chromatography: a new on-line system for analysis of polymers. II. Thermal decomposition of polyolefines: polyethylene, polypropylene, polyisobutylene

R. P. Lattimer, W. J. Kroenke, R. H. Backderf, *J. Appl. Polym. Sci. 27* (1982) 3633...6; Carbon-13 labeling studies of volatile pyrolyzate formation from poly(vinyl chloride)

R. S. Lehrle, J. C. Robb, J. R. Suggate, *Eur. Polym. J. 18* (1982) 443...61; An improved ("thermocouple-feedback") pyrolysis-*GLC* technique and its application to study polyacrylonitrile degradation kinetics

O. Mlejnek, *J. Chromatogr. 191* (1980) 181...6; Application of pyrolysis-capillary gas chromatography to the characterization of polyethylene

S. L. Morgan, *Org. Coat. Appl. Polym. Sci. Proc. 44* (1981) 600...3; Structure correlation and pattern recognition in analytical pyrolysis

H. Ohtani, T. Nagaya, Y. Sugimura, S. Tsuge, *J. Anal. Pyrolysis 4* (1982) 117...31; Studies on thermal degradation of aliphatic polyamides by pyrolysis-glass capillary gas chromatography

H. Ohtani, S. Tsuge, T. Ogawa, H.-G. Elias, *Macromolecules 17* (1984) 465...73; Studies on stereospecific sequence distributions in polypropylenes by pyrolysis-hydrogenation fused-silica capillary gas chromatography

H. Ohtani, S. Tsuge, T. Usami, *Macromolecules 17* (1984) 2557...61; Determination of short-chain branching up to C_6 in low-density polyethylenes by high-resolution pyrolysis-hydrogenation gas chromatography

H. Ohtani, T. Kimura, S. Tsuge, *Anal. Sci. 2* (1986) 179...82; Analysis of thermal degradation of terephthalate polyesters by high-resolution pyrolysis-gas chromatography

M. Seeger, E. M. Barrall, *J. Polym. Sci. Polym. Chem. Ed. 13* (1975) 1515...29; Pyrolysis-gas chromatographic analysis of chain branching in polyethylene

M. Seeger, E. M. Barrall, M. Shen, *J. Polym. Sci. Polym. Chem. Ed. 13* (1975) 1541...4; Pyrolysis and *GC* of plasma-polymerized ethylene

M. Seeger, H.-J. Cantow, *Makromol. Chem. 176* (1975) 2059...78; Thermische Spaltungsmechanismen in Homo- und Copolymeren aus α-Olefinen. 2. Polypropylene mit bekannter Taktizität, Polyisobutylen und Poly(1-buten)

M. Seeger, R. J. Gritter, J. M. Tibbitt, M. Shen, A. T. Bell, *J. Polym. Sci. Polym. Chem. Ed. 15* (1977) 1404...11; Analysis of plasma-polymerized hydrocarbons by pyrolysis/gas chromatography

H. Seno, S. Tsuge, T. Takeuchi, *Makromol. Chem. 161* (1972) 185...93; Estimation of chemical inversions of monomer placement in polypropylene by pyrolysis gas chromatography

T. Shimono, M. Tanaka, T. Shono, *J. Anal. Appl. Pyrol. 1* (1980) 189...96; Pyrolysis-gas chromatography of poly(3-methyl-1-alkene)s

C. G. Smith, R. Beaver, *TAPPI 63* (1980) 93ff.; Determination of styrene-containing polymers using pyrolysis gas chromatography

Y. Sugimura, S. Tsuge, *Macromolecules 12* (1979) 512...4; Pyrolysis hydrogenation glass capillary *GC* characterization of PE's and ethylene-α-olefin copolymers

Y. Sugimura, S. Tsuge, *J. Chromatogr. Sci. 17* (1979) 269...72; Studies on thermal degradation of aromatic polyesters by pyrolysis-gas chromatography

Y. Sugimura, T. Nagaya, S. Tsuge, T. Murate, T. Takeda, *Macromolecules 13* (1980) 928...32; Microstructural characterization of polypropylenes by high-resolution pyrolysis hydrogenation glass capillary gas chromatography

Y. Sugimura, T. Usami, T. Nagaya, S. Tsuge, *Macromolecules 14* (1981) 1787...91; Determination of short-chain branching in polyethylenes by pyrolysis-hydrogenation glass capillary gas chromatography

T. Székely, M. Blazsó, Analytical pyrolysis of inorganic and thermostable polymers, in C. E. Roland Jones, C. A. Cramers (eds.), *Analytical Pyrolysis*; Elsevier, Amsterdam 1977

S. Tsuge, Y. Sugimura, T. Nagaya, *J. Anal. Appl. Pyrol. 1* (1980) 221...9; Structural characterization of polyolefins by pyrolysis-hydrogenation glass capillary gas chromatography

S. Tsuge, *Chromatography Forum* Nov./Dec. 1986, 44...51; Characterization of polymers by pyrolysis/high resolution gas chromatography with fused-silica capillary columns

E. Urbas, M. Kaljurand, E. Kullik, *J. Anal. Appl. Pyrol. 1* (1980) 213...20; Study of the thermal decomposition of polymers by on-line cross-correlation gas chromatography

T. Usami, Y. Gotoh, S. Takayama, H. Ohtani, S. Tsuge, *Macromolecules 20* (1987) 1557...61; Branching structure in high-pressure low density polyethylene as a function of

molecular weight determination by ^{13}C nuclear magnetic resonance and pyrolysis-hydrogenation gas chromatography

C. J. Wolf, M. A. Grayson, D. L. Fanter, *Anal. Chem. 52* (1980) 348 A...58 A; Pyrolysis gas chromatography of polymers

J. Zulaica, G. Guiochon, *Bull. Soc. Chim. 4* (1966) 1351; Analyse des hauts polymères par chromatographie en phase gazeuse de leurs produits de pyrolyse. III. Application à quelques hydrocarbures macromoléculaire purs

7.5.3.3 Fibers

J. P. Bortniak, S. E. Brown, E. H. Sild, *J. Forens. Sci. 16* (1971) 380...92; Differentiation of microgram quantities of acrylic and modacrylic fibers using pyrolysis gas-liquid chromatography

J. S. Crighton, Characterisation of textile materials by thermal degradation: A critique of pyrolysis *GC* and thermogravimetry, in C. E. Roland Jones, C. A. Cramers (eds.), *Analytical Pyrolysis*; Elsevier, Amsterdam 1977

H. Haase, *Dünnschichtchromatographische und gaschromatographische Bestimmung von Kunststoff-Weichmachern und pyrolyse-gaschromatographische Untersuchungen an Faserstoffen*; Thesis, TH Stuttgart 1965

E. Heinsoo, A. Kogerman, D. Kirret, J. Coupek, S. Vilkova, *J. Anal. Appl. Pyrol. 2* (1980) 131...9; Stepwise pyrolysis-gas chromatography of viscose fibers

R. A. Janiak, K. A. Damerau, *J. Crim. Law Criminol. Pol. Sci. 59* (1968) 434...9; The application of pyrolysis and programmed temperature gas chromatography to the identification of textile fibers

O. Kirret, E. Küllik, *Lenzinger Ber. 36* (1974); Pyrolyse-Gaschromatographie der Chemiefaserstoffe

M. Krull, A. Kogermann, O. Kirret, L. Kutyina, D. Zapolski, *J. Chromatogr. 135* (1977) 212...6; *PGC* of capron (nylon 6) fibre stabilized with ethers of 4-oxydiphenylamine

E. Urbas, J. Küllik, *J. Chromatogr. 137* (1977) 210...4; Pyrolysis gas chromatographic analysis of some toxic compounds from nitrogen-containing fibers

7.5.3.4 Rubbers

A. V. Bratcikov, B. A. Berendeev, A. G. Rodionov, *Vysokomol. Soedin. A 27* (1985) 1107...12 (Russ.); Determination of the composition of ethylene-propylene copolymers by means of pyrolytic gas chromatography

D. Braun, E. Čanji, *Angew. Makromol. Chem. 29/30* (1973) 491; Pyrolyse-Gaschromatographie von Dien-Polymeren

D. Braun, E. Čanji, *Angew. Makromol. Chem. 33* (1973) 143...151; Pyrolyse-Gaschromatographie von Dien-Polymeren. I. Meßmethode; *ibid. 35* (1974) 27...38; II. Polybutadiene; *ibid. 36* (1974) 67...73; III. Polyisoprene

K. H. Burg, E. Fischer, K. Weissermel, *Makromol. Chem. 103* (1967) 268; Bausteinanalyse bei Homo- und Copolymerisaten des Trioxans mit Hilfe der katalytischen Pyrolysegaschromatographie

D. W. Carlson, H. C. Ransaw, A. G. Altenau, *Anal. Chem. 42* (1970) 1278...9; Determination of polymer composition of rubber vulcanizates

J. C. Chien, J. K. Kiang, *Eur. Polym. J. 15* (1979) 1059...65; Polymer reactions. X. Thermal pyrolysis of poly(isoprene)

J. Chih-An Hu, *Anal. Chem. 49* (1977) 537...40; Pyrolysis gas chromatography analysis of rubbers and other high polymers

H. M. Cole, D. L. Petterson, V. A. Sijaka, D. S. Smith, *Rubber Chem. Technol. 39* (1966) 259...69; Identification and determination of polymers in compounded cured rubber stocks by pyrolysis and two-channel gas chromatography

R. Davis, E. A. Ney, R. Peake, A. Proszynski, *J. Inst. Rubber Ind. 6* (1972) 197...203; Determination of the newer tyre rubbers in tyre treads

J. Dolinar, M. Jernejčič, L. Premru, *J. Chromatogr. 34* (1968) 89...95; The gas chromatographic analysis of industrial rubber compositions

I. Ericsson, *J. Chromatogr. Sci. 16* (1978) 340...4; Sequential pyrolysis gas chromatographic study of the decomposition kinetics of *cis*-1,4-polybutadiene

W. Fischer, H. Meuser, *Gummi Asbest Kunstst. 19* (1966) 1229...46; Analytische Bestimmung von Elastomeren in Vulkanisaten durch Pyrolyse-Gaschromatographie

A. A. Foxton, D. E. Hillman, P. R. Mears, *J. Inst. Rubber Ind. 3* (1969) 179...83; Identification of rubber vulcanisates by pyrolysis-gas chromatography

M. Galin-Vacherot, H. Eustache, P. Q. Tho, *Eur. Polym. J. 5* (1969) 211...8; Determination de la structure d'un produit de pyrolyse caracteristique des enchainements 3,4 dans les polyisoprènes de synthèse

M. Galin-Vacherot, *Eur. Polym. J. 7* (1971) 1455...71; Pyrolyse éclair de polyisoprenes. Essai de correlation entre les produits de degradation et la microstructure des polymères

M. Galin-Vacherot, *J. Macromol. Sci. A 7* (1973) 872...88; Study of polyisoprene microstructure by flash pyrolysis gas chromatography

M. A. Golub, R. J. Gargiulo, *J. Polym. Sci. Polym. Lett. Ed. 10* (1972) 41...9; Thermal degradation of 1,4-polyisoprene and 1,4-polybutadiene

M. A. Golub, M. Sung, *J. Polym. Sci. Polym. Lett. Ed. 11* (1973) 129...38; Thermal cyclization of 1,2-polybutadiene and 3,4-polyisoprene

M. J. Hackathorn, M. J. Brock, *J. Polym. Sci. Polym. Lett. Ed. 8* (1970) 617...25; Polyisoprene structure from thermal degradation data

M. J. Hackathorn, M. J. Brock, *Rubber Chem. Technol. 45* (1972) 1295...1302; The determination of "head-head" and "tail-tail" structures in poly(isoprene)s

K. G. Häusler, E. Schröder, B. Hartwich, *Plaste Kautsch. 23* (1976) 481; Lichtstrahl- und Curiepunkt-Pyrolyse von Elastomeren. I. Lichtstrahlpyrolyse; *ibid. 24* (1977) 175; II. Curiepunktpyrolyse von Polybutadienen

K. G. Häusler, E. Schröder, F.-W. Wege, *Plaste Kautsch. 24* (1977) 329...32; Lichtstrahl- und Curiepunktpyrolyse von Polymeren. III. Zur Strukturuntersuchung von Polybutadien mit der Pyrolyse-Kapillar-Gaschromatographie

K. Häusler, H. Hube, *Plaste Kautsch. 27* (1980) 78...81; Lichtstrahl- und Curiepunktpyrolyse von Polymeren. XI. Zur Strukturuntersuchung von vulkanisiertem Polybutadien mit der Pyrolysegaschromatographie

K.-G. Häusler et al., *Plaste Kautsch. 27* (1980) 19...22; Lichtstrahl- und Curiepunktpyrolyse von Polymeren. X. Pyrolysegaschromatographische Charakterisierung von strahlenchemisch vernetzten Polybutadienen

M. Jernejčič, L. Premru, *Rubber Chem. Technol. 41* (1968) 411...7; Pyrolysis gas chromatography of natural rubber and synthetic polyisoprene

A. Krishen, *Anal. Chem. 44* (1972) 494...7; Quantitative determination of natural rubber, styrene-butadiene rubber, and ethylene-propylene-terpolymer rubber in compounded cured stocks by pyrolysis-gas chromatography

A. Krishen, R. G. Tucker, *Anal. Chem. 46* (1974) 29...33; Quantitative determination of the polymeric constituents in compounded cured stocks by Curie-point pyrolysis-gas chromatography

H. Nakagawa, S. Tsuge, K. Murakami, *J. Anal. Appl. Pyrol. 10* (1986) 31...40; Characterization of sulphur-cured rubbers by high-resolution pyrolysis-gas chromatography with flame photometric detection

J. Naveau, H. Dieu, *J. Anal. Appl. Pyrol. 2* (1980) 123...30; Reproducibility of the pyrolysis-gas chromatography of the *cis*-1,4-polyisoprenes NR and IR. Influence of the chromatographic separation

E. A. Ney, A. B. Heath, *J. Inst. Rubber Ind. 2* (1968) 276...81; Analysis of tyre tread rubbers by gas chromatography

H. Ohtani, T. Kimura, K. Okamoto, S. Tsuge, Y. Nagataki, K. Miyata, *J. Anal. Appl. Pyrol. 12* (1987) 115...34; Characterization of polyurethanes by high-resolution pyrolysis-capillary gas chromatography

T. S. Radhakrishnan, M. Rama Rao, *J. Polym. Sci. Polym. Chem. Ed. 19* (1981) 3197...3208; Thermal decomposition of polybutadienes by pyrolysis gas chromatography

A. von Raven, H. Heusinger, *Angew. Makromol. Chem. 42* (1975) 183...92; Untersuchungen zur Struktur von gamma-bestrahltem 1,2-Polybutadien mittels Pyrolyse-Gaschromatographie

R. Schrafft, *Kautsch. Gummi Kunstst. 36* (1983) 851...8; Automatische Curie-Punkt-Pyrolysegaschromatographie mit Kapillarsäulen zur Analyse von Gummimischungen

T. Takeuchi, S. Tsuge, T. Okumoto, *J. Gas Chromatogr. 6* (1968) 542...7; Identification and analysis of urethane foams by pyrolysis-gas chromatography

L. Trojer, I. Ericsson, *J. Chromatogr. Sci. 16* (1978) 345...50; *PGC* studies of insoluble samples. Exemplified by vulcanized styrene-butadiene rubber

W. P. Tyler, *Rubber Chem. Technol. 40* (1967) 238; Analysis, composition and structure of rubber and rubber products

R. O. B. Wijesekera, M. R. N. Fernando, *J. Chromatogr. 65* (1972) 560...4; A method for distinguishing different types of processed rubber by gas-liquid chromatographic analysis of their volatile emanations

7.5.3.5 Copolymers and polymer mixtures

K. V. Alekseeva, L. P. Khramova, L. S. Solomatina, *J. Chromatogr. 77* (1973) 61 ff. (Russ.); Pyrolysis gaschromatography investigation of poly(butadiene-*co*-styrene), copolymers of isoprene with vinyl aromatic HC and NMA, polymethylmethacrylate-*b*-polystyrene and polystyrene-polybutadiene mixtures; differentiation of blocks and statistical copolymers

M. Blazsó, G. Várhegyi, *Eur. Polym. J. 14* (1978) 625...30; Calculation of kinetic parameters and sequence distribution from pyrolysis gas chromatographic data of styrene-methyl acrylate copolymers

D. Braun, R. Disselhoff, *Angew. Makromol. Chem. 23* (1972) 103...15; Analyse von Acrylnitril-Styrol-Copolymeren mit Hilfe der Pyrolyse-Gaschromatographie

D. Braun, E. Čanji, *Angew. Makromol. Chem. 36* (1974) 75; Pyrolyse-Gaschromatographie von Dien-Polymeren. IV. Butadien-Styrol-Copolymere

C. N. Cașcaval, I. A. Schneider, Ig. C. Poinescu, M. Butnaru, *Eur. Polym. J. 15* (1979) 661...6; Pyrolysis-gas chromatography of some crosslinked copolymers of styrene

J. K. Haken, D. K. M. Ho, *J. Chromatogr. 126* (1976) 239...47; Quantitative pyrolysis studies of styrene, acrylate ester systems, and their α-methyl-substituted homologs

K. G. Häusler, E. Schröder, P. Mühling, *Plaste Kautsch. 24* (1977) 554...9; Bestimmung der Mikrostruktur von Styrol-Butadien-Copolymeren durch *Py-GC*

K. G. Häusler, E. Schröder, G. Reinhold, *Plaste Kautsch. 26* (1979) 202...6; Lichtstrahl- und Curiepunktpyrolyse von Polymeren. IX. Zum Einsatz der Pyrolysegaschromatographie als Detektor für die analytische Fraktionierung von Styrol-Butadien-Copolymeren

K. P. Korneeva, V. V. Amerik, F. I. Yakobson, K. P. Orlova, V. F. Petrova, D. V. Ivanyukov, *Plast. Massy 1974* (3) 75 ff. (Russ.); Pyrolysis-gas chromatography of poly(propylene-*co*-vinylcyclohexane) and the corresponding polymer mixtures

I. Lüderwald, K. E. Müller, *Fresenius Z. analyt. Chem. 300* (1980) 277...9; Bestimmung des Einbauverhältnisses in Methylmethacrylat-Methylacrylat-Copolymeren durch Pyrolyse-Gas-Chromatographie

T. Nagaya, Y. Sugimura, S. Tsuge, *Macromolecules 13* (1980) 353...7; Studies on sequence distributions in acrylonitrile-styrene copolymers by pyrolysis-glass capillary gas chromatography

H. Nakagawa, S. Tsuge, *Macromolecules 18* (1985) 2068...72; Characterization of styrene-divinylbenzene copolymers by high-resolution pyrolysis-gas chromatography

H. Ohtani, T. Asai, S. Tsuge, *Macromolecules 18* (1985) 1148...52; Characterization of a multicomponent alkyl methacrylate copolymer by high-resolution pyrolysis-gas chromatography

T. Okumoto, T. Takeuchi, S. Tsuge, *Bull. Chem. Soc. Japan 43* (1970) 2080...2; Pyrolysis-gas chromatographic analysis of vinylchloride-vinylacetate copolymer

T. Okumoto, T. Takeuchi, S. Tsuge, *Macromolecules 6* (1973) 922; Pyrolysis gaschromatographic study on sequence distribution of dyads in styrene-*m*-chlorostyrene and styrene-*p*-chlorostyrene copolymers

T. Okumoto, S. Tsuge, Y. Yamamoto, T. Takeuchi, *Macromolecules 7* (1974) 376...80; Pyrolysis gas chromatographic evaluation on sequence distribution of dyads in vinyl-type copolymers: acrylonitrile-*m*-chlorostyrene and acrylonitrile-*p*-chlorostyrene copolymers

S. Paul, A. W. Becker, *J. Coating Techn. 52* (1980) 47...55; Pyrolysis gas chromatographic analysis (*PGC*) of methyl methacrylate (MMA) ethyl acrylate (EA) copolymers

T. Nagaya, Y. Sugimura, S. Tsuge, *Macromolecules 13* (1980) 353...7; Studies on sequence distributions in acrylonitrile-styrene copolymers by pyrolysis-glass capillary gas chromatography

G. S. Popova, B. I. Sazhin, N. E. Shadrina, *Vysokomol. Soedin. B 21* (1979) 758...61 (Russ.); Thermal degradation of poly(ethylene-*alt*-tetrafluoroethylene)

M. Seeger, H.-J. Cantow, *Makromol. Chem. 176* (1975) 2059...78; Thermische Spaltungsmechanismen in Homo- und Copolymeren aus α-Olefinen. 2. Polypropylen mit bekannter Taktizität, Polyisobutylen und Poly(1-buten)

H. Seno, S. Tsuge, T. Takeuchi, *J. Chromatogr. Sci. 9* (1971) 315...8; Pyrolysis-gas chromatographic analysis of 6-66-nylon copolymers

H. Seno, S. Tsuge, T. Takeuchi, *Makromol. Chem. 161* (1972) 195...205; Pyrolysis-gas chromatographic studies on the structures of ethylene/propylene copolymers

Y. Sugimura, S. Tsuge, T. Takeuchi, *Anal. Chem. 50* (1978) 1173...6; Characterization of ethylene-methyl methacrylate copolymers by conventional and stepwise *PGC*

S. Tsuge, T. Okumoto, T. Takeuchi, *Makromol. Chem. 123* (1969) 123...9; Pyrolysis-gas chromatographic studies on

sequence distribution of vinylidene chloride/vinyl chloride copolymers

S. Tsuge, S. Hiramitsu, T. Horibe, M. Yamaoka, T. Takeuchi, *Macromolecules 8* (1975) 721...5; Characterization of sequence distribution in methacrylate-styrene copolymers to high conversions by *PGC*

S. Tsuge, T. Takeuchi, Microstructures of vinyl-type copolymers by pyrolysis-gas chromatography, in C. E. Roland Jones, C. A. Cramers (eds.), *Analytical Pyrolysis*; Elsevier, Amsterdam 1977

S. Tsuge, T. Kobayashi, T. Nagaya, T. Takeuchi, *J. Anal. Appl. Pyrolysis 1* (1979) 133...41; Pyrolysis-gas chromatographic estimation of run numbers in methyl methacrylate-styrene copolymers using boundary effect

S. Tsuge, T. Kobayashi, Y. Sugimura, T. Nagaya, T. Takeuchi, *Macromolecules 12* (1979) 988...92; *PGC* characterization of highly alternating copolymers containing styrene and tetracyanquinodimethan, methyl acrylate, acrylonitrile, or methyl methacrylate units

S. Tsuge, Y. Sugimura, T. Kobayashi, T. Nagaya, H. Ohtani, *Adv. Chem. Ser. 203* (1983) 625...34; Microstructural characterization of copolymers by pyrolysis-glass capillary gas chromatography

J. Tulisalo, J. Seppälä, K. Hästbacka, *Macromolecules 18* (1985) 1144...7; Determination of branches in terpolymers of ethylene, 1-butene, and long α-olefin by pyrolysis-hydrogenation-gas chromatography

J. C. Verdier, A. Guyot, *Makromol. Chem. 175* (1974) 1543...59; Microstructure of propene-butene-copolymers studied by flash-pyrolysis-*GL* chromatography

R. Vuković, V. Gnjatovic, *J. Polym. Sci. Polym. Chem. Ed. 8* (1970) 139...46; Characterization of styrene-acrylonitrile copolymers by pyrolysis gas chromatography

K. L. Wallisch, *J. Appl. Polym. Sci. 18* (1974) 203...22; Pyrolysis of random and block copolymers of ethyl acrylate and methyl methacrylate

Y. Yamamoto, S. Tsuge, T. Takeuchi, *Macromolecules 5* (1972) 325...7; Study on the distributions of dyads in acrylonitrile-methyl acrylate copolymers by pyrolysis-gas chromatography

7.5.3.6 Resins, coatings

E. Blasius, H. Häusler, *Fresenius Z. analyt. Chem. 277* (1975) 9...17; Ermittlung des Vernetzungsgrades und Beladungszustandes von Ionenaustauschern auf Kunstharzbasis durch Pyrolyse-Gas-Chromatographie

P. J. Cardosi, *J. Forens. Sci. 27* (1982) 695...703; Pyrolysis-gas chromatographic examination of paints

W. Dankelman, J. M. H. Daemen, A. J. J. de Breet, J. L. Mulder, W. G. B. Huysmans, J. de Wit, *Angew. Makromol. Chem. 54* (1976) 187...201; Modern methods for the analysis of urea formaldehyde resins

N. C. Jain, C. R. Fontan, P. L. Kirk, *J. Forens. Sci. Soc. 5* (1965) 102...9; Identification of paints by pyrolysis and gas chromatography

E. J. Levy, The analysis of automotive paints by pyrolysis gas chromatography, in C. E. Roland Jones, C. A. Cramers (eds.), *Analytical Pyrolysis*; Elsevier, Amsterdam 1977

J. Martínez, G. Guiochon, *J. Gas Chromatogr. 5* (1967) 146...50; Identification of phenol-formaldehyde polycondensates by pyrolysis gas chromatography. II. Quantitative analysis of resins made with phenol, 3-methyl phenol, and 3,5-dimethyl phenol and their mixtures

R. W. May, E. Pearson, J. Porter, M. Scothern, *Analyst 98* (1973) 364...71; A reproducible pyrolysis-gas chromatographic system for the analysis of paints and plastics

H. Nakagawa, S. Tsuge, T. Koyama, *J. Anal. Appl. Pyrol. 12* (1987) 97...114; Studies on thermal degradation of epoxy resins by high-resolution pyrolysis-gas chromatography

J. Parrish, *Anal. Chem. 45* (1973) 1659...62; Analysis of ion-exchange resins by pyrolysis-gas chromatography

M. Ravey, *J. Polym. Sci. Polym. Chem. Ed. 21* (1983) 1...15; Pyrolysis of unsaturated polyester resin. Quantitative aspects

B. W. Schultz, T. P. Perros, *J. Assoc. Official Anal. Chem. 58* (1975) 1150; Pyrolysis gas chromatographic analysis of black paint

W. D. Steward, *J. Forens. Sci. 19* (1974) 121...9; Pyrolysis-gas chromatographic analysis of automotive paints

W. D. Steward, *J. Assoc. Official Anal. Chemists 59* (1976) 35...41; Pyrolysis-gas chromatographic techniques of the analysis of automobile finishes

B. B. Wheals, W. Noble, *J. Forens. Sci. Soc. 14* (1974) 23...32; The pyrolysis-gas chromatographic examination of car paint flakes as an aid to vehicle characterization

J. Zulaica, G. Guiochon, *J. Polym. Sci. B 4* (1966) 567...72; Identification of phenol-formaldehyde resins by gas chromatographic analysis of their pyrolysis products

7.5.3.7 Miscellaneous macromolecular systems

S. C. Brooks, J. F. Bates, *J. Mater. Sci. 20* (1985) 3890...6; The analysis of dental acrylic polymers by pyrolysis-gas chromatography

H. Ito, S. Tsuge, T. Okumoto, T. Takeuchi, *Makromol. Chem. 138* (1970) 111...8; Pyrolysis-gas chromatographic investigation on structure of chlorinated-1,4-polybutadiene

N. Sellier, C. E. Roland Jones, G. Guiochon, Pyrolysis/gas chromatography as a means of determining the quality of porous polymers of styrene cross-linked with divinyl benzene, in C. E. Roland Jones, C. A. Cramers (eds.), *Analytical Pyrolysis*; Elsevier, Amsterdam 1977

S. Tsuge, T. Okumoto, T. Takeuchi, *Macromolecules 2* (1969) 200...2; Structural investigation of chlorinated polyethylenes by pyrolysis-gas chromatography

S. Tsuge, T. Okumoto, T. Takeuchi, *Macromolecules 2* (1969) 277...80; Pyrolysis-gas chromatographic investigation on the structure of chlorinated poly(vinyl chlorides)

7.5.3.8 Quantitative pyrolysis-gas chromatography

D. H. Ahlstrom, S. A. Liebman, K. Abbås, *J. Polym. Sci. Polym. Chem. Ed. 14* (1976) 2479...95; Determination of branching in polyethylene and poly(vinyl chloride) using pyrolysis gas chromatography

K. V. Alekseeva, *Zh. Anal. Khim. 33* (1978) 348...52 (Russ.); *Py-GC* method for the quantitative determination of the composition of multicomponent polymers; application of this method to polyisoprene-polymethyl methacrylate-polystyrene mixtures and the corresponding block copolymers

V. P. Alishoyev, V. G. Berezkin, E. N. Viktorova, *J. Chromatogr. 108* (1975) 275ff.; Application of computer and external standards in determination of composition of polymer systems by *PGC*

A. G. Altenau, L. M. Headley, C. O. Jones, H. C. Ransaw, *Anal. Chem. 42* (1970) 1280...2; Termonomer analysis in ethylene propylene terpolymers

A. V. Bratcikov, B. A. Berendeev, A. G. Rodionov, *Vysokomol. Soedin. A 27* (1985) 1107...12 (Russ.); Determination of the composition of ethene-propene copolymers by pyrolysis-gas chromatography

G. L. Coulter, W. C. Thompson, Automatic analysis of tyre rubber blends by computer-linked pyrolysis gas chromatography, in C. E. Roland Jones, A. C. Cramers (eds.), *Analytical Pyrolysis*; Elsevier, Amsterdam 1977

R. Davis, E. A. Ney, R. Peake, A. Proszynski, *J. Inst. Rubber Ind. 6* (1972) 197...203; Determination of the newer tyre rubbers in tyre treads

P. Falke, G. Müller-Hagen, *Syspur Reporter 19* (1981) 53...9; P. Falke, H. Knopp, G. Müller-Hagen, *Acta Polymer. 35* (1984) 569...71; Zur Bestimmung des Acrylnitril- und Styrengehaltes in Polymerpolyolen mittels Pyrolysegaschromatographie

R. Gnauck, *Plaste Kautsch. 23* (1976) 649f.; Bestimmung des Gehalts an Ethylenoxid und Propylenoxid in deren Copolymeren aus der Ausbeute an Ethen und Propen bei der Pyrolyse

J. K. Haken, T. R. McKay, *Anal. Chem. 45* (1973) 1251ff.; Quantitative pyrolysis gas chromatography of some acrylic copolymers and homopolymers

J. K. Haken, T. R. McKay, *J. Chromatogr. 80* (1973) 75ff.; Quantitative pyrolysis gas chromatography of some terpolymers and three-component polyacrylic mixtures

M. Henkel, I. Lüderwald, *Fresenius Z. analyt. Chem. 321* (1985) 252...6; Bestimmung von synthetischen Polymeren in Humangewebe durch Pyrolyse-Gas-Chromatographie (*Py-GC*). 3. Polymethacrylat und Polyethylen

S. Hirayanagi, K. Kimura, M. Sato, K. Harada, *Int. Polym. Sci. Technol. 9* (1982) T54...T59; Analysis of polymers by pyrolysis gas chromatography. III. Quantitative determination of blend ratio in SBR vulcanisates

A. Krishen, *Anal. Chem. 44* (1972) 494...7; Quantitative determination of natural rubber, styrene-butadiene rubber, and ethylene-propylene-terpolymer rubber in compounded cured stocks by pyrolysis-gas chromatography

A. Krishen, R. G. Tucker, *Anal. Chem. 46* (1974) 29...33; Quantitative determination of the polymeric constituents in compounded cured stocks by curie-point-pyrolysis-gas chromatography

C. Landault, G. Guiochon, *Anal. Chem. 39* (1967) 713...21; Fast analysis of phenol, methylphenols, and polymethylphenols by gas chromatography using packed capillary columns

R. S. Lehrle, J. C. Robb, *J. Gas Chromatogr. 5* (1967) 89...95; The quantitative study of polymer degradation by gas chromatography

I. Lüderwald, K. E. Müller, *Fresenius Z. analyt. Chem. 300* (1980) 277...9; Bestimmung des Einbauverhältnisses in Methylmethacrylat-Methylacrylat-Copolymeren durch *Py-GC*

F. Maciejowski, J. Sokolowska, *Polimery (Warsaw) 22* (1977) 239...41 (Pol.); *Py-GC* determination of the MMA content of methyl methacrylate-butadiene-styrene terpolymers

N. MacLeod, *Chromatographia 5* (1972) 516ff.; Quantitative pyrolysis-gas chromatography of methylmethacrylate, styrene, butylmethacrylate, hydroxypropylmethacrylate and acrylic acid polymers

C. Merritt, R. E. Sacher, B. A. Petersen, *J. Chromatogr. 99* (1974) 301...8; Laser pyrolysis *GC/MS* analysis of polymeric materials

R. Milina, M. Pankova, *Faserforsch. Textiltechn. 26* (1975) 217...9; Bestimmung der Zusammensetzung von Acrylnitril-Methylmethacrylat-Copolymeren durch *Py-GC*

R. Milina, K. Kovaceva, *Faserforsch. Textiltechn.* 27 (1976) 443...5; Bestimmung der Monomerzusammensetzung von Butadien-Copolymeren mit Hilfe der *Py-GC*

S. Mori, *J. Chromatogr.* 194 (1980) 163...73; Determination of the composition of copolymers as a function of molecular weight by pyrolysis gas chromatography-size-exclusion chromatography

H. Mosimann, W. Weber, *Schweizer Archiv* 36 (1970) 402...11; Methode zur Bestimmung der Ausgangsphenole in Phenol-, Kresol- und Xylenolharzen mit Hilfe der Pyrolysen-Gaschromatographie

M. Seeger, H.-J. Cantow, *Colloid Polym. Sci.* 258 (1980) 527...44; Zur Berechnung und Auswertung der bei der Pyrolyse-Gaschromatographie entstehenden Fragmentverteilungen von Copolymeren mit langen Ethylensequenzen

J. Sokolowska, F. Maciejowski, *Polimery (Warsaw)* 22 (1977) 160...3 (Pol.); Determination of the composition of butadiene-methyl methacrylate-styrene terpolymers by Py-*GC*

J. Sokolowska, F. Maciejowski, *Chem. Anal. (Warsaw)* 22 (1977) 337...43 (Pol.); Determination of the styrene content of butadiene-styrene copolymers by pyrolysis-gas chromatography

A. S. Trynkina, V. V. Chebotarev, N. A. Baranov, L. F. Ovsyannikov, *Plast. Massy 1973* (2) 77ff. (Russ.); Determination of the composition of a trioxane-dioxolane copolymer by pyrolysis *GC*

S. Tsuge, T. Okumoto, T. Takeuchi, *Bull. Chem. Soc. Japan* 42 (1969) 2870...3; Pyrolysis-gas chromatographic determination of chlorine in chlorine-containing polymers

I. A. Tutorskii, E. G. Boikacheva, E. F. Bukanova, T. V. Guseva, I. G. Bukanov, *Izv. Vyssh. Uchebn. Zaved. Tekhnol. 18* (1975) 460...3 (Russ.); Determination of the distribution of styrene sequences in polybutadiene-*b*-polystyrene using *Py-GC* data from mixtures of polystyrene and polybutadiene

E. Urbas, A. Kogerman, E. Kuellik, O. Kirret, E. Heinsoo, Ju. D. Andricenko, T. V. Druzinina, *Acta Polymer. 31* (1980) 264...6; Über die quantitative Zusammensetzung der Pyrolyseprodukte beim thermischen Abbau halogenhaltiger Polyamidfasern

M. Vacherot, J. Marchal, *Compt. Rend. C 263* (1966) 210...3; *J. Gas Chromatogr. 5* (1967) 155...6; *Rubber Chem. Techn. 41* (1968) 418...20; Dosage des additions 1−4 et 3−5 dans les polyisoprènes par pyrolyse rapide et chromatographie en phase gazeuse

7.5.3.9 Coupling of pyrolysis-gas chromatography with other methods (see also 2.4.1 and 6.7.1)

A. Alajberg, P. J. Arpino, D. Deur-Šiftar, G. Guiochon, *J. Anal. Appl. Pyrol. 1* (1980) 203...12; Investigation of some vinyl polymers by pyrolysis-gas chromatography-mass spectrometry

A. Ballistreri, S. Foti, P. Maravigna, G. Montaudo, E. Scamporrino, *J. Polym. Sci. Polym. Chem. Ed. 18* (1980) 3101...10; Effect of metal oxides on the evolution of aromatic hydrocarbons in the thermal decomposition of PVC

E. Blasius, H. Lander, *Fresenius Z. analyt. Chem. 303* (1980) 177...87; Charakterisierung von Austauschern mit cyclischen Polyethern als Ankergruppen durch Pyrolyse-Gas-Chromatographie und Pyrolyse-Massenspektrometrie

M. Blazsó, T. Székely, F. Till, G. Várhegyi, E. Jakab, P. Szabó, *J. Anal. Appl. Pyrol. 8* (1985) 255...69; Pyrolysis-gas chromatographic-mass spectrometric and thermogravimetric-mass spectrometric investigation of brown coals

J. R. Brown, A. J. Power, *Polym. Degr. Stab. 4* (1982) 379...92; Thermal degradation of aramides. 1. Pyrolysis-gas chromatography-mass spectrometry of poly(1,3-phenylene isophthalamide) and poly(1,4-phenylene terephthalamide)

J. R. Brown, A. J. Power, *Polym. Degr. Stab. 4* (1982) 479...90; Thermal degradation of aramides. 2. Pyrolysis-gas chromatography-mass spectrometry of some model compounds of poly(1,3-phenylene isophthalamide) and poly(1,4-phenylene terephthalamide)

J. C. Chien, P. C. Uden, Ju-Li Fan, *J. Polym. Sci. Polym. Chem. Ed. 20* (1982) 2159...67; Pyrolysis of polyacetylene

J. Chiu, *Anal. Chem. 40* (1968) 1516...20; Polymer characterization by coupled thermogravimetry gas chromatography

K. S. Chiu, K. Biemann, K. Krishnan, S. L. Hill, *Anal. Chem. 56* (1984) 1610...5; Structural characterization of polycyclic aromatic compounds by combined gas chromatography/mass spectrometry and gas chromatography/Fourier transform infrared spectrometry

J. S. Crighton, Characterisation of textile materials by thermal degradation: A critique of pyrolysis *GC* and thermogravimetry, in C. E. Roland Jones, C. A. Cramers (eds.), *Analytical Pyrolysis*; Elsevier, Amsterdam 1977

B. Crossland, G. J. Knight, W. W. Wright, *Brit. Polym. J. 18* (1986) 156...60; A comparative study of the thermal stability and mechanism of degradation of poly(arylene sulphones)

B. Crossland, G. J. Knight, W. W. Wright, *Brit. Polym. J. 18* (1986) 371...5; The thermal degradation of some polymers based upon *p*-hydroxybenzoic acid

D. L. Doerfler, G. T. Emmons, J. M. Campbell, *Anal. Chem. 54* (1982) 832...3; Integration of a gas-flow proportional counter into a commercial gas chromatograph/mass spectrometer data system

H. Eustache, N. Robin, J. C. Daniel, M. Carrega, *Eur. Polym. J. 14* (1978) 239...43; Determination of multipolymer structure using pyrolysis gas chromatography

D. L. Evans, J. L. Weaver, A. K. Mukherji, C. C. Beatty, *Anal. Chem. 50* (1978) 857...60; Compositional determination of styrene-methacrylate copolymers by *PGC*, ^{1}H-*NMR*, and carbon analysis

H. Feuerberg, *GIT Fachz. Lab. 13* (1969) 1185...93; Kunststoff-Analyse durch Pyrolyse, Gas-Chromatographie und Massenspektrometrie

R. O. Gardner, R. F. Brown, *Anal. Chem. 52* (1980) 1360...4; Determination of polymer pyrolysis products by *GC* and *GC/MS*

M. Gazicki et al., *J. Appl. Polym. Sci. Appl. Polym. Symp. 38* (1984) 1...19; Pyrolysis as a means for the structure elucidation of plasma-polymerized organosilicones

J. Ghotra, G. Stevens, D. Bloor, *J. Polym. Sci. Polym. Chem. Ed. 15* (1977) 1155...67; *MS* and *PGC* studies of the monomer and polymer of *bis*(*p*-toluenesulfonate) of 2,4-hexadiyne-1,6-diol

R. J. Gritter, M. Seeger, E. Gipstein, *J. Polym. Sci. Polym. Chem. Ed. 16* (1978) 353...60; Study of the mechanism of polysulfone decomposition by pyrolysis/gas chromatography and pyrolysis/gas chromatography/mass spectrometry

R. J. Gritter, E. Gipstein, G. E. Adams, *J. Polym. Sci. Polym. Chem. Ed. 17* (1979) 3959...67; Pyrolysis/gas chromatography/mass spectrometry of polymers: polyisopropenylcyclohexane and copolymers with its aromatic counterpart, α-methylstyrene

L. Gunawan, J. K. Haken, *J. Polym. Sci. Polym. Chem. Ed. 23* (1985) 2539...55; The mechanism of thermal degradation of polymethyl acrylate using pyrolysis gas chromatography mass spectrometry

M. A. Haney, D. W. Johnston, B. H. Clampitt, *Macromolecules 16* (1983) 1775...83; Investigation of short-chain branches in polyethylene by pyrolysis-*GCMS*

E. Kiran, J. K. Gillham, *Polym. Eng. Sci. 19* (1979) 699...708; Pyrolysis-molecular weight chromatography-vapor phase infrared spectrophotometry. An on-line system for analysis of polymers — a review

J. D. Kleinert, C. J. Weschler, *Anal. Chem. 52* (1980) 1245...8; Pyrolysis gas chromatographic-mass spectrometric identification of poly(dimethylsiloxane)s

H.-J. Kretzschmar, D. Gross, J. Kelm, Pyrolysis-gas chromatography and spectroscopic identification of fluorine polymers, in C. E. Roland Jones, C. A. Cramers (eds.), *Analytical Pyrolysis;* Elsevier, Amsterdam 1977

R. P. Lattimer, W. J. Kroenke, R. H. Backderf, *J. Appl. Polym. Sci. 27* (1982) 3633...6; Carbon-13 labeling studies of volatile pyrolyzate formation from poly(vinyl chloride)

S. A. Liebman, D. H. Ahlstrom, C. R. Foltz, *J. Polym. Sci. Polym. Chem. Ed. 16* (1978) 3139...50; Thermal degradation studies of PVC with time-resolved *PGC* and derivative *TGA*

S. A. Liebman, D. H. Ahlstrom, W. H. Starnes, F. C. Schilling, *J. Macromol. Sci. Chem. A 17* (1982) 935...50; Short-chain branching in polyethylene and poly(vinyl chloride) using pyrolysis hydrogenation gas chromatography and ^{13}C nuclear magnetic resonance analysis

S. A. Liebman, T. P. Wampler, E. J. Levy, *J. High Resol. Chromatogr. Chromatogr. Comm. 7* (1984) 172...84; Developments in pyrolysis capillary *GC*

A. B. Littlewood, *Chromatographia 1* (1968) 37...42; The coupling of gas chromatography with methods of identification. I. Mass spectrometry; *ibid.* 133...9; II. The use of chemical methods; *ibid.* 223; III. *IR* spectrophotometry

J. B. Maynard, J. E. Twichell, J. Q. Walker, *J. Chromatogr. Sci. 17* (1979) 82...6; Determination of carboxyl-terminated-butadiene-nitrile polymer in commercial cresol-novolac epoxy resin systems by pyrolysis capillary gas chromatography and mass spectrometry

L. Michajlov, P. Zugenmaier, H.-J. Cantow, *Polymer 9* (1968) 325...43; Structural investigations on polyethylenes and ethylene-propylene copolymers by reaction gas chromatography and *X*-ray diffraction

G. Montaudo, C. Puglisi, E. Scamporino, D. Vitalini, *Macromolecules 19* (1986) 882...7; Thermal degradation of aromatic-aliphatic polyethers. 2. Flash pyrolysis-gas chromatography-mass spectrometry

G. Oehme, H. Baudisch, H. Mix, *Makromol. Chem. 177* (1976) 2657...67; Analyse von Polystyrolharzen mit funk-

tionellen Gruppen mittels *IR*-Spektroskopie und Pyrolyse-Gaschromatographie-Massenspektroskopie

H. Ohtani, T. Asai, S. Tsuge, *Macromolecules 18* (1985) 1148...52; Characterization of a multicomponent alkyl methacrylate copolymer by high-resolution pyrolysis-gas chromatography

M. M. O'Mara, *J. Polym. Sci. A-1 8* (1970) 1887...99; High-temperature pyrolysis of poly(vinyl chloride): gas chromatographic-mass spectrometric analysis of the pyrolysis products from PVC resin and plastisols

R. P. Philp, *Trends in Anal. Chem. 1/10* (1982) 237...41; Application of pyrolysis-*GC* and pyrolysis-*GC-MS* to fossil fuel research

N. Sellier, C. E. Roland Jones, G. Guiochon, *J. Chromatogr. Sci. 13* (1975) 383...5; The examination of some vinyl acetate/olefin copolymers by pyrolysis gas chromatography mass spectrometry

J. L. Sharp, G. Paterson, *Analyst 105* (1980) 517...20; Identification of small amounts of copolymerised unsaturated carboxylic acid in acrylic polymers by an alkylation-pyrolysis-gas chromatographic-mass spectrometric procedure

Y. Shimura, *J. Appl. Polym. Sci. 22* (1978) 1491...1507; Degradation products in weathered polymers

J. L. Wuepper, *Anal. Chem. 51* (1979) 997...1000; Pyrolysis gas chromatographic-mass spectrometric identification of intractable materials

7.5.4 Pyrolysis, followed by other chromatographic methods (thermofractography)

V. Brüderle, *G-I-T 21* (1977) 649...54; Thermische Schnellanalyse von Hochpolymeren in Kopplung mit der Dünnschicht-Chromatographie

E. Stahl, L. L. Oey, *Kunststoffe 64* (1974) 657...62; Thermofraktographie zur Schnellanalyse von Kunststoffen; Identifizierung von Polykondensaten nach Alkalischmelze

E. Stahl, L. S. Oey, *Angew. Makromol. Chem. 44* (1975) 107...17; Thermofraktographie zur Schnellanalyse von Kunststoffen. 2. Identifizierung von Phenolharzen

E. Stahl, L. S. Oey, *Z. analyt. Chem. 275* (1975) 187...91; Thermofraktographie zur Schnellanalyse von Kunststoffen. 3. Identifizierung von Vinylpolymeren

E. Stahl, V. Brüderle, *Angew. Makromol. Chem. 68* (1978) 87...116; Thermofraktographie zur Schnellanalyse von Kunststoffen. 4. Identifizierung der Basiskomponenten von Epoxidharzen

J. B. Maynard, J. E. Twichell, J. Q. Walker, *J. Chromatogr. Sci. 17* (1979) 82...6; Determination of carboxyl-terminated butadiene-nitrile polymer in commercial cresol-novolac epoxy resin systems by pyrolysis capillary *GC* and *MS*

Index

Index

Index